FOOD SCIENCE AND TECHNOLOGY

CHEMICAL FOOD SAFETY AND HEALTH

FOOD SCIENCE AND TECHNOLOGY

Additional books in this series can be found on Nova's website
under the Series tab.

Additional e-books in this series can be found on Nova's website
under the e-book tab.

PUBLIC HEALTH IN THE 21ST CENTURY

Additional books in this series can be found on Nova's website
under the Series tab.

Additional e-books in this series can be found on Nova's website
under the e-book tab.

FOOD SCIENCE AND TECHNOLOGY

CHEMICAL FOOD SAFETY AND HEALTH

FRANCO PEDRESCHI PLASENCIA
AND
ZUZANA CIESAROVÁ
EDITORS

New York

For permission to use material from this book please contact us:
Telephone 631-231-7269; Fax 631-231-8175
Web Site: http://www.novapublishers.com

Library of Congress Cataloging-in-Publication Data

ISBN: 978-1-62948-339-9

Library of Congress Control Number: 2013950458

Published by Nova Science Publishers, Inc. † New York

CONTENTS

INTRODUCTION

M. A. Fellenberg[1,*]

[1]Departamento de Ciencias Animales, Facultad de Agronomía e Ingeniería Forestal, Pontificia Universidad Católica de Chile, Santiago, Chile

In ancient times human beings hunted animals and collected plants to feed themselves. They were nomads and they moved following herds of animals and foraging for plants with fruits and seeds. After they learned to domesticate animals and plants, man ceased to wander and agriculture began. Often, primitive civilizations settled near water sources, which provided communication pathways across rivers and water for them, their animals and their crops.

The world has changed a lot since that age. In our modern world, animals and plant crops are produced all around the world and meat, dairy products, fish, vegetables, fruits, seeds, honey, etc. and their derivatives travel sometimes thousands of kilometres to their final consumers. All this has changed the manner of food production and commercialization. Now we need an organization to establish world rules to protect public health and facilitate food commerce. In 1962, at World Health Organization (WHO) meeting on food rules, an international group named "*Codex Alimentarius*", was established with the objective of protecting human health and facilitating world trade in food.

Public health is a constant concern for world health authorities because foodborne illnesses are increasingly prevalent. These diseases are caused by microorganisms or harmful chemicals present in the food people eat and drink. Most of the time, these illnesses are caused when certain bacteria, viruses, or parasites contaminate food or water. They also occur when food is contaminated by harmful chemicals or toxins, either during or after processing. Many different foodborne illnesses have been described. Probably most dramatic are those produced by microorganisms, because most of the time they produce an acute disease. On the other hand, chemicals can produce both acute and chronic diseases depending on the level of contaminants present in the food. When the level of contaminants is high, the result may be an acute disease with dramatic consequences, but when the level of contaminants is low; they

[*] Corresponding author: Dr. María Angélica Fellenberg. Departamento de Ciencias Animales, Facultad de Agronomía e Ingeniería Forestal, Pontificia Universidad Católica de Chile. Address: Avenida Vicuña Mackenna 4860, Santiago, Chile, Phone: + 56-2-3544147; Fax:+56-2-552 9435; E-mail: mafellen@uc.cl.

may accumulate in a live organism and produce a long term disease. Usually, chemical contaminants are found in the environment, both naturally and produced by human activity.

The best way to prevent foodborne illness is to prevent contaminants from getting into food. Prevention is therefore the principal focus of all safety quality systems. To this end, the food industry and food rules have changed, to assure people that food products are safe. In the past, the food producer was encouraged to produce safe food by assuring that the final product was safe. So, producers had to sample a large quantity of food and destroy it all if they found any contamination. This system was inefficient for various reasons, including: 1) It was not possible to detect in which part of the process contamination occurred, 2) If sampling failed, contaminated food could reach consumers, 3) When contaminated food resulted in foodborne illness, that produced public alarm and insecurity, 4) Some contaminations that happen at the beginning of production cannot be eliminated during processing. For these reasons, food safety has become an important issue for many world governments and consumers in general. Different countries have taken different actions to assure safe food for consumers. Some have created new rules or changed others, regulating the production of both human and animal food. Canada (1997), Ireland (1999), United Kingdom (2000), European Union (2002), New Zealand (2007), and United States of America (2010), among others, have promulgated food laws promoting global consistency in the production of safe food.

Contamination can happen at any place during processing. It is absolutely necessary to evaluate all the hazards that can occur all along the food production chain, identifying inputs, and analysing and controlling all critical points to keep hazards at acceptable levels. This, by reducing points where contamination can occur it is possible to prevent and avoid it, diminishing the probability of spread foodborne illness.

In a modern system of food safety, all actors in the food chain (producers, transporters and retailers) are responsible for their own segments of the chain and must assure the product they are receiving is in good condition. This is based on a system of trust, with clear rules about responsibilities and penalties.

The bases of this system are:

1) *Focus on whole food production chain*: all points of food production chain are evaluated and monitored. This approach permits focusing resources on those points where it is possible to reduce hazards to acceptable levels. This permits a better utilization of resources.
2) *Focus on preventing contamination*: the main idea is to prevent contamination thereby producing food that is safe for consumers.
3) *Focus on responsibilities*: in this system duties and responsibilities are shared among food producers (all the people involved in food chain), consumers, government authorities, and food safety researchers. Responsibility for safe foods is with the producers. Consumers must be informed and must handle food properly following producer's instructions. Authorities determine legal responsibilities and food safety researchers investigate different kinds of contaminants, safety levels, and the ways to avoid contamination.

In order for this system to work properly it must rely on scientific knowledge. The scientific community can establish through research which substances and which levels are harmful to human health.

As mentioned above, some chemical substances can produce either acute or chronic disease. Dioxins and furans are manmade environmental pollutants with deleterious effects in human health. Polychlorinated dibenzo-*p*-dioxin (PCDD) is the name of a family of 75 compounds formed per two benzene rings, linked by 2 oxygen, that can have 1 to 8 chlorine atoms linked to this structure. The most potent and toxic member of them is 2,3,7,8-tetrachlorodibenzo-*p*-dioxin (TCDD). Polychlorinated dibenzofurans (PCDFs) involve 135 molecules with similar origin and effects as dioxins. Both of them occur in a spontaneous and undesirable manner in many industrial processes. The main ways are: as byproducts of industrial processes involving chlorine molecules, and combustion processes of substances that have carbon and chlorine in their molecules, such as in incinerators or accidental fires. Dioxins and furans are: 1) toxic in small doses, 2) persistent (do not degrade easily) and they can remain in the environment for years, 3) bioaccumulative and biomagnificable, they are stored in fatty tissues and increase their concentration along the food chain. Due to their persistence, they can go far, being carried by atmospheric currents, rivers, or by migrant animals such as birds and whales.

The main way (90%) humans are exposed to dioxins and furans, is by contaminated food. Often, contamination occurs in food production chain because of grasses and animal feed that has been contaminated by dioxins and furans produced in industrialized places and then travel a long distances, and their products (beef, dairy products, etc) are finally consumed by humans. Fish and sea food can be contaminated as well, when water is contaminated by sewage. Thus, protecting the food supply is critical. "Good controls and practices during primary production, processing, distribution and sale are all essential to the production of safe food." (WHO)

Dioxins are highly toxic and can cause reproductive and developmental problems, interfere with hormones, damage the immune system, and also cause cancer. Dioxins are ubiquitous, anyone can be exposed to them, and due to their toxicity, efforts must be undertaken to reduce current exposure.

On the other hand, furan is well known to be found in a variety of foods that undergoes heat treatment. Coffee, sauces, soups and ready-to-eat baby food have been reported to have high furan levels. Concern about furan started twenty years ago when some studies based on laboratory animals indicated that they could possibly be carcinogenic to humans. Since then, the USA and the EU have been monitoring different kinds of food. Almost ten years ago they built a broad data base of many different foods and are updating it constantly. The main analytical method for furan detection in foods is headspace gas chromatography/mass spectrometry, its detection limit is less than 1 μg/kg in most of food matrices, however new methods are being developed to diminished the minimal level of detection. Both the mechanism of furan formation in foods and the effects of domestic cooking are not well understood yet, and it has been postulated that different precursors could be participating in their formation. More research is necessary to know clearly the toxicity of furan.

Acrylamide is the monomer of polyacrylamide which is used in some industries. Polyacrylamide is not toxic, but its monomer is. It is known that acrylamide produce cancer in some animals and affect the nervous system in both animals and humans. Although acrylamide has been present in foods for a long time, concerns about it arose in 2002 when the Swedish National Food Authority reported the presence of high levels of acrylamide in food processed at high temperatures. Then FAO/WHO did a consultation to better understand the risk to human health posed by acrylamide in food. Since then FAO (Food and Agriculture Organization of the United Nations)/WHO established an international network on acrylamide in food that allows all interested parties to share relevant data as well as information on ongoing investigations.

Even though hazardous substances can be found in foods we also find substances that protect human health. This is the case of polyphenols. Certain kinds of molecules found in plants, vegetables, fruits and seeds, produce several positives effects on human health such as: antioxidants, anti-inflammatories, anti-tumor, anti-carcinogenicity properties, anti-microbial activities and immune system protection, among others. There are more than 8,000 different kinds of molecules of polyphenols reported and they are currently widely studied, due to their beneficial effects on human health. Also in this category are selenium, magnesium and zinc. These important minerals form part of the different important enzymatic complexes, contributing to the oxidation-reduction balance.

Understanding risks, causes of contamination, and the production of hazardous chemicals is essential due to during food production, maintaining safe levels and avoiding contamination is vital to assure food safety for consumers around the world. Additionally, it is important to understand that there exist molecules in food that provide certain health benefits other than nutritional ones. It is necessary to know them, where they occur and what kind of health benefits they produce. With this knowledge, food producers can improve their processes to produce nutritional safe foods which will enhance the consumer's health and quality of life.

In: Chemical Food Safety and Health
Editors: F. Pedreschi Plasencia and Z. Ciesarová
ISBN: 978-1-62948-339-9

Chapter 1

ACRYLAMIDE MITIGATION IN HEAT PROCESSED FOODS: PATENTED TECHNIQUES

***M. Mariotti*[*1], *J. A. Carrasco*[2], *M. Inés Espinoza*[2] *and F. Pedreschi*[1]**
[1]Departmento de Ingeniería Química y Bioprocesos,
Pontificia Universidad Católica de Chile, Santiago, Chile
[2]DICTUC SA. Pontificia Universidad Católica de Chile, Santiago, Chile

ABSTRACT

Eating a balanced diet is one of the crucial aspects to reaching a healthier life. In order to accomplish this purpose, the overall quality of foods should be monitored in every step of the production chain. In this sense, processing of foods at high temperature is an antique way to preserve and make them readily available for consuming. Interestingly, another major advantage of food heating is that it adds taste and color, improving the consumer acceptation of the product while reducing microbial growth and inhibiting enzyme activity, that are critical factors for increasing shelf life. Both color and flavor compounds are generated during the thermal food processing mainly by Maillard reaction, along with some toxic compounds such as acrylamide. Maillard reaction is believed to be the main route for acrylamide formation between reducing sugars (glucose and fructose) and the amino acid asparagine. Consequently, a variety of technologies to reduce acrylamide concentration in foods processed at high temperatures have been developed by inhibiting this reaction through changes in process parameters and reductions in acrylamide precursor levels in raw materials. Although most of these techniques have successfully diminished acrylamide content in several foods, it is also critical to control acrylamide formation during food processing without impairing the sensorial attributes of the product. In this book chapter we will list and discuss several of the most recent patents developed for acrylamide mitigation in thermally processed foods. These technologies consider not only their effect on the safety of the product but also in its final sensorial quality. Finally, we propose in this chapter a new mitigation approach which can be transversally applied to different food matrices in order to reduce significantly acrylamide formation without considerable damage their sensorial attributes.

* Corresponding author: María Salomé Mariotti Celis, Departmento de Ingeniería Química y Bioprocesos, Pontificia Universidad Católica de Chile, Address: Avenida Vicuña Mackenna 4860, Santiago, Chile, Phone: 56223541269, e-mail:msmariot@uc.cl.

1. INTRODUCTION

In April 2002, the food safety world was alarmed when Swedish researchers announced the presence of acrylamide in some fried and baked foods, most notably potato chips and baked cereal products (*e.g.* ~ 2000μg/kg and ~ 1500 μg/kg of acrylamide in biscuits and in potato chips, respectively).

Acrylamide is a hazardous contaminant that has been classified by the International Agency for Research of Cancer (IARC) as "*probably carcinogenic for humans*"[1] and recognized by the European Union Scientific Committee on Food (EUSCF) as a genotoxic carcinogen in laboratory animals [2].

The presence of acrylamide in foods has provoked a worldwide concern, thus, in a number of countries several research projects concerning different aspects of acrylamide such as its exposure, mitigation and formation have been conducted. In this respect and considering acrylamide dietary exposure as a critical health issue the European Commission Scientific Committee on Food (SFC) emphasized that acrylamide exposure should be as low as reasonably achievable [2]. Likewise, according to The Joint Institute for Food Safety and Applied Nutrition (JIFSAN) recommendation, dated April 2006, the mitigation of acrylamide level in foods has been desirable and "*new ways for acrylamide reduction should be developed*" [3].

Regarding to its formation acrylamide has shown to be originated principally through the high temperatures reached in Maillard reaction during heat processing of various carbohydrate-rich foods [4]. However, Maillard reaction plays a relevant role during the heat processing of carbohydrate-rich foodstuffs. This highly temperature dependent reaction is instrumental in the development of desirable color, flavor and aroma compounds [5].

In order to that, a major challenge of both scientists and inventors has been to reduce acrylamide levels in foods as much as possible while maintaining their sensorial attributes intact [6].

During the last decade, patented reduction methods of acrylamide have principally focused on changing processing parameters such as pressure and temperatures (e.g. vacuum frying or atmospheric frying at low temperatures [7-12]. Some post-frying techniques of acrylamide removal in foods have been implemented; however its use is impractical since it destroys the product structure.

Moreover, other strategies for acrylamide mitigation have considered diminishing the levels of acrylamide precursors (reducing sugars and the amino acid asparagines) by using enzymes and other amino acids [13-22].

Likewise, modifying unit operations such as blanching of raw materials and Sodium Chloride (NaCl) solution soaking after blanching has also been implemented as a viable alternative [23] as well as novel methods which include genetic engineering, where modified plant DNA has led to reduced acrylamide contents [24].

While all of the mentioned technologies have shown a successful decrease in the acrylamide content of food products, consumer acceptation of these low-acrylamide foods remains a pending issue.

The present book chapter will focus on recent patented techniques for acrylamide mitigation in starchy foods in order to propose a new mitigation approach which can be applied to significantly reduce the acrylamide formation without damage the sensorial attributes of food products.

2. ACRYLAMIDE, A CHEMICAL APPROACH

Acrylamide, also known as acrylic amide, acrylic acid amide, ethylenecarboxamide, propenamide, and propenoic acid amide, is a low molecular weight vinyl compound (71.08 g/mol). It possesses two functional groups, an amide group and the electron-deficient vinylic double bond that makes it readily available for a wide range of reactions, including nucleophilic and Diel-Alder additions and radical reactions. These reactions are of significant importance in biological systems. Reactions of the amide residue include hydrolysis, dehydration, alcoholysis and condensation with aldehydes, while the vinylic double bond reacts with ammonia, aliphatic amines, phosphines, chlorine, bromine, bisulphite and dithiocarbamates, as well as proteins [23]. The structure of acrylamide molecule is shown in Figure 1.

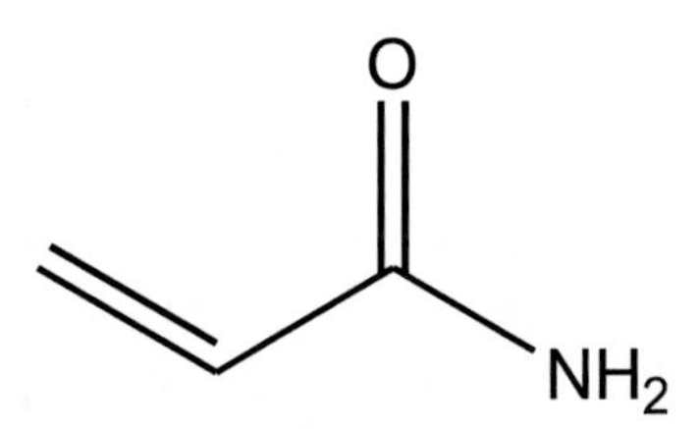

Figure 1. Chemical structure of acrylamide molecule.

Acrylamide is a small hydrophilic molecule [25]. It is an odorless solid and its color ranges from colorless to white. Also, it is soluble in a number of polar solvents, *e.g.* acetone, acetonitrile, water and susceptible to polymerization during heating, which prevents the determination of boiling point at ambient pressure. At 3.34 kPa (25 mm Hg), it boils at 125 °C. It is regarded as a thermally unstable compound. The most important chemical and physical parameters of acrylamide are listed in Table 1.

Table 1. Physicochemical parameters of acrylamide

Parameter	Specification
Chemical formula	C_3H_5NO
Molecular weight	71.08 g/mol
Melting point	84-85 °C
Solubility	216 g/100 g water at 30°C
Boiling point	125 °C at 3.34 kPa
Vapor pressure	0.007 mm Hg at 20 °C
Vapor density (Air=1)	2.4 at 175 °C
Specific gravity	1.122 kg/dm^3 at 30 °C

Despite its toxicity, polymers of acrylamide (polyacrylamide) are extensively used in modern chemical technology for a variety of purposes. These include their use as flocculants for sewage and wastewater treatment, as coagulants for clarifying drinking water, as sealants for construction of dams, tunnels and water reservoirs, as soil stabilizers in roadways construction, as binders in paper and pulp industry and as additives/adhesives/fixatives for manufacturing various industrial and cosmetic products. In analytical biochemistry, polyacrylamides are widely used for chromatography and electrophoresis (*e.g.* for separation and purification of proteins) [26, 27].

3. Acrylamide in Foods: Understanding of its Formation

Since the initial finding that acrylamide may be formed from naturally-occurring substances in certain foods processed at high temperature, food safety scientists have been undertaking studies to determine how acrylamide is formed *in situ* during the cooking of carbohydrate-rich foods.

In the early stages of research regarding to acrylamide formation mechanisms in heated foods, two mainly pathways were proposed: (i) Via reaction between reducing sugars and amino acids in the Maillard reaction and (ii) Via direct reaction between acrolein (a fatty acid oxidation product), with ammonia followed by oxidation to acrylamide [28].

In this respect, a number of mechanistic studies have shown that the first pathway is the most likely vehicle for acrylamide formation. For instance, Mottram, Wedzicha [4] found that considerable quantities of acrylamide were formed when asparagine, the most likely amino acid precursor of acrylamide, and glucose, a common reducing sugar, reacted at 185°C in phosphate buffer. Similarly, Stadler [29], [30] found that in equimolar glucose and asparagine model systems acrylamide pyrolysed at 180°. Additionally, Becalski, Lau [31] showed that ^{15}N-labeled glucose and asparagine in ratios similar to those found in potatoes produced ^{15}N labeled acrylamide.

Furthermore, both Stadler [29] and Mottram, Wedzicha [4] postulated that Maillard reaction was the main pathway of acrylamide formation, suggesting the sugar asparagine adduct N-glycosylasparagine as a possible direct precursor of acrylamide under pyrolytic conditions. In the same way, Zyzak [15] elucidated the mechanism of acrylamide formation confirming the presence of Maillard´s key intermediates such as a decarboxylated Schiff base and 3-aminopropionamide by using isotope substitution experiments.

Interestingly, real time monitoring of reducing sugars, asparagine and water contents in heated potato, wheat and rye systems have shown that precursor diminishing is accompanied by an increase in acrylamide formation, which reaches its maximum value near the end of the heating cycle [32].

Moreover, the non-enzymatic browning that is a consequence of Maillard reaction, has shown to be a good predictor of acrylamide content in starchy foods processed at high temperatures [33].

On the other hand, the acrolein route to acrylamide formation has been discarded since studies have confirmed that the addition of antioxidants did not affect acrylamide formation [34].

Most available data indicate that acrylamide´s major formation pathway in food is likely to be the Maillard reaction, in which the reducing sugars react with asparagine when the food is heated and, through a cascade of reactions, shows that the side chain of asparagine is converted to acrylamide.

4. ACRYLAMIDE REDUCTION METHODS

4.1. Changes in Process Parameters

Acrylamide formation in foods may be influenced differently by several factors during their processing, such as: temperature, heating time, browning level, water activity and pH. The effect of temperature, heating time, surface over volume ratio (SVR) and browning level on acrylamide formation in fried potatoes was studied by Taubert et al. It was found that in potato shapes with low SVR, acrylamide consistently increased while temperature and processing time increased as well [26]. On the other hand, in shapes with intermediate to high SVR, the maximum acrylamide formation took place at 160-180 °C, while higher temperatures or prolonged processing times made acrylamide level to decrease. Furthermore, studies on the effect of water activity on acrylamide formation in model systems concluded that by controlling moisture, it may be possible to uncouple concurrent reactions related to Maillard reaction [35].

The effect of metal ions over acrylamide formation has also been studied by several authors who concluded that the use of NaCl and $CaCl_2$ for instance could minimize the acrylamide formation during frying. These authors suggest that ionic and electronic associations between cations and asparagine suppress early-stage Maillard reactions [36, 37]. The preventive effect of Ca^{2+} ions may be due to the observed inhibition of the formation of the intermediate Schiff base that leads to acrylamide formation [38]. Model studies showed that acrylamide elimination, possibly via polymerization, increased in the presence of table salt [39]. Friedman and Levin [23] found that changes of the ionic strength induced by positively charged Na^+ ions affect the rate of addition reactions of amino groups of amino acids to the double bonds of conjugated vinyl compounds such as acrylamide. It is therefore also possible that changes in the ionic micro-environments near the potato strips contribute to the observed mitigating effects of positively charged metal ions.

On the other hand, frying products have shown one of the highest levels of acrylamide content, which has led several authors to study the effect of frying conditions on acrylamide formation in order to reduce it. Some results have shown that vacuum frying may be a mitigation alternative process for producing fried products with lower amounts of acrylamide [40]. For instance, in French fries, all the acrylamide is accumulated in the crust (no acrylamide presence in the core). Similarly, all the content of acrylamide in bread is located in the crust with no accumulation in the crumb; the amount of acrylamide in the bread crust increased with both baking time and temperature in the interval test [41]. These issues have led us to review recent information regarding to next challenges in processing for reducing acrylamide formation in foods. In that sense, researchers have focused using different approaches. For example, a patented method and an apparatus applied vacuum or/and light radiation to starchy foods. The starchy food could be flushed with a stream of gas such as air, oxygen, nitrogen, carbon dioxide, ozone, or a combination of them. Besides, the starchy food could be heated at a temperature among the ambient temperature to about the boiling point of acrylamide. This method was applied for removing acrylamide in potato chips and the treated samples (vacuum treatment: 85 °C, 0.001 torr, 10 min; light radiation: UV, 30 min), presented much lower acrylamide contents that the control samples [11]. Similarly, Bourg, Desai [42] and Bourg, Desai [43] disclosed a method for reducing the level of acrylamide in starch based food ingredients such as corn, wheat, barley, rye among other whole grains and mixtures thereof that are used to make fabricated food products. In a first invention, a method is presented towards reducing enzymes in corn, describing a process that comprises roasting corn, cooking the roasted corn, steeping the roasted corn, washing the corn to remove the pericarp layer and grinding the roasted corn to make roasted dough with reduced final acrylamide levels. In a second invention, acrylamide was removed from the food ingredients by polymerizing (using steam heat), dissolving (using an aqueous solution) and/or causing the vaporization (using vacuum pressure) of the acrylamide. These authors tested their invention in raw materials (corn kernels) in which it was possible to separate the germen by soaking. Then, they applied a sufficient heat to form polyacrylamide over the germen (since in this portion the most acrylamide is produced). The obtained product presented an acrylamide reduction about 90 % (from an initial value of 900 ppb of acrylamide).

In this way, another invention was developed to offer an efficient and easy way for restaurants and fine dining establishments to provide high quality fried foods that have a reduced acrylamide level. This invention may also be fully or partially applied to domestic preparation of fried food and considered a water blanching system to parboil high glycemic food immersed in water to remove reducing sugars. Potato samples were cut to the desired shape and size, and then they were blanched in water for 3 to 10 minutes depending on the size and shape of potato strips at a temperature of about 76 °C to about 88 °C. The acrylamide reduction level obtained with this method reached 80% to 90% (from an initial acrylamide amount of 2200 ppb) [7].

Another invention for reducing acrylamide concentration in thermally processed foods relied on the manipulation of various unit operations, particularly the peeling, cooking and selection unit operations [9]. For example, the peeling operation could be modified to provide a fully peeled potato slice. This invention comprised providing a continuous feed of peeled and sliced raw potatoes wherein the continuous feed of raw potato slices had at least 80% of potato peel removed. Then, potato chips could be analyzed and defective chips were removed before packaging. It is worth noting that the use of blanching solution with some amino acids (1% L-cysteine) to reduce acrylamide content in final products was also included in the flow sheet of the process. The authors also tested different kinds of heating methods, such as atmospheric and vacuum frying, microwave assisted frying and baking (in atmospheric and vacuum conditions). All the examples showed that vacuum conditions and pre-treatment applied in order to diminish the acrylamide precursors (*e.g.* blanching and soaking in amino acid solutions) resulted to be efficient technologies for mitigating acrylamide content in high acrylamide products (foods with acrylamide content at least about 1000 ppb). Finally, the optimized acrylamide reduction in products was about 90 % (from an initial acrylamide amount of 1900 ppb for potato chips) while keeping intact their sensorial properties (texture, flavor and color).

On the other hand, some authors have developed acrylamide mitigation technologies based on lowering the pH of the food products. Rydberg, Eriksson [44] and Rydberg, Eriksson [45] studied the effect of pH on acrylamide formation concluding that the dependence of acrylamide formation exhibited a maximum around at pH value of 8. Lower pH values enhanced acrylamide elimination and decelerated its formation. Besides, the following organic acids also induced acrylamide diminishing in French fries: benzoic, propionic, and sorbic acids. Citric acid and the amino acid glycine also mitigated acrylamide formation in a potato model system indicating that increased acidity may be used to decrease acrylamide formation in potatoes and possibly other foods [46]. The beneficial effects of low pH could result not only from protonation of the reactive free $R\text{-}NH_2$ group of asparagine to the nonreactive $R\text{-}NH_3^+$ form, but also from partial acid-catalyzed hydrolysis of asparagine to aspartic acid and of acrylamide to acrylic acid. However, low pH may adversely affect the taste of foods according to the organic acid concentration [47].

In this sense, many studies were conducted [48, 49] in an attempt to develop a method to effectively reduce the formation of acrylamide finding that, when a nucleophilic alpha-amino group of the asparagine is protonated and converted into a non-nucleophilic amine, the formation of asparagine can be effectively reduced. Therefore, their inventive method has the effect of highly reducing acrylamide by a simple treatment with a pH-lowering agent. So, foods should be treated with a pH-lowering agent whose pH was lower at least about 0.5 to 2.0 units lower than the intrinsic pH of the food. For this purpose, the pH-lowering agent was added to the foods at a concentration of about 0.02%-20.0% by weight. The pH-lowering agent which could be used included organic acids or their salts, a buffer solution containing the organic acid or it salt, inorganic acid or its salt, a buffer solution containing the inorganic acid or its salt, fruit juice, and a mixture of them. These inventors tested the effect of citric acid in two concentrations on acrylamide formation in fried and baked corn chips (0.1 % and 0.2%, respectively). In fried products the acrylamide amount was reduced from 45% to 80% for each concentration, respectively. In the same way, treated baked products also presented an acrylamide reduction of about 59 % and 73% for each concentration, respectively. This inventive method has the effect of highly reducing the formation of acrylamide without affecting the flavor and color of the foods or food ingredients tested. Additionally, Tomoda, Hanaoka [8] developed a similar method to diminish acrylamide content in instant fried noodles by using "*kansui*": a pH -lowering agent, which contains potassium carbonate, sodium carbonate, sodium hydrogen carbonate, potassium salt or sodium salt of phosphoric acids as well as an aqueous solution or a dilution with wheat flour, as specified in the food additive official regulation of Food Sanitation Japanese Law. In this way, acrylamide levels in the different kind of noodles tested were reduced from 100 ppb to 30 ppb. These results indicated that by changing some parameters of food processing such as time, temperature, pressure and pH; it would be possible to diminish the acrylamide content of high-temperature processed foods while maintaining intact their acceptability.

4.2. Reduction of Precursor's Levels in Raw Materials

One strategy to reduce acrylamide content in heat-processed foods would be to reduce the precursor levels in the raw materials. In this sense, various patented pre-treatments have been studied such as incorporating and/or exposing the food piece to: (i) Food grade micro-organisms (yeasts, bacteria and fungi) [19, 37, 50-52]); (ii) Asparaginase enzyme that converts free asparagine into aspartic acid [14-21]; (iii) Another amino acid that does not form acrylamide [13, 17, 20, 31, 45, 49, 53-60]; (iv) Saccharides and/or phenolic compounds having the ability of suppressing the formation of acrylamide [13, 38, 61-63]. (v) Divalent or tri valent cations[17, 23, 36-39, 64, 65].

4.2.1. Acrylamide Mitigation by Using Microorganisms

Yeast and other microorganisms are believed to suppress the formation of acrylamide in various high temperature heated foods by two mechanisms. (i) The live yeasts and other microorganisms assimilate the free sugars (especially glucose, fructose and sucrose) that react with asparagine to produce acrylamide under elevated temperatures conditions; (ii) Yeast and other microorganisms may also assimilate the free asparagine, thus removing a key precursor in the formation of acrylamide. Additionally, yeast and other microorganisms may possess the specific enzyme asparaginase which would simply de-amidate asparagine to yield aspartic acid and ammonia, again removing a key precursor for acrylamide formation.

Lindsay et al. patented a method for suppressing acrylamide formation and restoring browned color and flavor by treating and intermediate food material with a food – grade microorganism and/or a caramel coloring agent before the high temperature heating step [64]. The microorganisms (natural or genetically engineered) that can be used in this methodology include yeast (*Torula sp., Klyveromyces sp., Saccharomyces cerevisiae* and other sp.), bacteria (lactic bacteria such us: *Lactobacillus sp, Lactococcus sp., Leuconostoc sp.* among others) and fungi (*Aspergillus sp., Mucor sp and Rhizopus sp*.). These inventors applied yeast to reduce acrylamide level in different food materials that have not been traditionally treated with food-grade microorganisms mentioned previously. These tests considered yeast addition during the mixing process with the others ingredients in fabricated food products such as deep fried potato flake nuggets, fresh plant puree and deep fried corn strip. Finally, all the products were incubated by 60 minutes at 30 °C before to the heating process and the acrylamide reduction was of 50-70 %, 72 % and 40 %, respectively. The use of yeast and caramel agents for restoring browned flavor and brown color in potato chips was also studied achieving potato chips with desirable brown color while maintaining low levels of acrylamide.

Similarly, Aziz [19] developed a method for acrylamide reduction in starchy foods without altering their regular cooking process parameters (temperature and time) but by using microbial cell fermentation. In the invention, reducing sugar precursors of acrylamide were metabolized by yeast and bacteria in starchy foods prior to cooking. The process could be applied to both fabricated starchy foods, and fried potatoes (chips and French fries) which are extruded, baked or fried. In this process, raw food materials were introduced in a stirred fermentation tank with distilled water, dry yeast extract, active yeast or bacterial cells for 2.5 hr at pH 4 and 30 °C. This inventor tested the effect of different concentrations of microorganism (yeast or bacteria), pH, time and temperature of fermentation on acrylamide mitigation finding that the highest tested microorganism concentrations in the order of 2.5 g of yeast *(Saccharomyces cerevisiae)* and 10 x 10^9 CFU/ml of bacterial cell *(Streptococcus thermophilus)* provoked acrylamide reduction levels of 24 % and 70 %, respectively. It is worth to noting that for yeast, higher amounts than 2.5 g had the same acrylamide reduction effect. On the other hand, the effect of the time involved in the reaction was dependent upon the level of microbial cells used. Best results were obtained at 4 hr for yeast (2.5 g) and bacteria (5.9 x 10^{9} CFU/ml) with an acrylamide reduction of 24% and 64%, respectively (experimental conditions of pH 6 and 30 °C). On the other hand, fermentation temperature is not a trivial factor in the process due to its ability to change the fermentation rate and inactive microbial cells. In these experiments, highest acrylamide reduction was obtained at fermentation temperature of 30 °C for both yeast and bacterial cells. Finally, pH process around 4 produced the highest acrylamide reduction in the processed foods tested. This invention provides an inexpensive method to diminish acrylamide content, which preserves the flavor and texture of the cooked starchy food and which can be easily scaled-up to large volumes using available equipment. Similar processes such as fermentation of the raw food material prior to cooking in microbial cell brew have been patented by other inventors using different food grade microorganisms. For instance, Baardseth et al. [2004a, 2004b] developed three patents in which acrylamide reduction in fried, baked, grilled and roasted cereal foods and vegetables and also French frieswas obtained by using lactic acid treatments generating microorganisms and/or with acid. Acrylamide reduction for each group of products by using this method was 75 %, 60% and 38%, respectively; concluding that the use of food grade microorganisms to reduce acrylamide content in starchy food seems to be a useful and inexpensive process which can also maintain properly the desirable sensorial properties of the final products.

4.2.2. Acrylamide Mitigation by Using Asparaginase

Asparaginase, an enzyme that hydrolyzes asparagine to aspartic acid is a very effective mean for reducing acrylamide formation in foods via removal of one of the precursors (asparagine) of Maillard reaction. For instance, some researchers have pre-treated potato pieces with asparaginase after blanching, and the acrylamide levels in the resulting fried potatoes could be lowered by 60% - 85% in French fries and 60% in potato chips [66]. Besides, Zyzak, Sanders [67] developed a method for acrylamide reduction in low moisture starchy foods by using the enzyme asparaginase capable of hydrolyzing the amide group of free asparagine . This invention could be applied in batch, semi-batch and continuous processes. This enzyme could be added to food materials in different suitable forms such as powder or solution. Furthermore, the enzyme could be added to the food material in any suitable manner such as directly (*e.g.* sprinkled, poured or sprayed on the food material) or indirectly. Additionally, the enzyme could also be added to the food material at any suitable stage of the process (*e.g.* during the mixing of a dough or before, during or after maceration and by soaking the piece in an enzyme solution). This invention was tested in dehydrated potato product, potato chips and French fries finding that in all the cases the acrylamide reduction percentage was 95. Similarly, Elder, Fulcher [57] also patented the use of asparaginase for diminishing acrylamide content in foods which suffered Maillard reaction when they were processed at high temperatures . These authors also remarked that for higher enzymatic acrylamide reductions, pH control is crucial. The best performance is achieved by asparaginase at slightly acidic pH values (*e.g.* pH: 5) and/or when the pH is slightly basic (*e.g.* pH: 9).

On the other hand, Dria, Zyzak [16] developed a method to reduce the acrylamide content in roasted coffee beans using asparaginase. The enzyme could be added to coffee beans in various ways, either directly (*e.g.* sprinkled or poured) or indirectly (as a soaking solution). In order to obtain a higher acrylamide reduction, coffee beans should be pre-treated to facilitate the contact between the enzyme and it substrate (asparagine). For this purpose, coffee beans could be dried or steamed to open their pores. Another option for increasing the contact between asparaginase and asparagine implies particle size reduction of the product to create a larger surface area to allow solution uptake and/or extraction to occur more completely, uniformly and rapidly. All the examples in which the present invention was applied, presented an acrylamide reduction at least of 10%.

The enzymatic effectiveness of asparaginase in acrylamide reduction has been demonstrated by several authors. However, a relevant challenge for many inventors appears to be to discover which of the enzymes the best option is. Budolfsen, Jensen [14] studied the effect of different enzymes on acrylamide reduction and defined the alignment and encoding sequence of the tested enzymes (in order to homologize them). Extraction, purification and characterization of the enzymes were also described. Finally, they tested their enzyme effect on acrylamide reduction in potato chips concluding that asparaginase was the most effective.

Continuing, with this research, Matsui, Friis [68] developed a new asparaginase with improved activity at high temperatures. Based on such structural and functional considerations, asparaginase variants were constructed having modified amino acid residues at the identified positions and having altered physiochemical properties, especially improved thermo stability. The authors compared the half-life of the improved enzyme and wild type one, over French fries. For wild type enzyme it was 135 min and for the thermostable variant 157 min, corresponding to a 16 % increase. Considering that the cost is the main problem for using asparaginase, this invention is an important step to make it viable industrial application.

Boer [69] developed a novel process for enzymatic acrylamide reduction in food products processed at high temperatures. In this invention, a novel enzyme composition comprising asparaginase and at least one enzyme capable to oxidize reducing sugars was used for reducing acrylamide content in bakery products, deep frying products and roasted products. For this purpose, the author added the both enzymes prior to heating step in all mentioned food products, concluding that the addition of asparaginase together at least one sugar hydrolyzing enzyme resulted in a synergetic effect with respect to decrease acrylamide levels. The acrylamide remaining amount depended on the specific combination of both enzymes.

The use of asparaginase appears to be one of the most effective pre-treatment to mitigate acrylamide in foods processed at high temperatures. However, it is worth to mention that this pre-treatment is more expensive than others such as the using of amino acids, microorganisms and sugars.

4.2.3. Acrylamide Mitigation by Using Amino Acids

Addition of free amino acids other than asparagine or from a protein rich food component to a model or food matrix are reported to strongly reduce the acrylamide content as well in the heated products, probably by promoting competing reactions and/or by covalent binding the acrylamide formed .[17, 31, 45, 53].

The acrylamide molecule has two reactive sites: the conjugated double bond and the amide group, and thus can be eliminated by reaction with numerous food constituents [54]. Several studies about the effect of some amino acids different from asparagine on acrylamide formation/elimination kinetics, have shown that the addition of cysteine or lysine to model systems, significantly lowered the acrylamide formation, whereas the addition of glutamine had a strong promoting effect in acrylamide formation; interestingly, alanine shows a rather neutral effect on the acrylamide formation [13, 49, 53, 55] . Finally, glutamine together with asparagine are the most important free amino acids in potato tubers which could partly explain the high amount of acrylamide observed in fried or baked potato products [56].

Additionally, many inventors have developed some process to acrylamide mitigation by using amino acids. For instance, Kim, Park [21] patented a process for preparing snacks characterized by adding one or more amino acids selected from the group consisting of glycine, lysine and cysteine into raw materials of wheat based snacks prepared by a conventional process in order to diminish the acrylamide content in the final products without altering significantly quality parameters such as taste, flavor and appearance. In order to achieve the aforementioned objective, the inventors provided two processes for preparing the snacks: One based on wheat and the other based on potato. For wheat snacks, amino acids should be added to the dry raw ingredients during the mixing process. For potato snacks, peeled, cut, washed and blanched potatoes should be soaked in warm water containing one or more selected amino acids. In this case, potatoes could be blanched in a solution containing the amino acids or they could also be first blanched and then soaked in warm water with amino acids. The highest acrylamide reduction, while maintaining their desirable sensorial properties, was obtained when 1.5 % of cysteine was added. It is to note that higher acrylamide mitigation in wheat based snack was obtained when 3 % of amino acid was added, but the final product was very strong, dark, rough and dark. On the other hand, best results in acrylamide reduction of potato snack were obtained when 1.5 % of cysteine was added to the blanching solution (70 °C, 5 min). When higher amounts of amino acids were added, the final product lost their desirable organoleptic attributes. Similarly, Elder, Fulcher [57] have developed a process to diminish acrylamide content in fabricated, thermally processed snack foods by adding cysteine or lysine to the formula. In this way, the amino acids were first dissolved in water prior to adding to the dough and the best percentage of acrylamide reduction (~90) was obtained when using the highest cysteine amount (8.4 g cysteine/5496 g potato flakes). In order to skip organoleptic alterations in the final product, lower amounts of amino acids could be added in order to achieve significant acrylamide reduction while maintaining intact their attractive sensorial properties (texture, color and flavour). Finally, the inventors tested the effect of cysteine over acrylamide reduction in sliced fried potatoes. For this purpose, potato slices were immersed in an aqueous solution containing 1% of cysteine for 15 min at room temperature. Under this conditions the acrylamide level was reduce in the order of 100-200 ppb in the final product. Likewise, Tomoda, Hanaoka [20] developed a method capable of decreasing acrylamide formation during the cooking process of the food. This method comprised the addition to the food piece of at least one compound selected from the group consisting of (i) Neutral amino acids and salts, basic amino acids and salts; and (ii) Sulfonic acids and salts and/or least one peptide complex of peptides having, as constituting components, any one of the amino acids of (i). The inventors found that was possible to prepare instant fried noodles with lower acrylamide contents by adding a compound selected from the group (i) or (ii) to the noodles before the cooking. The effectiveness of different amino acids relied on the specific formulation of the final product.

Finley [58] used a N-acetyl-cysteine, rich peptide, and mixtures thereof to diminish the acrylamide content of food processed at high temperature. This invention could be applied to fabricated snack and also to fried potatoes and the inhibitor agent was added in the same way as detailed in previous examples: during mixing in fabricated snacks or into a soaking solution for sliced fried potatoes or French fries. The acrylamide reduction levels obtained were in the order of 30% - 50 % respectively. On the other hand, Eyal, Vitner [59] developed a method for preparing heat-treated foods from plants containing asparagine and at least one reducing sugar (*e.g.* potato and coffee among others). The method included contacting the raw ingredient with a reagent comprised an amino acid of low asparagine concentration (less than 5%) so that the coating layer could be formed. Any non-containing asparagine amino acid was suitable for this purpose. The coating was prepared by mixing amino acids and water at a concentration greater than 100 ppm and then this solution was added to the food by using a spraying system. The use of a coating over the raw ingredient could reduce the amount of acrylamide in the heated final product.

Kelleher and Basian [60] patented a method for minimizing acrylamide content in heated foods (fried and/or baked foods) by adding a dry protein mixture, a dry alkaline protein mixture, an aqueous alkaline protein mixture or an aqueous acidic protein mixture to a food prior to cooking. All inhibitor agents comprised myofibrillar and sarcoplasmatic proteins substantially free of myofibrils and sarcomeres. Both dry mixtures and aqueous solutions could be applied to the surface of the food to be cooked, injected or mixed with it. These inventors obtained acrylamide reduction levels of around 30% in deep fried potatoes by using extracted chicken proteins and the final product maintained its desirable sensorial properties. These results suggest that the use of amino acids to reduce acrylamide levels in food processed at high temperature seems to be viable process, however, the amount of inhibitor agent added could affect some quality parameters of the final product, especially in fabricated snacks, which not only can suffer undesirable changes over their color by acrylamide reduction, but also in their texture.

4.2.4. Acrylamide Mitigation by Using Non Reducing Sugars

Reducing sugars are essential precursors for acrylamide reaction. Replacing inverted sugar and honey in the recipe with the non reducing sugar sucrose resulted in a 20-fold decrease in acrylamide formation in gingerbread [13]. Adding the non reducing disaccharide trehalose (currently used in many commercial food applications) to glucose/asparagine or ascorbic acid/asparagine mixtures inhibited acrylamide formation, presumably by suppressing the generation of the intermediate carbonyl compounds such as pyruvaldehyde [61] . Significantly, less acrylamide was formed in cookies when the dough contained sucrose instead of glucose [38]. However, when the pH of the dough was lowered with the addition of citric acid, acrylamide content was decreased in glucose-containing dough, but unexpectedly increased in sucrose-containing dough, presumably due to hydrolysis of sucrose to the reducing sugars glucose and fructose. These results indicate that replacing the reducing sugars glucose and fructose with the non reducing sugars sucrose or trehalose may mitigate acrylamide formation under specific conditions.

Oku, Kubota [62] patented a method to diminish the acrylamide content of food processed at high temperature by testing the effect of non reducing sugars over acrylamide reduction not only in low humidity aqueous model systems (L-asparagine and D-glucose) with different amino acids but also in foods which suffers Maillard reaction. The specific organic substances used as acrylamide inhibitor agents were saccharides and/or phenolic substances (one or more saccharides selected from the group consisting of α,α-trehalose; α,β-trehalose; reduced palatinose; α-glucosyl α,α-trehalose; α-maltosyl α,α-trehalose; D-mannitol; D-erythritol; and β-cyclodextrin; and/or one or more phenolic substances selected from the group consisting of catechins and those saccharides derivatives). The results obtained in model systems revealed that the formation of acrylamide from L-asparagine and D-glucose was remarkably suppressed in the presence of some saccharides. Particularly, the formation of acrylamide from L-asparagine and D-glucose was suppressed to less than 50% by α,α-trehalose; α,β-trehalose; reduced palatinose; α-glucosyl α,α-trehalose; α-maltosyl α,α-trehalose; D-mannitol; D-erythritol; and β-cyclodextrin. Besides, different commercial non reducing sugars and phenolics were tested in fried potatoes, potato chips, crackers, butter rolls, roasted slices almonds, roasted wheat germ, coating for tempura, sweet potato snack, pretzels and seasoned instant noodles, and in all the cases the acrylamide inhibitor agent was effective achieving an acrylamide reductions higher than 30%. Lately, Bhaskar and Topor [63] developed a method for producing a thermally processed food with a low reducing sugar concentration in the former dough. The dough was cooked according to prior art methods to make low moisture, ready to eat product with acrylamide content lower than products with prior art potato flakes. Because reducing sugars drive both flavor and acrylamide, it can be difficult to lower the level of acrylamide while retaining their desired sensorial properties. This invention achieved that balance by adding dextrose to potato flakes with low reducing sugar concentration (0.5 %). The potatoes flakes were made from potato varieties with native low reducing sugar concentration (*e.g.* Saturna, Lady Rosett, Lady Clair, Hermes, Maris Piper among others) and/or treated with enzymes, blanching, fermentation or other suitable method to achieve a total reducing sugar concentration of less than about 0.5 %. Then, the dextrose was added to the low reducing sugar potato flakes (0.7 %) since it advantageously provided the necessary flavor drivers in the final product and because of the rate of acrylamide formation for dextrose is about six times slower than other sugars as fructose. These "enhanced" potato flakes contained less than 0.5 % and 0.7 % of native reducing sugars and dextrose, respectively. Acrylamide reduction achieved by using this method was at least 25%. Finally, the replacement of reducing sugars with the non reducing sugars or processing native varieties of potatoes with low reducing sugar content seems to be a useful way to diminish the acrylamide content of final products while maintaining their desired sensorial attributes.

In another invention, Zhang, Wu [70] presents a method for using bamboo leaf extract as an acrylamide inhibitor. It is stated that the extract, which can be comprised of a group of gingko extract, tea extract, rosemary extract, apple polyphenol extract, haw extract, onion extract, licorice extract, root of kudzuvine extract, grape seed extract and leech extract, can be either applied by mixing it with a coating material, soaking the food in an aqueous solution or spraying it with the solution. Measurements showed that the acrylamide inhibition rate varied between 15% and 98%.

4.2.5. Acrylamide Mitigation by Using Di-Valent and Tri-Valent Cations

It has been further discovered that acrylamide formation in heated foods can be reduced by adding multivalent cations before cooking. The advantages of using multivalent cations in food processing are numerous, which include: (i) They generally suppress the acrylamide reaction without causing unwanted side reactions; (ii) They are active under very mild conditions of temperature and pH; (iii) They are active at low concentration and (iv) Some of multivalent cations such as calcium are already widely approved for use in food processing [65]. In order to that, the effect of metal ions over acrylamide formation has been studied by several authors who concluded that the use of NaCl and $CaCl_2$ for instance could minimize the acrylamide formation during frying. These authors suggest that ionic and electronic associations between cations and asparagine suppress early-stage Maillard reactions [36, 37]. The preventive effect of Ca^{2+} ions may be due to the observed inhibition of the formation of the intermediate Schiff base that leads to acrylamide formation [38]. Model studies showed that acrylamide elimination, possibly via polymerization, increased in the presence of table salt [39]. Friedman et al. found that changes of the ionic strength induced by positively charged Na^+ ions affect the rate of addition reactions of amino groups of amino acids to the double bonds of conjugated vinyl compounds such as acrylamide [23]. It is therefore also possible that changes in the ionic micro-environments near the potato strips contribute to the observed mitigating effects of positively charged metal ions.

Elder, Fulcher [17] developed a method to diminish acrylamide content in fabricated, thermally processed foods by adding one of a select group of divalent or trivalent cations to the recipe. In preferred embodiment, the cation could come from the group including calcium, magnesium and aluminum salts. In this inventive process, a divalent or trivalent cations or combination of such cations was added to fabricated foods prior to cooking during milling, dry mix or wet mix, so that the cation was present throughout the food product. The cation was added to the dough in a sufficient amount to reduce acrylamide formation in the finished product to a desired level. These authors also tested the use of calcium chloride in baked potato flakes before heating and concluded that the acrylamide reduction level was directly proportional to the concentration of calcium chloride solutions (10% calcium chloride solutions presented the highest acrylamide reduction level).

On the other hand, Corrigan [65] patented a method for the reduction of acrylamide in heat processed foods. This method comprised adding to a food material a water soluble, non-chelated and multivalent cation: calcium lactate and calcium chloride, either in solid or liquid form (*e.g.* in solution). The multivalent cation could be added with the other ingredients during the mixing and preparing of the dough. It also could be added to the food before, during or after maceration. The effective amount of the multivalent cation to be used would depend upon its complexing ability and the level of asparagine present in the food to be heat processed. This method was tested in fried fabricated potato crisps, French fries, tortilla and corn chips, and acrylamide reduction levels around 90% could be achieved by using this invention. The addition of divalent cations effectively reduced the amount of acrylamide found in the end product while minimally affecting its sensorial quality. Further, such a method of acrylamide reduction is generally easy to implement and adds little or no cost to the overall process. Despite the use of cations is an inexpensive alternative for acrylamide mitigation, it is important to note that the use of chelating compounds has been associated with the formation of allergen compounds.

4.2.6. Acrylamide Mitigation by Using Genetic Modification

Genetic approaches for reducing the levels of acrylamide precursors (asparagine, reducing sugars) in cereal and potato plants are active areas of research [71-73]. Ideally, breeding and/ or suppressing genes that encode enzymes governing the biosynthesis of free asparagine may achieve decreasing in asparagine content. Besides, selection from available varieties that contain low levels of asparagine for dietary use offers another approach to mitigate acrylamide content. Asparagine levels in wheat grown under conditions of severe sulfate depletion were up to 30 times greater as compared to levels in wheat grown in soils with sufficient amounts of sulfate fertilizer [74]. This was also reflected in observed acrylamide levels of baked products. Levels in products prepared from high-asparagine wheat flours ranged from 2600 to 5200 μg/kg and those from wheat grown under normal conditions, from 600 to 900 μg/kg. These observations suggest the need to develop new wheat varieties with low asparagine content and that wheat should be either be grown in soils with adequate amounts of sulfates or that the soil should be amended to provide adequate sulfates to the crops. The acrylamide content of breads largely depended on the wheat used to prepare the dough and is linked the levels of free asparagine and crude protein [75]. Nitrogen fertilization of the soil induced elevated amino acid and protein contents, resulting in increased acrylamide levels in breads.

Elmore, Mottram [76] and Muttucumaru, Halford [74] showed that for three potato varieties (a) low sulfur levels in the soil led to a decrease in acrylamide formation and in an increase in free amino acids and sugars; (b) elevated reducing sugar levels caused by the low-sulfur soils did not correlate with elevated acrylamide content; and (c) free asparagine levels as a proportion of the total free amino acid pool did correlate with acrylamide content. These authors proposed that free asparagine as a percent of total amino acids is rate limiting and suggested that when the sugar content is low, as it is in potato tubers, competition between asparagine and other amino acids for participation in the Maillard reaction may be a key determinant of the amount of acrylamide that is formed during processing. Due to this issue, it seems to be a relevant topic to develop a method to reduce acrylamide by using genetic modification of raw materials.

Rommens, Ye [77], developed an invention which provided polynucleotide and polypeptide sequences isolated from plants, methods for reducing free asparagine levels in plants, methods for producing heat processed foods containing reduced levels of acrylamide. This invention employed methods from genetic engineering to reduce the levels of asparagine in the starchy tissues of a crop plant by 50 %. The level of asparagine was reduced by lowering the level of asparagine biosynthesis and/or increasing the level of asparagine metabolism. Either mechanism could entail down-regulating genes that were directly or indirectly involved in each asparagine pathway. The gene involved in asparagine biosynthesis encoded an asparagine synthetase. In another aspect, genes that were indirectly involved in an asparagine pathway were selected from the group consisting of a glutamine synthetase gene, a nitrate reductase gene, a 14-3-3 gene, and a hexokinase gene. The inventors tested their method in breakfast cereals, cookies, ground coffee, chocolate, crackers, wheat bread, French fries, baked fries and chips. All products produced by a transgenic plant of specific variety presented lower acrylamide levels (5% - 90 % of reduction) than those from non-transgenic plant of the same variety.

Additionally, Rommens [71] developed his last invention by designing a new plant breeding process which improved the agronomic performance of crop plants by using genetic material that is also used in classical breeding. Instead of sexually recombining entire genomes at random, as done in classical breeding, specific genetic elements were rearranged in vitro and inserted back into individual plant cells. Plants obtained through this new plant breeding process do not contain foreign nucleic acid but only contain nucleic acid from the plant species selected for transformation or plants that are sexually compatible with the selected plant species. Plants developed through this new plant breeding process presented improved tuber storage and health characteristics allowing the acquirement of final products with lower acrylamide content.

In another invention, Soyka, Frohberg [78] approaches acrylamide reduction by genetically modifying the plant material in order to reduce the contents of soluble sugars glucose, fructose and sucrose. In this invention, it is shown that potato chips and potato crisps produced from potato tubers having decreased R1 gene expression show less acrylamide content compared with corresponding products which were produced from potato tubers from corresponding non-genetically-modified wild type plants.

5. Several Technologies Combined

Some authors have patented inventions in which several of the above acrylamide mitigation technologies are combined in order to improve the effectiveness of the method. Elder, Fulcher [18] patented an invention in which the structure of a starch-based food containing asparagine was disrupted, and the acrylamide reducing agent was added to the food prior to drying. The agent can include any of a divalent or trivalent cations or combination of such cations, and acids or amino acids. The agent could be added during milling, dry mix or wet mix, so that the agents are present throughout the food. In preferred embodiments, calcium cations were used in conjunction with phosphoric acid, citric acid and/or cysteine. The combination of agents could be adjusted in order to reduce the acrylamide formation in the finished product to desired level, while minimally affecting its sensorial quality. Thus, potato chips, French fries and tortilla chips produced according to this method presented acrylamide concentrations of 5ppb, 10ppb and 10ppb respectively; for all the above cases the acrylamide formation was reduced about over 90%.

Boudreaux, Desai [79] proposed an invention to reduce the acrylamide level in foods by solubilizing the cell wall of a plant-based food and contacting the asparagine with asparaginase an asparagine reducing agent in combination with various amino acids, polyvalent cations, and free thiols to enhance the destruction of the acrylamide precursor. Solubilization of the cell wall and contacting the cell wall with asparaginase could be done in sequence or simultaneously. Further, cell weakling mechanisms could be used alone or in combination. For instance, the cell wall could be solubilized by microwave energy followed by application of a pressure differential. These inventors found that the use of a combination of lysine, cysteine and calcium chloride on baked fabricated potato chips provided almost a total reduction of acrylamide content in the product. On the other hand, new health trends are looking for fresh technologies which are capable to produce allergen free products. Respecting to this requirement, Shannon and Markus [80] developed a fresh fry cooking and handling system for reducing acrylamide in carbohydrate glycemic foods without the use of chelating compounds, chemicals, carbonyl group blockers, multivalent cations or other additives. This invention included different steps: product storage conditions, size of the product, blanching temperature and monitoring of the cooking oil. The authors tested their method in baked (1 hour at 190.6 °C) potatoes (Idaho Russet Burbank Variety , 21 % solids), obtaining an acrylamide level of 0. The obtained results could indicate that the correct manage of storage and blanching temperatures should be a good alternative for producing organic starchy products. Likewise the monitoring of oil represents an essential issue to produce healthy fried products.

6. Is it Possible to Produce a "Reduced-Acrylamide" Product That Has a Good Consumer Acceptance?

Most of the examples showed that not only the changes in process parameters but also the pre-treatment applied to diminish the levels of acrylamide precursors resulted to be efficient technologies for reducing acrylamide content, while keeping intact their sensorial properties (texture, flavor and color).

Table 2. Patented techniques for acrylamide mitigation in foods processed at high temperatures. Adapted from Mariotti, Pedreschi [81]

ID US Patent	Name	Inventors	Impacted specific foods (examples)	Category Method
US20060083832A1	Reducing acrylamide in fried food.	Shannon, G.	Fried starchy products (potato chips and French fries)	Changes on processing parameters
US20040105929A1	Instant fried noodles with lowered acrylamide and method of preparing the same.	Tomoda, Y., Hanaoka, A., Yasuda, T., Takayama, T., Hiwatashi, A.	Intant fried noodles	Changes on processing parameters
WO2009152348A1	Method for reducing acrylamide formation in thermally processed foods.	Cantley, C., Desai, P., Michel, E., Rao, M., Vindiola, G.	Fried starchy products (potato chips)	Changes on processing parameters
US20040115321A1	Method for preventing acrylamide formation during heat treatment of food	Tricoit, J., Salucki, G., Rousset, G.	Fried starchy products (potato chips and French fries)	Changes on processing parameters
US20030219518A1	Process and apparatus for reducing residual level of acrylamide in heat processed food	Zhaoaying, L.	Potato chips, cereal, fried flour products	Changes on processing parameters
US20100255167A1	Method for reducing acrylamide in food products	Bourg, W., Desai, M., Shepard, B., Topor, M., Vogel, G.	Potato chips, cereal, fried flour products	Changes on processing parameters
US20070196556A1	Process for the roasting of cocoa	Van der Meer, H.	Potato chips, cereal, fried flour products	Changes on processing parameters
US20070281062A1	Process for neutralizing enzymes in corn	Bourg, W.	Corn kernels	Changes on processing parameters
US20090304879A1	Method for using bamboo leaf extract as actylamide inhibitor for heat processing food.	Zhang, Y., Wu, X., Zhang, Y., Zhang, G., Lou, D., Dong, Y.	Potato, cereals, bakery products.	Changes on processing parameters
WO2004098313A1.	Acrylamide Reduction in Food.	Ritter, A., Moglich, B.	Bakery products, potato deep frying products and roasted starchy products	pH lowering agents
US20060240174 A1	Method for the reduction of acrylamide formation.	Jung, M.Y., Choi, D.S., and Ju, J.W	Fried and baked corn chips, fried potatoes	pH lowering agents
US 20040086597 A1	Reduction of acrylamide formation in cooked starchy foods.	Aziz, A.	Bakery products, potato deep frying products and roasted starchy products	Reduction of precursors (Microorganism)
WO2004028276 A2	Reduction of acrylamide formation in cereal-based food processing.	Baardseth, P., Blom, H., Enersen, G., Skrede G., Slinde, E., Sundt, T., Thomassen, T.	Fried, baked, grilled and roasted cereal foods	Reduction of precursors (Microorganism)

Table 2. (Continued)

ID US Patent	Name	Inventors	Impacted specific foods (examples)	Category Method
WO2004028276 A2	Reduction of acrylamide formation in cereal-based food processing.	Baardseth, P., Blom, H., Enersen, G., Skrede G., Slinde, E., Sundt, T., Thomassen, T.	Fried, baked, grilled and roasted cereal foods	Reduction of precursors (Microorganism)
WO2004028277 A2	Reduction of acrylamide formation in food processing.	Baardseth, P., Blom, H., Enersen, G., Skrede G., Slinde, E., Sundt, T., Thomassen, T.	Vegetables	Reduction of precursors (Microorganism)
WO2004028278 A2	Reduction of acrylamide formation.	Baardseth, P., Blom, H., Enersen, G., Skrede G., Slinde, E., Sundt, T., Thomassen,T.	French Fries	Reduction of precursors (Microorganism)
US7396670B2	Asparaginases and method of preparing a heat-treated product.	Budolfsen, G., Jensen, M., Heldt-Hansen, H.P., Stringer, M.A	Potato chips	Reduction of asparagine (Asparaginase)
US20040081724A1	Method for reduction of acrylamide in roasted coffee beans having reduced levels of acrylamide, and article of commerce	Dria, G., Zyzak, D., Gutwein, R., Villagran, F., Young, H., Bunke, P., Yau Tak Lin, P., Howie, J., Schafermeyer, R.	Coffee beans	Reduction of asparagine (Asparaginase)
US20050074538.	Method for reducing acrylamide formation in thermally processed foods.	Elder, V.A., Fulcher, J.G., Leung, H., Topor, M.G	Cereal foods	Reduction of asparagine (Asparaginase)
US20040109926A1.	Method of decreasing acrylamide in food cooked under heat.	Tomoda, Y., Hanaoka, A., Yasuda, T., Takayama, T., Hiwatashi, A.	Bakery products, potato deep frying products and roasted products	Reduction of asparagine (Asparaginase)
US20050058757A1	Snacks having lower acrylamide levels and process for preparation thereof	Kim, J.H., Park, S.H., Kang, W. S., Min, B.J., Kim, H.J., Seong, B.G., Kim, C.T., Lee, C.Y., Oh, S.S.	Bakery products, potato deep frying products and roasted products	Reduction of asparagine (Asparaginase)
US20050214411A1	Methods for suppressing acrylamide formation and restoring browned color and flavor.	Lindsay, R., Jang, S.	Deep fried potato flake nuggets, fresh plant puree and deep fried corn strip	Reduction of asparagine (Asparaginase)
US20040058046A1.	Method for reducing acrylamide in foods, foods having reduced levels of acrylamide, and article of commerce	Zyzak, V. , Sanders, R., Stojanovic, M., Gruber, D., Yau Tak Lin, P., Martínez-Serna, M.D., Howie, J., Schafermeyer, R.	Bakery products, potato deep frying products and roasted products	Reduction of asparagine (Asparaginase)

ID US Patent	Name	Inventors	Impacted specific foods (examples)	Category Method
US20060127534	Method for reducing acrylamide formation in thermally processed foods.	Elder, V., Fulcher, J., Leung, H.	Bakery products, potato deep frying products and roasted products	Reduction of asparagine (Asparaginase)
US20100221385A1	Asparaginases.	Matsui, T., Friis, E., Yamagishi, A.	French Fries	Reduction of asparagine (Asparaginase)
US20110070333A1	Novel process for enzymatic acrylamide reduction in food products	Boer, L.	Bakery products, potato deep frying products and roasted products	Reduction of asparagine (Asparaginase)
US20040166227A1	Method for reducing acrylamide formation in thermally processed foods.	Elder, V., Fulcher, J., Leung, H., Topor, M	Bakery products, potato deep frying products and roasted products	Use of other amino acids
US7267834B2	Method for reducing acrylamide formation in thermally processed foods.	Elder, V., Fulcher, J., Leung, H., Topor, M.	Bakery products, potato deep frying products and roasted starchy products	Use of other amino acids
US20050196504 A1.	Reduction of Acrylamide in processed foods.	Finley, J.W.	Bakery products, potato deep frying products and roasted products	Use of other amino acids
US20070031559 A1	Low Acrylamide Food.	Eyal, A., Vitner, A., Purtle, I.	Bakery products, potato deep frying products and roasted products	Use of other amino acids
US20070042092 A1	Process for reducing acrylamide in cooked food.	Kelleher, S., Basian, K.	Bakery products, potato deep frying products and roasted products	Use of other amino acids
US20040058045A1	Method for reducing acrylamide in thermally processed foods.	Elder, V.A., Fulcher, J.G., Leung, H., Topor, M.G.	Potato chips, French fries	Use of non reducing sugars
US20060194743A1	Method for inhibiting acrylamide formation and use thereof.	Oku, K., Kubota, H., Fukuda, S., Miyake, T.	Bakery products, potato deep frying products and roasted products	Use of non reducing sugars
20100143540 A1	Method for making a low-acrylamide content snack with desired organoleptical properties.	Bhaskar, A., Topor, M	Bakery products, deep frying products and roasted products	Use of non reducing sugars
US20050079254 A1	Method for reducing acrylamide in foods, foods having reduced levels of acrylamide, and article of commerce	Corrigan, P.	Tested in fried fabricated potato crisps, French fries, tortilla and corn chips	Use of divalent and tri-valent cations
US20070074304	Low Acrylamide Foods	Rommens, C.	Potatoes	Use of genetic modification
US20100015319A1	Precise Breeding – Low Acrylamide Foods.	Rommens, C.	Potatoes	Use of genetic modification

Table 2. (Continued)

ID US Patent	Name	Inventors	Impacted specific foods (examples)	Category Method
US20060233930A1	Process for Reducing the Acrylamide content of heat-treated foods	Soyka, C., Frohberg, C., Quanz, M., Essigmann, B.	Dough mixtures, potato slices, granules and maize grains.	Use of genetic modification
US20070178219A1	Method for reducing acrylamide formation.	Boudreaux, E., Desai, P., Elder, V., Fulcher, J., Leung, H., Li, W., Topor, M.	Bakery products, potato deep frying products and roasted products	Several combined technologies

In this sense, vacuum frying may be considered as an alternative process for producing fried and baked products with lower amounts of acrylamide (50% - 90% of reduction). However, one critical barrier for the implementation of this technology is the high cost that working in vacuum pressure conditions could implicate, moreover if it is used at domestic level.

On the other hand the blanching of raw food or food ingredients in hot water (~80 °C) with or without some amino acids added, has shown to be an efficient and easy way for restaurants and fine dining establishments to provide high quality fried foods that have a reduced acrylamide level (reduction of ~80% to 90%).

Likewise, acrylamide mitigation technologies based on lowering the pH of the food products have been recognized as successful and inexpensive inventions, reaching acrylamide reductions near to the 80% both in fried and baked products without affecting the flavor and color of the foods or food ingredients tested.

Additionally, the reduction of acrylamide precursor's levels in raw materials to diminish the acrylamide content in starchy food seems to be a useful and inexpensive mitigation approach which can also maintain properly the desirable sensorial properties of the final products. In these sense several method have been proposed in order to diminish the sugar and/or asparagines content.

For instance, the use of yeast and other microorganisms that could assimilate free sugars and/or react with asparagines has presented satisfactory results in several food products. However in some cases the use of a caramel colorant which restores the desirable color and flavor was mentioned as necessary in order to maintain the consumer acceptation. In the same way, the use of asparaginase appears to be one of the most effective pre-treatment to mitigate acrylamide in foods processed at high temperatures. The most important aspects of this approach lies on the ease of use and the quality of results. In French fries, acrylamide reduction can attain 95%. It is worth to note that it is more expensive than other pre-treatment such as amino acids, microorganisms and sugars, but thanks to improved technology and growing market adoption this approach has become one of the main trends in acrylamide reduction methods. Furthermore, considering that glutamine together with asparagine are the most important free amino acids in potato tubers, many inventors have developed processes to mitigate acrylamide by using other amino acids, which are available in commercial formats. The use of these inventions has permitted a reduction of acrylamide levels close to 90% in potato flakes. However, it is to note that the amount of inhibitor agent added could affect some quality parameters of the final product, especially in fabricated snacks, which not only can suffer non desirable changes in their color to reduce acrylamide, but also in their texture.

By using the same previous approach inventors have developed alternatives for replacing sugars, most notably glucose and fructose with non-reducing sugars such as disaccharides, saccharides and/or phenolic substances. Because reducing sugars drive both flavor and acrylamide, it can be difficult to lower the level of acrylamide while retaining desired sensorial properties. Although both the use of other amino acids as non reducing sugars are methods that still represent a field of research and invention; it is worth to noting that they are being slowly replaced by recent trends, such as genetic engineering and more successful approaches such as enzymes. Another invention found to effectively reduce the acrylamide content in the end thermally processed foods is the addition of divalent or trivalent cations (reduction up to 90% in potato products) while minimally affecting its sensorial quality. In general terms this method of acrylamide reduction is generally easy to implement and adds little or no cost to the overall process, however it could cause the formation of other compound harmful to health. Currently, the use of use of genetic tools to reduce the acrylamide precursor′s levels has been the driver for several studies and inventions, which have led to methods that enable acrylamide reduction up to 90% in cereals, snacks, chocolate and chips based on transgenic plants, compared with the same variety of the non transgenic plants. However the food safety of transgenic foods is still a not concluding issue, thus although genetic modification is an active area of investigation and it would arguably become an important source of patents with novel methods, its application could be rejected by some consumers. Finally, the use of several technologies combines has been found as the most effective approach in dietary acrylamide mitigation due to the reduced-acrylamide products present a better conservation of their desirable sensorial attributes because of it is possible to decrease the intensity and duration of each treatment alone. Table 2 summarizes most current patent information previously discussed in this book chapter.

CONCLUSION

Maillard reaction is the main route for acrylamide formation in foods processed at high temperature. Thus a variety of methods for acrylamide reduction have been developed by inhibiting this reaction through changes in process parameters and reductions in acrylamide precursor levels in raw materials. Although most of these techniques have successfully diminished acrylamide content in several foods, sensorial quality of treated products is still a pending issue. For developing technologies for acrylamide mitigation is neccesary consider not only their effect on the safety of the product but also in its final sensorial quality. In this sense, we propose a new mitigation approach which can be transversally applied to different food matrices in order to reduce significantly acrylamide formation without considerable damage their sensorial attributes.

ACKNOWLEDGMENTS

The authors appreciate the financial support of the FONDEF Project, FONDEF D10I1109.

REFERENCES

[1] IARC, Some industrial chemicals. *Monographs on the evaluation of carcinogenic risks to humans.* I.A.f.R.o. Cancer, Editor 1994: Lyon, France.

[2] EC, *Opinion of the Scientific Committee on Food on new findings regarding the presence of acrylamide in food.*, E. Commission, Editor 2002: Belgium.

[3] Ciesarova, Z., M. Suhaj, and J. Horvathova,et al., Correlation between acrylamide level and antioxidant activity of spice extracts in a model food system. *Journal of Food and Nutrition Research*, 2008. 47(1): p. 1-5.

[4] Mottram, D.S., B.L. Wedzicha, and A.T. Dodson, Acrylamide is formed in the Maillard reaction. *Nature*, 2002. 419: p. 448-449.

[5] Tareke, E., et al., Analysis of acrylamide, a carcinogen formed in heated foodstuffs. *Journal of Agricultural and Food Chemistry*, 2002. 50: p. 4998-5006.

[6] Pedreschi, F., et al., Color kinetics and acrylamide formation in NaCl soaked potato chips. *Journal of Food Engineering*, 2007. 79(3): p. 989-997.

[7] Shannon, G., *Reducing acrylamide in fried food*, 2006.

[8] Tomoda, Y., et al., *Instant fried noodles with lowered acrylamide and method of preparing the same*, 2004.

[9] Cantley, C., et al., *Method for reducing acrylamide formation in thermally processed foods,* 2009.

[10] Tricoit, J., G. Salucki, and G. Rousset, *Method for preventing acrylamide formation during heat treatment of food.*, 2004.

[11] Zhaoaying, L., *Process and apparatus for reducing residual level of acrylamide in heat processed food.*, 2003.

[12] Van der Meer, H., *Process for the roasting of cocoa*, 2007.

[13] Amrein, T.M., et al., Acrylamide in gingerbread: Critical factors for formation and possible ways for reduction. *Food Chem.,* 2004. 52: p. 4282-4288.

[14] Budolfsen, G., et al., *Asparaginases and method of preparing a heat-treated product.,* 2008.

[15] Zyzak, D.V.S., R. A.; Stojanovic, M.; Tallmadge, D. H.; Eberhart, B. L.; Ewald, D. K.; Gruber, D. C.; Morsch, T. R.; Strothers, M. A.; Rizzi, G. P.; Villagran, M. D., Acrylamide formation mechanism in heated foods. . *Journal of Agricultural and Food Chemistry*, 2003. 51: p. 4782-4787.

[16] Dria, G., et al., *Method for reduction of acrylamide in roasted coffee beans having reduced levels of acrylamide, and article of commerce*, 2004.

[17] Elder, V.A., et al., *Method for reducing acrylamide in thermally processed foods*, 2004.

[18] Elder, V.A., et al., *Method for reducing acrylamide formation in thermally processed foods.*, 2005.

[19] Aziz, A., *Reduction of acrylamide formation in cooked starchy foods.*, 2004.

[20] Tomoda, Y., et al., *Method of decreasing acrylamide in food cooked under heat*, 2004.

[21] Kim, J.H., et al., *Snacks having lower acrylamide levels and process for preparation thereof.* , 2005.

[22] Ritter, A. and B. Moglich, *Acrylamide Reduction in Food*, 2004.

[23] Friedman, M. and C.E. Levin, Review of methods for the reduction of dietary content & toxicity of acrylamide. . *Journal of Agricultural and Food Chemistry,* 2008. 56: p. 6113-6140.

[24] Kempken, F., J. C., and R. C., Precise Breeding Through All-Native DNA Transformation. Genetic Modification of Plants. . *Biotechnology in Agriculture and Forestry,* 2010. 64(1): p. 61-77.

[25] Anon, Acrylamide Health and Safety Guide, W. *IPCS International Programme on Chemical Safety In Health and Safety*, Editor 1991.

[26] Bologna, L.S., et al., Analysis of residual acrylamide in field crops. *Journal of Chromatographic Science* 1999. 37: p. 240-244.

[27] Smith, E.A., S.L. Prues, and F.W. Oehme, Environmental degradation of polyacrylamides. 1. *Effects of artificial environmental conditions: Temperature, light, and pH. Ecotoxicology and Environmental Safety*, 1996. 35: p. 121-135.

[28] Gertz, C. and S. Klostermann, Analysis of acrylamide and mechanisms of its formation in deep-fried products. *European Journal of Lipid Science and Technology,* 2002. 104: p. 762-771.

[29] Stadler, R., Blank, I., Varga, N., Robert, F., Hau, J. r., Guy, P., Robert, M., & Riediker, S. , Acrylamide from Maillard reaction products. *Nature*, 2002. 419: p. 449-450.

[30] Stadler, R. and G. Scholz, Acrylamide: an update on current knowledge in analysis, levels in food, mechanisms of formation, and potential strategies of control. *Nutrition reviews*, 2004. 62: p. 449-467.

[31] Becalski, A., et al., Acrylamide in foods: occurrence, sources, and modeling. *Journal of Agricultural and Food Chemistry*, 2003. 51: p. 802-808.

[32] Elmore, J.S., et al., Measurement of Acrylamide and Its Precursors in Potato, Wheat, and Rye Model Systems. *Journal of Agricultural and Food Chemistry*, 2005. 53(4): p. 1286-1293.

[33] Pedreschi, F., et al., Color changes and acrylamide formation in fried potato slices. *Food Research International*, 2005. 38(1): p. 1-9.

[34] Vattem, D.A. and K. Shetty, Acrylamide in food: a model for mechanism of formation and its reduction. *Innovative Food Science and Emerging Technologies,* 2003. 4: p. 331-338.

[35] De Vleeschouwer, K., et al., Kinetics of Acrylamide Formation/Elimination Reactions as Affected by Water Activity. *Biotechnology Progress.* , 2007. 23(3): p. 722-728.

[36] Lindsay, R.C. and S. Jang, *Chemical intervention strategies for substantial suppression of acrylamide formation in fried potato products, in Chemistry and Safety of Acrylamide in Food,* M. Friedman, Mottram, D. S., Editor 2005, Springer: New York. p. 393-404.

[37] Lindsay, R.C. and S.J. Jang, Chemical intervention strategies for substantial suppression of acrylamide formation in fried potato products. . *Advances in Experimental Medicine and Biology,* 2005. 561: p. 393-404.

[38] Gokmen, V. and T. Palakzaglu, Acrylamide formation in foods during thermal processing with a focus on frying. *Food and Bioprocess Technology*, 2008. 1: p. 35-42.

[39] Kolek, E., P. Simko, and P. Simon, Effect of NaCl on the decrease of acrylamide content in a heat-treated model food matrix. *Journal of Food and Nutrition Research,* 2006. 45: p. 17-20.

[40] Granda, C., Moreira, R. and Tichy, S. , Reduction of Acrylamide Formation in Potato Chips by Low-temperature Vacuum Frying. *Journal of Food Science*, 2004. 69: p. E405-E411.

[41] Brathen, E. and S.H. Knutsen, Brathen, E., & Knutsen, S. H. (2005). Effect of temperature and time on the formation of acrylamide in starch-based and cereal model systems, flat breads and bread. *Food Chemistry,* 2005. 92: p. 693-700.

[42] Bourg, W., et al., *Process for neutralizing enzymes in corn*, 2007.

[43] Bourg, W., et al., *Method for reducing acrylamide in food products*, 2010.

[44] Rydberg, P., et al., Investigations of factors that influence the acrylamide content of heated foodstuffs. *Journal of Agricultural and Food Chemistry*, 2003. 51: p. 7012-7018.

[45] Rydberg, P., et al., *Factors that influence the acrylamide content of heated foods, in Chemistry and Safety of Acrylamide in Food*, M. Friedman, Mottram, D.S., Editor 2005: New York. p. 317-328.

[46] Low, M.Y., et al., Effect of Citric Acid and Glycine Addition on Acrylamide and Flavor in a Potato Model System. *Journal of Agricultural and Food Chemistry,* 2006. 54(16): p. 5976-5983.

[47] Mestdagh, F., et al., Impact of additives to lower the formation of acrylamide in a potato model system through pH reduction and other mechanisms. *Food Chemistry,* 2008. 107(1): p. 26-31.

[48] Jung, M.Y., D.S. Choi, and J.W. Ju, *Method for the reduction of acrylamide formation*, 2006.

[49] Jung, M.Y., D.S. Choi, and J.W. Ju, A novel technique for limitation of acrylamide formation in fried and baked corn chips and in French fries. *Journal of Food Science*, 2003. 68: p. 1287-1290.

[50] Baardseth, P., et al., *Reduction of acrylamide formation*, 2012.

[51] Baardseth, P., et al., *Reduction of acrylamide formation.*, 2004.

[52] Baardseth, P., et al., *Reduction of acrylamide formation in food processing.,* 2004.

[53] Biedermann, M., et al., Methods for determining the potential of acrylamide formation and its elimination in raw materials for food preparation, such as potatoes. *Mitteilungen aus Lebensmitteluntersuchung und Hygiene* 2002. 93: p. 653-667.

[54] Leufvén, A. and H. Lingnert, Influencing Acrylamide Formation in Food Processing-Introductory Model Experiments Performed at SIK, in Public report of the *Swedish Institute for Food and Biotechnology*, 2003: Sweden.

[55] Claeys, W., K. De Vleeschouwer, and M. Hendrickx, Effect of Amino Acids on Acrylamide Formation and Elimination Kinetics. *Biotechnology*, 2005. 21: p. 1525-1530.

[56] Eppendorfer, W.H. and S.W. Billie, Free and total amino acids composition of edible parts of beans, kale, spinach, cauliflower and potatoes as influenced by nitrogen fertilization and phosphorus and potassium deficiency. *Journal of the Science of Food and Agricultural,* 1996. 71: p. 449-458.

[57] Elder, V., et al., *Method for reducing acrylamide formation in thermally processed foods.,* 2007.

[58] Finley, J.W., *Reduction of Acrylamide in processed foods.,* 2005.

[59] Eyal, A., A. Vitner, and I. Purtle, *Low Acrylamide Food.* , 2007.

[60] Kelleher, S. and K. Basian, *Process for reducing acrylamide in cooked food.,* 2007.

[61] Oku, K., et al., Suppressive Effect of Trehalose on acrylamide formation form asparagine and reducing saccharides. *Bioscience, Biotechnology, and Biochemistry*, 2005. 69(8): p. 1520-1526.
[62] Oku, K., et al., *Method for inhibiting acrylamide formation and use thereof.*, 2006.
[63] Bhaskar, A. and M. Topor, *Method for making a low-acrylamide content snack with desired organoleptical properties,* 2010.
[64] Lindsay, R. and S. Jang, *Methods for suppressing acrylamide formation and restoring browned color and flavor* , 2005.
[65] Corrigan, P., *Method for reducing acrylamide in foods, foods having reduced levels of acrylamide, and article of commerce* , 2005.
[66] Pedreschi, F., et al., Acrylamide reduction under different pre-treatments in French fries. *Journal of Food Engineering*, 2007. 79: p. 1287-1294.
[67] Zyzak, V., et al., *Method for reducing acrylamide in foods, foods having reduced levels of acrylamide, and article of commerce.*, 2004.
[68] Matsui, T., E. Friis, and A. Yamagishi, *Asparaginases*, 2010.
[69] Boer, L., *Novel process for enzymatic acrylamide reduction in food products.*, 2011.
[70] Zhang, Y., et al., *Methods for using bamboo leaf extract as acrylamide inhibitor for heat processing food*, 2009.
[71] Rommens, C., *Precise Breeding – Low Acrylamide Foods.* , 2010.
[72] Gerenda´s, J. and F. Heuser, Influence of nitrogen and potassium supply on contents of acrylamide precursors in potato tubers and on acrylamide accumulation in French fries. *Journal of Plant Nutrition,* 2007. 30: p. 1499-1516.
[73] Halford, N.G., et al., Genetic and agronomic approaches to decreasing acrylamide precursors in crop plants. *Food Additives & Contaminants*, 2007. 24: p. 26-36.
[74] Muttucumaru, N., et al., Formation of high levels of acrylamide during the processing of flour derived from sulfate-deprived wheat. *Journal of Agricultural and Food Chemistry,* 2006. 54: p. 8951-8955.
[75] Claus, A., et al., Influence of agronomic factors and extraction rate on the acrylamide contents in yeast-leavened breads. *Journal of Agricultural and Food Chemistry,* 2006. 54: p. 8968-8976.
[76] Elmore, J.S., et al., Changes in free amino acids and sugars in potatoes due to sulfate fertilization and the effect on acrylamide formation. *Journal of Agricultural and Food Chemistry,* 2007. 55: p. 5363-5366.
[77] Rommens, C.M., et al., Improving potato storage and processing characteristics through all-native DNA transformation. *Journal of Agricultural and Food Chemistry*, 2007. 54: p. 9882-9887.
[78] Soyka, S., et al., *Process for reducing the acrylamide content of heat-treated food*, 2006.
[79] Boudreaux, E., et al., *Method for reducing acrylamide formation.*, 2007.
[80] Shannon, G. and M.E. *Markus, Fresh fry cooking and handling systems for reducing acrylamides in carbohydrate glycemic foods and preventing carcinogenic contaminants in cooking oil.* , 2010.
[81] Mariotti, S., et al., Patented techniques for acrylamide mitigation in high-temperature processed foods. *Recent Patents on Food, Nutrition & Agriculture*, 2011. 3(3): p. 158-71.

In: Chemical Food Safety and Health
Editors: F. Pedreschi Plasencia and Z. Ciesarová
ISBN: 978-1-62948-339-9

Chapter 2

THE RELEVANCE OF ACRYLAMIDE IN THE FOOD INDUSTRY: OCCURRENCE, EXPOSURE AND IMPACT OF MITIGATION TOOLS

Z. Ciesarová*[1]
[1]VÚP Food Research Institute, Bratislava, Slovak Republic

ABSTRACT

Acrylamide is a toxic compound with potential carcinogenic effects. It is found in many types of processed foods as a consequence of its formation during an intense heat treatment. Due to its occurrence in many foods, the exposure to acrylamide and the risk to health of consumers cannot be ignored. A group of consumers with higher exposure to acrylamide are people between the ages of 14 and 20 years. Their daily acrylamide intake is near 2.6 μg per kg of body weight, which is a suggested tolerable level. The adoption of acrylamide mitigation tools leads to the significant reduction of the acrylamide burden. Among effective mitigation tools in cereal based food production are sodium bicarbonate replacement, asparaginase treatment, and addition of calcium chloride. This chapter includes the findings of several scientific reports of the presence of acrylamide in various foods, and outlines tools for mitigation of the levels of this probably carcinogenic substance.

1. INTRODUCTION

The great concern regarding acrylamide and its carcinogenicity stems from the fact that it belongs to the Group 2A, meaning it is "probably carcinogenic to humans" based on the evaluation of the International Agency for Research on Cancer since 1994 [1]. This category is used when there is a limited evidence of carcinogenicity in humans and a sufficient evidence of carcinogenicity in experimental animals as well as a strong evidence that

* Corresponding author: Zuzana Ciesarová, VÚP Food Research Institute, Priemyselná 4, Address: 824 75 Bratislava, Slovak Republic. Phone: + 421-2-250237 (ext. 192); Fax: + 421-2-50237111; e-mail:ciesarova@vup.sk.

carcinogenesis is mediated by a mechanism that also operates in humans. A study published by Swedish scientists in 2002 [2], discovered unexpected high levels of acrylamide in various common foods. This attracted the attention of many researchers and food safety institutions around the world. Throughout the last decade, many details regarding the mechanism of acrylamide formation were confirmed. And since, several acrylamide mitigation tools, suitable for various food processing, were developed.

2. Concern of European Institutions about Acrylamide Occurrence in Foods

The first document discussing the acrylamide issue was released in June 2002 as a report from the Joint FAO/WHO Consultation on Health Implications of Acrylamide in Food [3]. This document also evaluated existing data and research on acrylamide and provided a range of recommendations for further information and new studies to better understand the risk to human health posed by acrylamide in food. The next recommendation of the Joint FAO/WHO Expert Committee on Food Additives (JECFA) in February 2005 [4], concluded that "appropriate efforts to reduce acrylamide on the concentration as low as reasonably achievable should continue". The wave of new findings in subsequent years led responsible institutions to include the acrylamide issue into their agenda and re-evaluate recommendations and limits related to acrylamide. In March 2010, the Environmental Protection Agency (EPA) refreshed the data concerning acrylamide [5]: i) Reference Dose (RfD) for Chronic Oral Exposure; ii) Reference Concentration (RfC) for Chronic Inhalation Exposure; iii) Carcinogenicity assessment. Fortunately, epidemiological studies have since reported that daily exposure to acrylamide from food substances is too low to be of carcinogenic concern. Despite this, in March 2010 the European Chemical Agency (ECHA) inserted acrylamide in the Candidate List of Substances of Very High Concern [6]. Acrylamide levels in food have been monitored by Member States of the European Union from 2007 following the Commission Recommendation 2007/331/EC of 3 May 2007 [7]. This monitoring exercise has been extended by the Commission Recommendation 2010/307/EU of 2 June 2010 [8] with a special target to foodstuffs with high acrylamide levels and a significant contribution to the human dietary intake. In May 2010, the European Food Safety Authority (EFSA) reported results of monitoring acrylamide levels in various types of food sampled in 2008 [9]. Although data collected in 2007 showed no consistent trend towards lower levels of acrylamide across food categories, new results show an apparent downward trend in some categories. However, crisps, instant coffee, and substitute coffee products, such as those based on barley or chicory showed higher levels in 2008 than the previous year. Based on the evidence, the European Commission in January 2011 released a document recommending the investigations of certain food categories with evidence of high acrylamide levels that exceeded the indicative values reported in the mentioned document [10]. Indicative values have been set for ten food categories as main contributors to acrylamide intake (Table 1). The scientific report of EFSA, which summarized results on acrylamide levels in food from years 2007 – 2009 and an exposure assessment, was published in March 2011 [11]. Based on the findings it can be inferred that acrylamide decreased in 'crackers', 'infant biscuits' and 'gingerbread', but increased in 'crisp bread' and 'instant coffee', while showing no statistically significant change in six out of the ten food groups. As the last initiative in 2011, the Food Drink Europe updated the Acrylamide Toolbox guidance that summarized agronomic, processing and ingredient mitigation techniques, including enzyme treatments [12]. Since 2012, updated acrylamide brochures have been available in 22 EU community languages addressed mainly for producers' usage to enhance their understanding and acceptance of available acrylamide mitigation tools in food processing [13].

Table 1. Indicative values of acrylamide based on the EFSA monitoring data from 2007 – 2008 [10]

Foodstuffs	Indicative value [µg/kg]
French fries ready-to-eat	600
Potato crisps	1000
Soft bread	150
Breakfast cereals (excluding muesli and porridge)	400
Biscuits, crackers, wafers, crisp bread and similar, excluding ginger bread	500
Roast coffee	450
Instant (soluble) coffee	900
Baby foods, other than processed cereal based foods	80
Biscuits and rusks for infants and young children	250
Processed cereal based foods for infants and young children, excluding biscuits and rusks	100

3. Sources of Acrylamide Intake in a Human Diet

The main source of acrylamide in the human diet is found in carbohydrate rich thermally treated foods with high asparagine level in raw material. Acrylamide is formed as an undesirable by-product of the Maillard reaction, which is responsible for flavour, colour, and aroma when food is cooked, baked, or fried. By thermal degradation of free amino acid asparagine in the presence of carbonyl compounds, through a cascade of reactions with different intermediates, acrylamide formation has been repeatedly proven, and the resulting measurements yielded a range between 0.2 and 0.5 mmol/mol asparagine in the presence of α-dicarbonyls, approximately 4.0 mmol/mol asparagine for hydroxyacetone, and 15.8 mmol/mol asparagine in the case of unstable 2-hydroxy-1-butanal [14]. The yields of acrylamide depend on reactivity of carbonyl reactants, particularly the functional group in α-position to carbonyl group. Besides the main Strecker aldehyde route mentioned before, there are minor formation pathways directly through cyclization of asparagine [15], or via acrylic acid generated during thermal decomposition of some amino acids (β-alanine, aspartic acid, serine, cysteine) or dipeptides (carnosine) [16], or via acrolein which is formed from lipids upon oxidation [17].

The largest dietary intake of acrylamide found in food is divided in three main categories: potatoes, cereals and coffee. Generally, popular potato-based snack products such as potato crisps and French fries are known to have high levels of acrylamide and are commonly consumed among younger age groups. On the other hand, brewed coffee and cereal based products (bread, crisp bread, cookies, crackers, cakes, gingerbreads, and breakfast cereals), despite their lower level of acrylamide (usually up to 1000 μg/kg) are frequently consumed by general population, thus substantially contribute to human exposure. Exceptions in low-acrylamide cereal products are gingerbread and ginger cakes with typically high levels of acrylamide more than 1000 μg/kg. The reason for the high levels stems from the mechanism of acrylamide formation: the simple saccharides, such as glucose and fructose, act as precursors and promoters to acrylamide formation [18,19]. Fortunately, ginger cakes are usually consumed in many European countries seasonally, typically during the Christmas season. This means these products do not significantly contribute to the long-term acrylamide exposure.

Other consumed sources of acrylamide include grilled or fried vegetables and thermally processed fruits. There is now clear evidence that free asparagine, as a precursor of acrylamide formation, is accumulated in most, if not all, plant organs with a plentiful supply of reduced nitrogen during periods of low protein synthesis. The accumulation of asparagine occurs during normal physiological processes such as germination and nitrogen transport, particularly in leguminous plants. Vegetables other than potatoes found to have significant levels of acrylamide after grilling and roasting include asparagus, pumpkin, zucchini, eggplant [20], squash, carrot, red paprika, chestnuts, onion, beans, olives, almonds, among others. Similarly, dried fruit, mostly prunes and pears, and fruit crisps can contain acrylamide in significant levels usually up to 1000 μg/kg [21].

4. Estimation of Acrylamide Exposure

The Opinion of Scientific Committee on Food from 3 July 2002 reported findings of estimated acrylamide exposure in foods [*3*]. This report was again confirmed in February 2010 by the Joint FAO/WHO Expert Committee on Food Additives at their 72nd meeting in Roma, Italy [*22*]. Levels of acrylamide exposure for the general population are approximately 1 μg per kg of body weight per day. For a group of consumers with higher consumption of acrylamide-rich foods it is approximately 4 μg per kg of body weight per day. Exposure estimations from 2002-2004 in various European countries compiled by Dybing et al. (2005) [23] varied between 0.28 to 1.4 μg per kg of body weight per day. Comparison of data from various countries is difficult due to different models which were used for collecting data. To perform a long-term exposure assessment several approaches are available. Approaches are based on calculations of dietary intake by multiplying a mean concentration of acrylamide level in particular food items, reported in databases or determined on-site, with a mean consumption level of particular food items. Consumption data are derived from Food Balance Sheet statistics or from individual reporting of consumption collected through food consumption surveys. It must be said that all of these models bring unquantified uncertainty related to the exposure assessment. Despite this inconvenience, the processing of this data enables researchers to identify the most vulnerable group of consumers as well as recognize main contributors to acrylamide intake. For example, Table 2 summarizes food consumption preferences among 285 subjects from the Slovak and the Czech Republics based on a preliminary survey. It also includes acrylamide content in the various food categories, as well as acrylamide levels in particular foodstuffs available in international and local databases [24].

Table 2. Acrylamide content in foodstuffs and its contribution to acrylamide intake

Food category	Foodstuffs	Acrylamide content [μg/kg]		Acrylamide intake [μg/day]	
		Min	Max	Min	Max
French fries/Potato products	French fries	5	1407	0.073	20.651
	Baked potatoes	23		0.441	
Potato crisps	Potato crisps	5	4108	0.062	50.769
Biscuits, crackers, crisp bread and similar	Extruded bread	5	916	0.016	2.765
	Toast, roasted toast	30	3200	0.412	43.913
	Crisp breads	30	3200	0.089	9.537
	Salty snacks (sticks, etc.)	5	896	0.052	9.307
	Gingerbread stuffed	5	1582	0.022	7.022
	Icing gingerbread	5	698	0.036	4.958
	Honey cakes	401		0.176	
	Wafers filled	71	101	1.865	2.653
	Baby biscuits	5	24	0.023	0.112
	Sweet biscuits	16	2561	0.456	72.966
Soft bread	Bread	5	162	0.463	11.584
	Rolls, French bread	18	500	2.012	55.896
Breakfast cereals	Breakfast cereals	5	1346	0.052	11.697
Coffee and coffee substitutes	Coffee	175	3025	0.692	11.960
	Coffee substitutes	50	70	0.038	0.054
Other products	Pastry	5	278	0.047	2.322
	Potato pancakes	531	692	1.629	2.123
	Corn puffs	5	32	0.017	0.106
	Muesli bars	5	70	0.025	0.346
	Cocoa	1203		3.865	
	Hot chocolate	32		0.081	
	Chocolate	17		0.334	
	Chocolate/ chocolate-nut spread	17		0.084	

This study revealed an age dependent distribution of acrylamide exposure. The consumers with the highest acrylamide exposure risk were young people below the age of 20 years (Figure 1). The following report specifically targeted the consumption habits of high-school students. The survey had 388 respondents with the identical proportionality between girls and boys (109:85) in both the Slovak and the Czech Republics. The results revealed relatively high acrylamide exposure in boys from both countries (P50 (median) = 2.2 μg/kg bw/day) (Table 3) which can be associated with their preference for eating snack-foods. Contrarily, adolescent girls had slightly lower acrylamide exposure. This could be attributed to both lower body weight and the pressure to control their weight, therefore eating smaller portions and "healthier" low-caloric products.

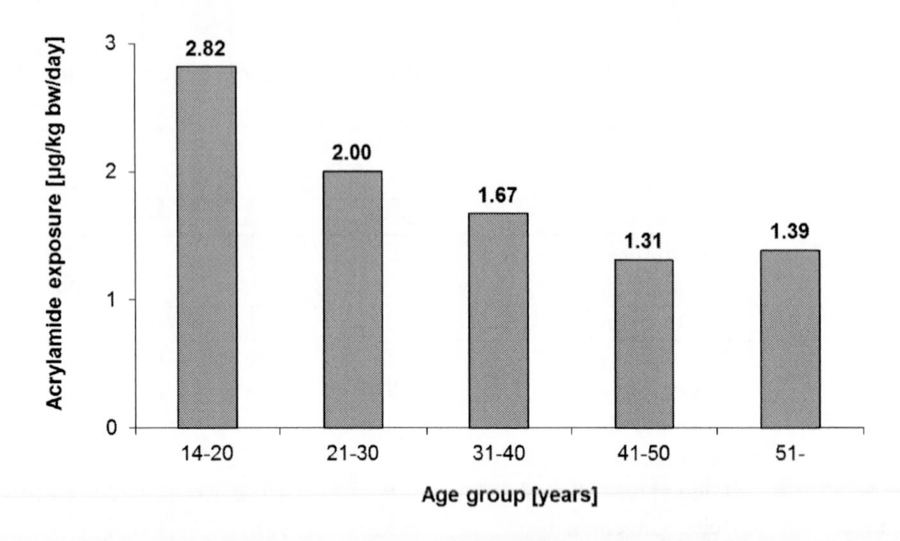

Figure 1. Consumer´s age dependent distribution of acrylamide exposure from foods.

Similar results of higher exposure of young people, children and babies were observed by other authors [25-29] despite the mentioned diversity related to various methods of exposure assessment and wide variability in acrylamide level of similar food items belonging to the same food category (Table 4).

Upon the European Commission´s May 2007 request issued in the Commission Recommendation 2007/331/EC on the monitoring of acrylamide levels in foods [7], member states monitored the acrylamide levels in certain foods annually in 2007, 2008, and 2009. The report of this recently published exercise describes results, as well as presents exposure estimates for the aforementioned target populations [11]. Exposure to acrylamide was estimated by pooled acrylamide occurrence values obtained through the monitoring program described above. Individual dietary information was derived from the EFSA Comprehensive European Food Consumption Database. The results confirm previous estimations for European countries with increasing tendency of acrylamide burden to younger consumers (Table 5).

Table 3. Estimation of acrylamide exposure of high-school students in the Slovak and the Czech Republics

Acrylamide exposure [ug/kg body weight/day]	The Slovak Republic		The Czech Republic	
	Median (P50)	High (P90)	Median (P50)	High (P90)
All	1.87	3.92	2.05	3.83
Boys	2.19	4.36	2.24	3.96
Girls	1.62	3.63	1.94	3.33

Median (P50) – median exposure; High (P90) – 90th percentile of exposure distribution

Table 4. Overview of acrylamide exposure assessments reported in different countries

Country	Age of consumers	Acrylamide exposure (µg/kg body weight/day)		Reference
		Median (P50)	High (P90; P95*; P97.5†)	
Brazil	11-17	0.12	1.92	[30]
France	18-79	0.43	1.02*	[26]
	15+	0.5	0.98†	[26]
	3-17	0.69	1.80*	[26]
	3-14	1.25	2.54†	[26]
Germany	1-18	0.45	2.04	[31]
	adults	0.85		[32]
Ireland	18-64	0.59	1.75	[25]
Netherlands	1-97	0.5	1.2	[27]
	1-6	1.1	2.0	[27]
Norway	Pregnant women	0.48	0.92	[33]
	Adult men	0.49	1.04*	[23]
United Kingdom	19-64	0.61	1.29	[25]
USA	2+	0.44	0.95*	[34]
	2-5	1.06	2.33*	[34]
Poland	0.5-1	2.10		[28]
	1-96	0.43		[35]
Saudi		0.86		[20]
Spain	17-60	0.409		[36]
Sweden	18-74	0.45	1.03†	[37]
Czech Republic and Slovakia	14-73	1.43	3.33	[29]
Czech Republic	15-20	2.05	3.83	[29]
Slovakia	15-20	1.87	3.92	[29]

Median (P50) – median exposure; High (P90, P95, P97.5) – 90th; 95th; 97.5^{th} percentile, respectively, of exposure distribution

5. MAIN CONTRIBUTORS OF ACRYLAMIDE INTAKE

The data presented above now enable us to identify main contributors of acrylamide exposure from foods. The Scientific report of EFSA [11] recognized the major contributors for adults as fried potatoes (including French fries), coffee, and soft bread, whereas for adolescents and children, major acrylamide exposure contributors also included fried potatoes, and soft bread, along with potato crisps and biscuits. However, the specific findings vary from country to country. According to observations of Keramat et al. [38] potato products account for 50% of human exposure to acrylamide, while bakery products account for only 20 % of exposure. Based on the evaluation of data from the survey in the Slovak and the Czech Republics, the main contributors for adolescents were cereal foods consumed either as snacks (biscuits, crackers, salty sticks etc.) or for breakfast (bread, rolls, French bread, crisp bread, toasts, breakfast cereals etc.) (see Table 6). Similar observations were also published by Mojska et al. [35] with bread making up more than 45 % of the total acrylamide exposure in humans. Similarly, Mojska et al. demonstrate that acrylamide exposure is associated with people living in nearby regions that favor a cereal based diet. Our survey, however, was given to students that regularly utilize school cafeteria services, which significantly limited their consumption of fast food, while simultaneously providing balance to their diets. Surprisingly, however, these students frequently consumed biscuits as a mid-morning snack, which increased their exposure to acrylamide significantly. Other findings indicated that main source of acrylamide intake was crisp bread (22%) [33], and even spices (13%) [26].

Table 5. Estimation of acrylamide exposure compiled from monitoring period 2007-2009 in 22 EU Member Countries and Norway adapted from the Scientific report of EFSA (2011) [11]

	Acrylamide exposure [µg/kg body weight/day]	
	Median (P50)	**High (P95)**
Adults (18-75 > years)	0.31 – 1.07	0.58 – 2.26
Adolescents (11-17 years)	0.43 – 1.36	0.94 – 3.06
Children (3-10 years)	0.70 – 2.05	1.50 – 4.22
Toddlers (12-35 months)	1.16 – 2.37	2.44 – 6.58
Infants (1-12 months)	0.73 – 1.29	2.20 – 3.97

Median (P50) – median exposure; High (P95) – 95th percentile of exposure distribution

Table 6. Food contribution to acrylamide intake (%) in a diet of high school students in the Slovak and the Czech Republics

Food category	**Food contribution to acrylamide intake (%)**	
	The Slovak Republic	**The Czech Republic**
French fries/potato products	5.7	6.9
Potato crisps	14.3	15.6
Soft bread	20.5	20.8
Breakfast cereals	5.0	2.1
Biscuits, crackers, crisp bread and similar	47.6	45.0
Coffee and coffee substitutes	1.8	5.5
Other products	5.1	4.0

6. POTENTIALITY OF ACRYLAMIDE MITIGATION TOOLS TO REDUCE EXPOSURE

Tardiff et.al´s (2010) safety evaluation of human acrylamide exposure in the EU [39] revealed that the maximum intake of acrylamide that the human body tolerates is 2.6 μg per kg of body weight per day. A greater intake or exposure to the chemical runs the risk of producing carcinogenic effects. From the presented data it is obvious that this value is achieved especially in the group of young consumers that eat large quantities of these foods. Thus, the continuous efforts to create safer, noncarcinogenic food products and encourage responsible consumption of the foods are not only relevant, but absolutely necessary. The Acrylamide Toolbox [12] reflects this, as well as summarizes the tools applicable for acrylamide mitigation in food processing and technology. This document, issued by Food Drink Europe, is organized into four sections, each of which offers verified ways of acrylamide mitigation in a particular processing step:

1) Intervention in raw material selection;
2) Alteration in recipes;
3) Adjustment of processing conditions;
4) Final preparation before eating.

The application of these tools is divided accordingly to three sectors: cereal production, potato production, and coffee production. The document was built on the authors´ collected evidence of the molecular mechanism of acrylamide formation and elimination that was gathered in previous work. Methods to reduce adverse effects of dietary acrylamide that were noted here include:

a) selecting potato, cereal, and other plant varieties for dietary use that contain low levels of the acrylamide precursors, namely, asparagine and glucose;
b) removing precursors before processing the foods;
c) using the enzyme asparaginase to hydrolyze asparagine to aspartic acid;
d) selecting processing conditions (pH, temperature, time, processing and storage atmosphere) that minimize acrylamide formation;
e) adding food ingredients (acidulants, amino acids, antioxidants, nonreducing carbohydrates, chitosan, garlic compounds, protein hydrolysates, proteins, metal salts) that have been reported to prevent acrylamide formation;
f) removing/trapping acrylamide after it is formed with the aid of chromatography, evaporation, polymerization, or reaction with other food ingredients; and
g) reducing toxicity *in vivo* [40].

Adoption of aforementioned tools can lead to the significant reduction of acrylamide intake. It is demonstrated on a simulation of dietary acrylamide intake in which verified interventions to the food processing were projected.

7. Substitution of Ammonium Hydrogen Carbonate

One commonly used baking agent responsible for acrylamide formation in cereal products, especially in cookies, wafers and biscuits is ammonium hydrogen carbonate. There is no exception if biscuits contain about 1500 – 2500 μg of acrylamide per kg [41]. Since the evidence from our survey and other previously published studies reveals that children frequently consume these products for mid-morning snacks, it can be inferred from this that their resulting acrylamide intake level is very high (approximately 40 μg per day). To mitigate these levels to a level of the tolerable acrylamide intake, one solution would be to replace the ammonium baking agent with sodium salts. This intervention was tried in the industrial production of ginger biscuits with acrylamide levels before any intervention at about 1220 μg/kg. The full replacement of ammonium hydrogen carbonate with sodium hydrogen carbonate and sodium acid pyrophosphate resulted in the decrease of acrylamide in this product on 77 μg/kg [42]. The intake of acrylamide through the consumption of these products by young people would be decreased from 2.1 μg per day before any intervention to 0.1 μg per day after the intervention. However, it should be noted that this intervention is associated with an undesirable side effect on quality properties of final products. For that reason, this method of acrylamide reduction cannot be entirely recommended as the exclusive solution.

8. Application of Asparaginase

One very promising choice of effective acrylamide elimination in products that contain large amounts of the substance seems to pre-treatment using enzyme asparaginase. This enzyme allows the conversion of amino acid asparagine to the aspartic acid which does not enter into reactions leading to acrylamide formation. The undeniable advantage of asparaginase application is that it has no significant impact on the quality and expected organoleptic properties of final products. This intervention was successfully applied in several food processing trials [43]. In particular, this method is especially appropriate for biscuits production as the quality properties are crucial parameters of consumers' acceptability of the products, and moreover, these goods contribute to acrylamide intake in high portion.

Industrially produced whole-grain biscuits with dried fruits contained more than 2500 μg of acrylamide per kg before any intervention. The application of asparaginase prior heat treatment during kneading of dough resulted in the decrease of acrylamide on the level of 100 μg/kg (own unpublished data). The daily intake of acrylamide due to this intervention could be reduced from 36.7 to 1.6 μg per day. The quality properties of final products after intervention were not significantly impacted. Moreover, the application of asparaginase combined with a partial replacement of ammonium salt in ginger biscuits, kept organoleptic properties on acceptable level and support reduction of acrylamide from 1220 μg/kg to 40 μg/kg [42].

9. Additives in Bread Making

Soft bread belongs to the most frequently consumed staple food group. Based on the survey of consumption habits of young people between 14 and 20 years, the consumption of common industrially produced wheat-rye-potato bread resulted in an intake of acrylamide of 8.2 μg per day. As an alternative to this bread with determined acrylamide content of 257 μg/kg, the domestic bread preparation in home bread machine from improved bread mix is considered. Due to the fact that domestic bread preparation is generally rising and production of bread premix for home bread machine are frequently innovated taking in account new trends, the inclusion of improving ingredients into the formulas of bread premix is easily under control. Among various additives the calcium chloride was recognized as the salt which suppressed acrylamide formation up to 10% and concurrently improved organoleptic as well as functional properties of final bread loaf (Table 7). The systematic study of the impact of inorganic salts on acrylamide formation was published previously [44]. The home prepared bread is characterized by reduced level of acrylamide (approximately 20 μg/kg) due to softer conditions during baking and improving formula with $CaCl_2$ and extra yeast addition. The acrylamide intake from soft bread as a consequence of alternative consumption of homemade bread would be reduced to 1.0 μg per day.

Table 7. Impact of additives on acrylamide content and sensory evaluation of bread loaves

Additives in bread mix	Acrylamide content [μg/kg dry bread crust]	Sensory evaluation (total score)
Control (without additives)	151 ± 6	91
$CaCl_2$ (3.0 g/kg)	137 ± 23	92
Ca-Lactate (3.0 g/kg)	159 ± 1	81
NH_4Cl (3.0 g/kg)	295 ± 11	88
KH_2PO_4 (2.5 g/kg)	188 ± 13	84
NaH_2PO_4 (2.5 g/kg)	263 ± 2	86
$Na_2H_2P_2O_7$ (2.5 g/kg)	160 ± 14	84
$Na_4P_2O_7$ (2.5 g/kg)	123 ± 21	84

10. Addition of Natural Antioxidants

One of less known methods of acrylamide mitigation with insufficiently described mechanism of their effect is the addition of antioxidants. Some of them are present in naturally occurred food additives such as spices [45]. Their action can be exploited for a suppression of acrylamide level in those kinds of products such as gingerbreads. Their contribution to the acrylamide intake is not so dominant due to their occasional consumption but seasonally they can represent a significant source of acrylamide. The application of a special spice mix with endorsed ability to reduce acrylamide supported acrylamide mitigation strategy as a whole. A specially composed spice mix enabled producers to decline acrylamide content in gingerbreads up to half which resulted also in the decrease of daily acrylamide intake. The effect of various spices on acrylamide content in ginger cookies was recently presented [24, 46, 47].

Conclusion

The case studies presented above offer potential strategies to combat the challenge of acrylamide mitigation in foodstuffs. Adoption of the aforementioned interventions would be projected in the decrease of daily acrylamide intake which is calculated by appropriate specified food groups. Implementation of presented interventions could reduce acrylamide exposure of highly exposed young people aged between 14 and 20 up to 30%. Additional improvements could be achieved by the application of mentioned methods to another food processing. Research needs are suggested that may further facilitate reducing the acrylamide burden of the diet. Researchers are challenged to (a) apply the available methods and to minimize the acrylamide content of the diet without adversely affecting the nutritional quality, safety, and sensory attributes, including colour and flavour, while maintaining consumer acceptance; and (b) educate commercial and home food processors and the public about available approaches to mitigating undesirable effects of dietary acrylamide. Consumers themselves can reduce acrylamide intake by their own appropriate adjustment of dietary habits arising from the latest information about acrylamide occurrence and exposure. For this purpose a widespread dissemination of scientific information and appropriate communication with consumers play the crucial role leading to the higher responsibility for their own healthy life.

Acknowledgments

Support for this work was provided by the project implementation "The Centre of Excellence for Contaminants and Microorganisms in Foods" ITMS 26240120024, and "Strategy of acrylamide elimination in food processing" ITMS 26240220050, supported by the Research & Development Operational Programme funded by the European Regional Development Fund. The research was supported also by the Slovak Research and Development Agency, under the contract Nos. LPP 0310-09 and VMSP-P-0089-09.

References

[1] IARC. 1994. Acrylamide. In: *IARC Monographs on the Evaluation of Carcinogenic Risks to Humans. Some Industrial Chemicals*, International Agency for Research on Cancer: Lyon, France, 1994; Vol. 60, 389-433.

[2] Tareke, E.; Rydberg, P.; Karlsson, P.; Eriksson, S.; Törnqvist, M., Analysis of acrylamide, a carcinogen formed in heated foodstuffs. *Journal of Agricultural and Food Chemistry* 2002, *50*, 4998-5006.

[3] Health implications of acrylamide in food: report of a joint FAO/WHO consultation. In FAO/WHO, Ed. WHO Headquarters.: Geneva, Switzerland, 2002; 1-35.

[4] Summary and conclusions from the 64th meeting of the Joint FAO/WHO Expert Committee on Food Additives (JECFA). In FAO/WHO, Ed. Food and Agriculture Organization of the United Nations/World Health Organization: Rome, 2005; 1-6.

[5] U.S.EPA Integrated Risk Information System. Acrylamide (CASRN 79-06-1). In EPA, Ed. Environmental Protection Agency: 2010.

[6] ECHA (2010). Candidate List of Substances of Very High Concern for authorisation. In Agency, E. C., Ed. 2010.

[7] Commission Regulation (EC) No 333/2007 of 28 March 2007. *Official Journal of the European Union*, L 88/29, 2007; Vol. EC 333/2007, 1-10.

[8] Commission Recommendation of 2 June 2010 on the monitoring of acrylamide levels in food. (2010/307/EU). *Official Journal of the European Union*, L 137/4: 2010; 4-10.

[9] EFSA (2010). Results on acrylamide levels in food from monitoring year 2008. *EFSA Journal, 8*, European Food Safety Authority: 2010; 1-31.

[10] Commision Recommendation of 10.1.2011 on investigations into the levels of acrylamide in food. C(2010) 9681. *Official Journal of the European Union*, 2011; 1-7.

[11] Results on acrylamide levels in food from monitoring years 2007-2009 and Exposure assessment. *EFSA Journal* 2011, *9*, 2133-2181.

[12] Acrylamide Toolbox. In Food Drink Europe: 2011; p 47.

[13] Acrylamide brochures. http://ec.europa.eu/food/food/chemicalsafety/contaminants/acrylamide_en.htm

[14] Blank, I.; Robert, F.; Goldmann, T.; Pollien, P.; Varga, N.; Devaud, S.; Saucy, F.; Huynh-Ba, T.; Stadler, R. H., Mechanisms of acrylamide formation: Maillard-induced transformation of asparagine. In 2005; Vol. 561, 171-189.

[15] Yaylayan, V. A.; Stadler, R. H., Acrylamide formation in food: A mechanistic perspective. *Journal of AOAC International* 2005, *88*, 262-267.

[16] Stadler, R. H.; Verzegnassi, L.; Varga, N.; Grigorov, M.; Studer, A.; Riediker, S.; Schilter, B., Formation of Vinylogous Compounds in model Maillard reaction systems. *Chemical Research in Toxicology* 2003, *16*, 1242-1250.

[17] Zamora, R.; Hidalgo, F. J., Contribution of lipid oxidation products to acrylamide formation in model systems. *Journal of Agricultural and Food Chemistry* 2008, *56*, 6075-6080.

[18] Zieliński, H.; Ciesarová, Z.; Troszyńska, A.; Ceglińska, A.; Zielińska, D.; Amarowicz, R.; Przygodzka, M.; Kukurová, K., Antioxidant properties, acrylamide content and sensory quality of ginger cakes with different formulations. *Polish Journal of Food and Nutrition Sciences* 2012, *62*, 41-50.

[19] Amrein, T. M.; Schönbächler, B.; Escher, F.; Amadò, R., Acrylamide in gingerbread: Critical factors for formation and possible ways for reduction. *Journal of Agricultural and Food Chemistry* 2004, *52*, 4282-4288.

[20] El-Ziney, M. G.; Al-Turki, A. A.; Tawfik, M. S., Acrylamide status in selected traditional Saudi foods and infant milk and foods with estimation of daily exposure. *American Journal of Food Technology* 2009, *4*, 177-191.

[21] Becalski, A.; Brady, B.; Feng, S.; Gauthier, B. R.; Zhao, T., Formation of acrylamide at temperatures lower than 100°C: The case of prunes and a model study. *Food Additives and Contaminants - Part A Chemistry, Analysis, Control, Exposure and Risk Assessment* 2011, *28*, 726-730.

[22] Summary and conclusions from the 72th meeting of the Joint FAO/WHO Expert Committee on Food Additives (JECFA). In FAO/WHO, Ed. Food and Agriculture Organization of the United Nations/World Health Organization: Rome, 2010; 1-16.

[23] Dybing, E.; Farmer, P. B.; Andersen, M.; Fennell, T. R.; Lalljie, S. P. D.; Müller, D. J. G.; Olin, S.; Petersen, B. J.; Schlatter, J.; Scholz, G.; Scimeca, J. A.; Slimani, N.; Törnqvist, M.; Tuijtelaars, S.; Verger, P., Human exposure and internal dose assessments of acrylamide in food. *Food and Chemical Toxicology* 2005, *43*, 365-410.

[24] Ciesarová, Z.; Suhaj, M.; Horváthová, J., Correlation between acrylamide contents and antioxidant capacities of spice extracts in a model potato matrix. *Journal of Food and Nutrition Research* 2008, *47*, 1-5.

[25] Mills, C.; Tlustos, C.; Evans, R.; Matthews, W., Dietary acrylamide exposure estimates for the United Kingdom and Ireland: Comparison between semiprobabilistic and probabilistic exposure models. *Journal of Agricultural and Food Chemistry* 2008, *56*, 6039-6045.

[26] Sirot, V.; Hommet, F.; Tard, A.; Leblanc, J. C., Dietary acrylamide exposure of the French population: Results of the second French total diet study. *Food and Chemical Toxicology* 2012, *50*, 889-894.

[27] Boon, P. E.; De Mul, A.; Van Der Voet, H.; Van Donkersgoed, G.; Brette, M.; Van Klaveren, J. D., Calculations of dietary exposure to acrylamide. *Mutation Research - Genetic Toxicology and Environmental Mutagenesis* 2005, *580*, 143-155.

[28] Mojska, H.; Gielecińska, I.; Stoś, K., Determination of acrylamide level in commercial baby foods and an assessment of infant dietary exposure. *Food and Chemical Toxicology* 2012, *50*, 2722-2728.

[29] Ciesarová, Z., Successes and limitations in acrylamide mitigation efforts: Part 1: Relevance, occurrence and exposure. *Agro Food Industry Hi-Tech* 2011, *22*, 26-28.

[30] Arisseto, A. P.; Toledo, M. C. d. F.; Govaert, Y.; van Loco, J.; Fraselle, S.; Degroodt, J. M.; Caroba, D. C. R., Contribution of selected foods to acrylamide intake by a population of Brazilian adolescents. *LWT - Food Science and Technology* 2009, *42*, 207-211.

[31] Hilbig, A.; Kersting, M., Dietary acrylamide exposure, time trends and the intake of relevant foods in children and adolescents between 1998 and 2004: Results of the DONALD study. *Journal fur Verbraucherschutz und Lebensmittelsicherheit* 2006, *1*, 10-18.

[32] Schettgen, T.; Weiss, T.; Drexler, H.; Angerer, J., A first approach to estimate the internal exposure to acrylamide in smoking and non-smoking adults from Germany. *International Journal of Hygiene and Environmental Health* 2003, *206*, 9-14.

[33] Brantsæter, A. L.; Haugen, M.; Mul, A. d.; Bjellaas, T.; Becher, G.; Klaveren, J. V.; Alexander, J.; Meltzer, H. M., Exploration of different methods to assess dietary acrylamide exposure in pregnant women participating in the Norwegian mother and child cohort study (MoBa). *Food and Chemical Toxicology* 2008, *46*, 2808-2814.

[34] U.S. FDA 2006. The 2006 Exposure Assessment for Acrylamide. Available from: http://www.fda.gov/downloads/Food/FoodborneIllnessContaminants/UCM197239.pdf.

[35] Mojska, H.; Gielecińska, I.; Szponar, L.; Ołtarzewski, M., Estimation of the dietary acrylamide exposure of the Polish population. *Food and Chemical Toxicology* 2010, *48*, 2090-2096.

[36] Arribas-Lorenzo, G.; Morales, F. J., Dietary exposure to acrylamide from potato crisps to the Spanish population. *Food Additives and Contaminants - Part A Chemistry, Analysis, Control, Exposure and Risk Assessment* 2009, *26*, 289-297.

[37] Wilson, K. M.; Bälter, K.; Adami, H. O.; Grönberg, H.; Vikström, A. C.; Paulsson, B.; Törnqvist, M.; Mucci, L. A., Acrylamide exposure measured by food frequency questionnaire and hemoglobin adduct levels and prostate cancer risk in the cancer of the prostate in Sweden study. *International Journal of Cancer* 2009, *124*, 2384-2390.

[38] Keramat, J.; LeBail, A.; Prost, C.; Jafari, M., Acrylamide in baking products: A review article. *Food and Bioprocess Technology* 2011, *4*, 530-543.

[39] Tardiff, R. G.; Gargas, M. L.; Kirman, C. R.; Leigh Carson, M.; Sweeney, L. M., Estimation of safe dietary intake levels of acrylamide for humans. *Food and Chemical Toxicology* 2010, *48*, 658-667.

[40] Friedman, M.; Levin, C. E., Review of methods for the reduction of dietary content and toxicity of acrylamide. *Journal of Agricultural and Food Chemistry* 2008, *56*, 6113-6140.

[41] Ciesarová, Z., Kukurová, K., Bednáriková, A., Marková, L., Baxa, S., Influence of food processing on acrylamide level in gingerbreads and cookies. *Aspects of Applied Biology* 2010, *97*, 87-92.

[42] Ciesarová, Z.; Kukurová, K.; Bednáriková, A.; Morales, F. J., Effect of heat treatment and dough formulation on the formation of Maillard reaction products in fine bakery products - benefits and weak points. *Journal of Food and Nutrition Research* 2009, *48*, 20-30.

[43] Ciesarová, Z.; Kukurová, K.; Benešová, C., Enzymatic elimination of acrylamide in potato-based thermally treated foods. *Nutrition and Food Science* 2010, *40*, 55-63.

[44] Kukurová, K.; Ciesarová, Z.; Bednáriková, A.; Marková, L., Effect of inorganic salts on acrylamide formation in cereal matrices. *Czech Journal of Food Sciences* 2009, *27*, S425-S428.

[45] Ou, S. Y.; Shi, J. J.; Huang, C. H.; Zhang, G. W.; Teng, J. W.; Jiang, Y.; Yang, B. R., Effect of antioxidants on elimination and formation of acrylamide in model reaction systems. *Journal of Hazardous Materials* 2010, *182*, 863-868.

[46] Zieliński, H.; Del Castillo, M.D.; Przygodzka, M.; Ciesarová, Z.; Kukurová, K.; Zielińska, D., Changes in chemical composition and antioxidative properties of rye ginger cakes during their shelf-life. *Food Chemistry* 2012*, 135,* 2965-2973.

[47] Marková, L.; Ciesarová, Z.; Kukurová, K.; Zieliński, H.; Przygodzka, M.; Bednáriková, A.; Šimko, P., Influence of various spices on acrylamide content in buckwheat ginger cakes. *Chemical Papers* 2012, *66*, 949-954.

In: Chemical Food Safety and Health
Editors: F. Pedreschi Plasencia and Z. Ciesarová
ISBN: 978-1-62948-339-9

Chapter 3

5-Hydroxymethyl-Furfural and Furfuryl Alcohol: Occurrence, Exposure and Detection

M. Murkovic** and Y. R. Swasti
Institute of Biochemistry, Graz University of Technology, Graz, Austria

Abstract

During the recent years a new class of food borne heat generated compounds became the focus of risk evaluation. The identification of a new mechanism of activation of vinylogous alcohols by sulphotransferases has given insight into a possible contribution of these types of substances to carcinogenesis. In this chapter two of these compounds – 5-hydroxymethyl-furfural (HMF) and furfuryl alcohol (FA) – are described. These two compounds occur in high amounts in some selected foods and even if the mutagenic/carcinogenic activity is low, there might be a risk due to the high exposure. Both compounds are formed by heating of carbohydrate rich foods. HMF could be formed via the Maillard reaction or via direct dehydration of fructose and FA from hexoses or pentoses. The concentrations of FA can reach several hundred μg/g and of HMF several mg/g.

1. Introduction

HMF is one of the compounds that are formed during the Maillard reaction or by direct dehydration of hexoses. Higher temperatures, an acidic environment, and a low water activity favour the formation of HMF. However, even at lower temperatures (e.g. storage at room temperature) – which means under practically any conditions of food processing – HMF is formed; sometimes rather high concentrations are occurring. Estimates of the mean daily

* Corresponding author: Dr. Michael Murkovic. Institute of Biochemistry, Graz University of Technology; Address: Petergasse 12/2, 8010 Graz. Phone: 43-316-873 6495. Fax: 43-316-873 6952; E-mail: Michael.murkovic@tugraz.at.

intake are in the range of 30 to 150 mg/capita. Various studies conducted in the 1960's and 1970's consistently showed a low acute and chronic toxicity of HMF in mice and rats. It was therefore concluded that HMF, which is formed in foods during processing or as a result of sterilisation of parenteral solutions, does not seem to pose any significant toxicological problem. Because of the reactive chemical structural moieties of HMF that include a furan ring, an α,β-unsaturated carbonyl, and an allylic hydroxyl group there might be a genotoxic and carcinogenic hazard [1]. Indeed, HMF initiated and promoted preneoplastic lesions, aberrant crypt foci (ACFs), in the rat colon [2]. The initiation of these lesions implies the induction of gene mutations in the colon mucosa. It is not only HMF but also furfuryl alcohol that can be activated to highly reactive metabolites [3]. Although HMF showed a very low chronic and acute toxicity the exceptionally high human exposure, the induction of ACFs and the genotoxicity prompted the National Toxicological Program [NTP] of the USA to conduct long-term carcinogenicity studies with HMF in mice and rats. The NTP reported that ...*There were increased incidences of lesions (degeneration and metaplasia) of the olfactory and respiratory epithelium of the nose in male and female rats and male and female mice that received 5-(hydroxymethyl)-2-furfural. Many of the male and female mice receiving 750 mg/kg died before the end of the study, and some exhibited seizures or other signs of neurological response. In the other two groups of female mice receiving 5-(hydroxymethyl)-2-furfural, there were increased incidences of hepatocellular adenoma of the liver...* In this report it was concluded that ...*5-(hydroxymethyl)-2-furfural caused liver cancer in female mice but did not cause cancer in male or female rats or male mice. In addition, 5-(hydroxymethyl)-2-furfural was associated with increased lesions of the olfactory and respiratory epithelium of the nose in male and female rats and mice*. [4].

2. Analysis of 5-Hydroxymethyl-Furfural

Normally the analysis of HMF is carried out by HPLC. Older methods for analysis of HMF in honey use photometry after reaction with e.g. bisulfite [e.g. AOAC 980.23, [5]] or after derivatization with p-toluidine [Winkler method] and barbituric acid [e.g. [6]]. However, the routine analysis is normally carried out by HPLC with UV detection at 280 nm. For the separation a reversed phase (RP-18) column can be used and the HMF is eluted with 5% methanol in water [7]. Another method was published earlier using a RP-8 column with 5% acetonitril in water [8]. When a better selectivity or even a higher sensitivity is needed HMF can be derivatized with dinitrophenyl-hydrazine (DNPH) to give a stable hydrazone that can be detected at 380 to 400 nm or with a good response by ESI-MS. Since the product occurs in both *Z*- and *E*-configuration the limit of detection is reduced but both peaks can be used for quantification.

Due to the good solubility of HMF in water this can be used for extraction of the analyte. The extract can be clarified by the use of Carrez I and Carrez II instead of acids (trichloroacetic TCA, m-phosphoric, sulfosalycilic). TCA was evaluated in detail by Ameur and co-workers [9] which gave the best recovery without the formation of artefactual HMF during sample preparation. The addition of TCA to the extraction solvent was also used in other matrices such as milk [10], [11] and fruit preparations [12], [13].

Other possibilities of separation include the use of flow injection analysis [14] or micellar electrokinetic chromatography (MEKC) using sodium dodecyl sulphate (SDS) as background electrolyte buffered at pH 8.5 [15] or with sodium tetraborate at pH 9.3 [16]. With this method a limit of quantification of 2.5 mg/kg could be reached. This method was applied for breakfast cereals, toasts, honey, orange juice, apple juice, jam, coffee, chocolate, and biscuits. After derivatization with e.g. BSTFA it is also possible to analyse HMF by GC-MS. In this method a clean-up including a solid phase extraction was necessary resulting in a limit of quantification of 6 mg/kg [15].

Zappala and co-workers [17] published a comparison of the routine methods for measuring the HMF content in honey. They concluded that the HPLC method and the photometric method according to White gave similar results, whereas the photometric method according to Winkler generally resulted in higher values.

3. Formation of 5-Hydroxymethyl Furfural

Antal and co-workers [18] proved experimentally that the mechanism of the HMF formation goes through cyclic intermediates as is shown in Figure 1. Their interpretation was supported by the experimental results that 1) HMF is easily formed from fructose or sucrose, 2) 2,5-anhydro-D-mannose converts easily into HMF (this compound is a parent aldehyde to the enol), 3) when the reaction was carried out in D_2O starting from fructose, deuterium was absent in HMF.

Similar results were obtained by Perez-Locas and Yaylayan [19] who showed by pyrolysis GC-MS that especially in dry and high temperature systems at temperatures above 250 °C, 90% of HMF originated from the fructose moiety and only 10% originated from the glucose. Alternatively, when sucrose was refluxed in acidic methanol at 65 °C, 100% of HMF was generated from the glucose moiety.

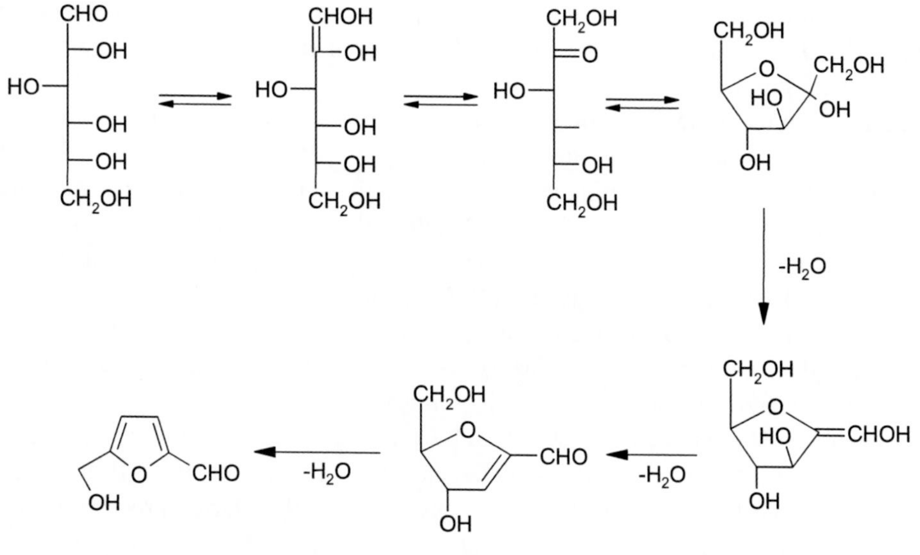

Figure 1. Formation of HMF by dehydration reactions [20].

When comparing the conversion efficiency of the well known HMF precursor 3-deoxyglucosone with glucose, fructose, and sucrose they could show that fructose and sucrose had a significantly higher conversion rate which indicated that glucose is not a major precursor of HMF in fructose and sucrose solutions. Based on the data generated, they proposed a mechanism of HMF formation from sucrose in which sucrose degrades into glucose and a very reactive fructofuranosyl cation. Subsequently, in dry conditions this cation can be effectively converted directly into HMF.

Cämmerer and co-workers [21] suggested a different mechanism of formation of HMF by isomerization of glyceraldehyde followed by dehydration to methylglyoxal and its subsequent condensation with another molecule of glyceraldehyde. They also concluded that HMF is formed by the two competing reactions presented here. [21]

Looking at the concentration of HMF in similar products it can be seen that depending on the raw materials, variation in composition, and variation in heat load during processing a huge variation in the formation of HMF can occur. Ameur and co-workers [9] observed a strong variation in the HMF concentration within the 17 commercial cookies, ranging from 0.5 to 74.6 mg/kg. These results are comparable to other reports e.g. between 0.4 and 65.5 mg/kg in infant cereals [22], [23], and between 3.7 and 193 mg/kg in breakfast cereals [24].

The processing of balsamic vinegar (especially traditional balsamic vinegar) includes a cooking step of the must. During cooking the must temperature is raised to the boiling point followed by skimming to remove dispersed solids and denatured proteins. Then the temperature is kept at 80 – 90 °C for several hours to evaporate water and concentrate the soluble solids up to 35 – 60 °Brix.

During the heat treatment non-enzymatic browning reactions are occurring that are giving the product the typical dark brown colour. The high temperature, low pH value and reducing water activity enhance the formation of HMF. The high sugar concentrations – typically 236 g/L glucose and 211 g/L fructose – lead to such high concentrations as indicated in table 1 [25]. In addition, traditional balsamic vinegar is stored for at least 12 years.

During the storage of a juice of peaches the content of HMF increases from ca. 0.3 up to 8 mg/kg. In these experiments the storage temperature was kept at 37 °C which is rather high but this should simulate the longer storage times which reflects a typical shelf life of 12 months of these products [26].

The legal limit for HMF in honey was set due to restricted processing conditions to 40 mg/kg. This limit is not based on toxicological reasons [EC Directive 74/409/EEC]. In the fair trade standards a quality grading system is used to produce honey with a HMF content as low as possible suggesting values of below 20 mg/kg [Fair-trade Standards, 2005].

Comprehensive surveys of average honey composition have established that the major components are fructose (38.4%), glucose (30.3%), and water (17.2%). In addition to the two major sugars an array of more than 20 higher sugars is present, which is formed by linking the fructose and glucose in various combinations. Honey is therefore primarily a carbohydrate material, and sugars comprise over 95% of its solids [27].

The average pH of honey was determined by White [28] as 3.91 which ranges from 3.4 to 6.1. Because of this special composition honey is extremely sensitive to HMF formation and especially if heated the HMF concentration rises significantly. During processing of honey heating is not allowed *...to such an extent that its natural enzymes are destroyed or made inactive...* [Council Directives 74/409/EEC, 2001/110/EEC] and HMF is analysed as an indicator for heat treatment.

Table 1. Occurrence of HMF (mg/kg; mg/L) in different foods

Food item	HMF	References
Honey	0.1 – 140	[29], [30], [15], [16], [15].
Breakfast cereals	4 – 193	[24], [31], 15].
Infant cereals	0.4 – 66	[22], [23].
Orange juice	< LOD – 22	[32], [15].
Apple juice	< LOD – 3.5	[33], [34], [15].
Jam	2.7 – 160	[13], [35], [36], [15].
Caramel containing drinks	0.8 – 80	[37]
Biscuits	< LOQ – 180	[38], [39], [15].
Cookies	0.5 – 75	[9].
Bread	2.2 – 88	[40], [41], [42].
Toasted bread	1.7 – 2,030	[41], [15].
Pasta	0.08 – 7	[43].
Coffee	110 – 1,900	[7], [44], [15].
Coffee, instant	24 – 4,020	[45], [7], [15].
Chocolate	42 – 99	[15].
Wines, fortified	20 – 170	[46].
Ketchup	0.8 – 190	[36].
Tomato purée	2.8 – 84	[36].
Dried fruits	1 – 2,200	[7].
Syrup	1.3 – 27	[36].
Fruit baby food	2.1 – 9.8	[36].
Special regional products		
Abbamele (honey decoction)	880 – 4,800	[47].
Bread with dried fruits	450	[7].
Aged sugar cane spirits	0.8 – 3.1	[48].
Pekmez (concentrated juice from grapes or mulberries)	< 14,000	[49].
Balsamic vinegar	246 – 4,040	[50], [51].
Churros (deep fried dough pastry)	74 ± 48	[52].
Treacle (black honey)	66 – 180	[53]

4. EXPOSURE

The exposure to HMF was evaluated by Husoy and co-workers recently [54]. In this study a group of 47 non-smokers was evaluated using a 24 hour dietary recall. The food list obtained from this dietary recall was collected and analysed for HMF and 5-hydroxymethyl-furanoic acid (HMFA).

Since most of the HMF is metabolised to HMFA in the kidneys the urine was collected during the testing period. From this study the daily mean exposure was calculated being 5.6 mg. The 95th percentile of the estimated daily dietary intake of HMF was 27.6 mg. In the tested group the most important source of HMF was coffee (63%), both because of the high levels of HMF in coffee and because of the high consumption of coffee among the participants. The second most important food sources of HMF were milk products (11%) followed by juice (9%), bread (7%), and beer (4%). The calculated uptake correlated well with the urinary excretion of HMFA [55].

5. Furfuryl Alcohol

Although furfuryl alcohol can polymerize in acid conditions the concentration of the monomer is still high in heated foods; especially in roasted coffee [82]. Furfuryl alcohol gives a burnt [76], [83], cooked-sugar [74], and rubber-like odour [71]; when furfuryl alcohol interacts with dihydroxy benzene or trihydroxy benzene as it is occurring during roasting of coffee it will produce a bitter taste [56]. Nevertheless, furfuryl alcohol is used as a flavouring agent with an acceptable daily intake of up to 0.5 mg/kg BW [57].

5.1. Analysis of Furfuryl Alcohol

The analysis of furfuryl alcohol can be done either by liquid or gas chromatography. Due to the better separation and more sensitive detection the analysis by GC-MS is preferred. In most of the products the furfuryl alcohol concentration is comparably low and these foods do not contribute significantly to the exposure. A method using head space solid phase microextraction (SPME) coupled to GC-MS was introduced by Yand and Peppard [58]. They analysed roasted coffee and fruit juice beverages using a fused silica fibre coated with poly(dimethylsiloxane) (100 μm). The extraction of the furfuryl alcohol could be done by solvent extraction, simultaneous distillation extraction and nitrogen purge and steam distillation [59]. The applicability of headspace GC-MS for the furfuryl alcohol analysis was shown by Kumazawa and Masuda [60]. Another method using liquid chromatography with UV detection was published by Yuan and Chen in 1999 [61]. Different furanic compounds were separated on an Aminex HPX-87H column (300 × 7.8 mm) with a mobile phase consisting of acetonitrile and 5 mM sulfuric acid (16:84, v/v). With the diode array detector measuring at 254 nm they were able to analyse furfuryl alcohol in fruit juices.

5.2. Formation of Furfuryl Alcohol

Glucose or fructose can undergo isomerization reactions at high temperatures. The key intermediate in this isomerization reaction, 1,2-enediol, is also considered as the starting intermediate in the degradation reactions by β-elimination producing an unstable compound 3-deoxyaldoketose which then undergoes a cleavage reaction producing formic acid and a C_5-compound [62], [63], [84], [85]. The C_5-compound (2-deoxypentose) will react further by cyclization and aromatization forming furfuryl alcohol (Figure 3) [63]. Besides that, heating of quinic acid at 250°C for 30 min under a stream of nitrogen produces furfuryl alcohol (250 μg/g quinic acid), Figure 2 [64]. Quantitatively, furfural alcohol as a furan derivative is predominating in roasted coffee [56].

5.3. Furfuryl Alcohol in Foods

Although the polymerization proceeds during the roasting of coffee the concentration of the monomeric furfuryl alcohol is still high in the finished products.

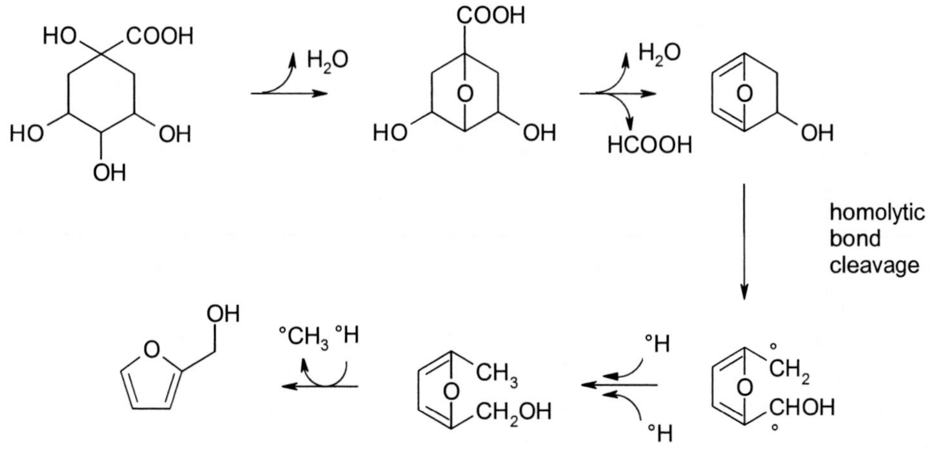

Figure 2. Formation of furfuryl alcohol from degradation of quinic acid [64].

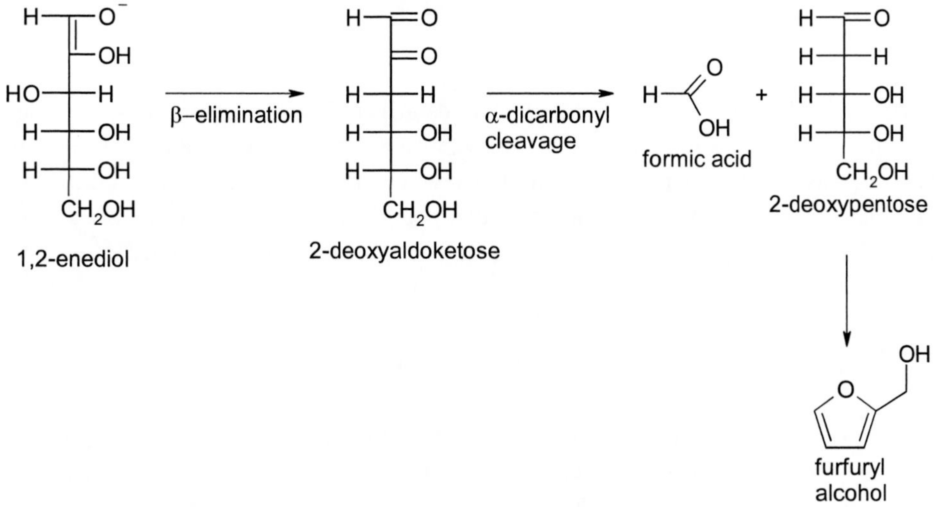

Figure 3. Formation of furfuryl alcohol from degradation of reducing sugars [63].

The concentration of furfuryl alcohol is 267 µg/g in instant coffee and in 564 µg/g coffee roasted at 210 °C for 3 min [65]. Coffee of a medium roast contains more furfuryl alcohol compared to a light roast [66]. Furthermore, furfuryl alcohol is also found in rice cakes 2 – 2.3 µg/g [67], bread 187 µg/g [68], honey 1.55 µg/g [69], toasted almond cv. Marcona 5.97 ± 1.09 µg/g, toasted almond cv. Comuna 8.88 ± 1.39 µg/g, toasted almond cv. California 4.40 ± 1.23 µg/g [70], non fat dried milk stored for 3 months at room temperature 14.5 µg/g [71], popcorn 0.0382 – 0.0821 µg/g [72], corn tortilla chips 0.54 µg/g [73], roasted cocoa powder 0.021 µg/g [74], palm sugar made by a traditional heating process at 210°C 0.139 µg/g, palm sugar which was made by an increased temperature of 240°C contains significantly more furfuryl alcohol (0.518 µg/g) [75], baked "Jewel" sweet potato 0.014 µg/g fresh weight [76], and citrus honey 0.011 µg/g [77]. In addition, furfuryl alcohol was found in oil that was used for frying of beef, veal, and chicken [78].

5.4. Health Issues of Furfuryl Alcohol

Estimated furfuryl alcohol intake is 130 μg/kg BW/day with a margin of safety of 462 mg/kg BW/day [79]. Furfuryl alcohol is mutagenic to *Salmonella typhimurium* strains TA100 engineered for the expression of human SULT1A1 because sulphotransferases can activate furfuryl alcohol into a mutagenic compound, 2-sulfooxymethylfuran. The 2-sulfooxymethylfuran is formed intracellularly near the bacterial DNA leading to the formation of 2-methylfuranyl adduct. The covalent 2-methylfuranyl adduct causes the mutagenic effect. The mutagenicity of furfuryl alcohol is dose dependent and increases its mutagenicity when the amount of furfuryl alcohol is increased from 3 to 200 nmol per plate [80]. In mice which received furfuryl alcohol with the drinking water the DNA samples of liver, kidney, and lung contain DNA adducts. In rodents which were exposed to furfuryl alcohol tumours that contained 2-methylfuranyl adducts were formed [80] but at lower concentration exposure (0.06μg furfuryl alcohol/kg BW/day) no tumors are formed [81].

CONCLUSION

Furfuryl alcohol and HMF can occur in foods at very high concentrations. Although the acute toxicity of these compounds is not relevant in the foods they could be activated with sulphotransferases to highly reactive compounds which are then mutagenic/carcinogenic. The detailed risks of these compounds and other compounds that could be metabolized to similar substrates for these enzymes is not yet known and additional work is pending.

REFERENCES

[1] Glatt, H. and Y. Sommer, Health risks of 5-hydroxymethylfurfural (HMF) and related compounds., in *Acrylamide and other hazardous compounds in heat-treated foods* K. A. Skog, J., Editor 2007. p. 328-357.

[2] Zhang, X.M., et al., Initiation and promotion of colonic aberrant crypt foci in rats by 5-hydroxymethy1-2-furaldehyde in thermolyzed sucrose. *Carcinogenesis*, 1993. 14(4): p. 773-775.

[3] Glatt, H., et al., Hydroxymethyl-substituted furans: mutagenicity in Salmonella typhimurium strains engineered for expression of various human and rodent sulphotransferases. *Mutagenesis*, 2012. 27(1): p. 41-48.

[4] Program, N.T. 2010; Available from: http://ntp.niehs.nih.gov/ntp/htdocs/LT_rpts/TR554.pdf.

[5] White, J.W., Spectrophotometric method for hydroxymethylfurfural in honey. *Journal of the Association of Official Analytical Chemists,* 1979. 62: p. 509-514.

[6] DIN10751-1, Untersuchung von Honig - Bestimmung des Gehaltes an Hydroxymethylfurfural - Teil 1: *Photometrisches Verfahren nach Winkler*, 2010-08.

[7] Murkovic, M. and N. Pichler, Analysis of 5-hydroxymethylfurfual in coffee, dried fruits and urine. *Molecular nutrition & Food research*, 2006. 50(9): p. 842-846.

[8] Mijares, R.M., et al., HPLC analysis of HMF in orange juice. *J. Food Sci.*, 1986. 51(3): p. 843-844.

[9] Ameur, L.A., G. Trystram, and I. Birlouez-Aragon, Accumulation of 5-hydroxymethyl-2-furfural in cookies during the backing process: Validation of an extraction method. *Food Chemistry*, 2006. 98(4): p. 790-796.

[10] Morales, F.J. and S. Jiménez-Pérez, Hydroxymethylfurfural determination in infant milk-based formulas by micellar electrokinetic capillary chromatography. *Food Chemistry*, 2001. 72(4): p. 525-531.

[11] van Boekel, M.A.J.S. and R. Zia Ur, Determination of hydroxymethylfurfural in heated milk by high-performance liquid chromatography. *Netherlands Milk and Dairy Journal,* 1987. 41: p. 297-306.

[12] Ibarz, A., J. Pagán, and S. Garza, Kinetic models of non-enzymatic browning in apple puree. *Journal of the Science of Food and Agriculture*, 2000. 80(8): p. 1162-1168.

[13] Rada-Mendoza, M., A. Olano, and M. Villamiel, Determination of hydroxymethylfurfural in commercial jams and in fruit-based infant foods. *Food Chemistry,* 2002. 79(4): p. 513-516.

[14] la Iglesia, F., et al., Automatic determination of 5-hydroxymethylfurfural (5-HMF) by a flow injection method. *Food Chemistry*, 1997. 60(2): p. 245-250.

[15] Teixidó, E., et al., Analysis of 5-hydroxymethylfurfural in foods by gas chromatography–mass spectrometry. *Journal of Chromatography* A, 2006. 1135(1): p. 85-90.

[16] Rizelio, V.M., et al., Development of a fast MECK method for determination of 5-HMF in honey samples. *Food Chemistry*, 2012. 133(4): p. 1640-1645.

[17] Zappalà, M., et al., Methods for the determination of HMF in honey: a comparison. *Food Control*, 2005. 16(3): p. 273-277.

[18] Antal Jr, M.J., W.S.L. Mok, and G.N. Richards, Mechanism of formation of 5-(hydroxymethyl)-2-furaldehyde from d-fructose and sucrose. *Carbohydr. Res.,* 1990. 199(1): p. 91-109.

[19] Perez Locas, C. and V.A. Yaylayan, Isotope labeling studies on the formation of 5-(hydroxymethyl)-2-furaldehyde (HMF) from sucrose by pyrolysis-GC/MS. *J. Agric. Food Chem.,* 2008. 56(15): p. 6717-6723.

[20] Lewkowski, J., Synthesis, chemistry and applications of 5-hydroxymethylfurfural and its derivatives. *Arkivoc.*, 2001. 1: p. 17-54.

[21] Cämmerer, B., B.L. Wedzicha, and L.W. Kroh, Nonenzymatic browning reactions of retro-aldol degradation products of carbohydrates. *European Food Research and Technology*, 1999. 209(3): p. 261-265.

[22] Fernández-Artigas, P., E. Guerra-Hernández, and B. García-Villanova, Browning Indicators in Model Systems and Baby Cereals. *J. Agric. Food. Chem.*, 1999. 47(7): p. 2872-2878.

[23] Ramírez-Jiménez, A., E. Guerra-Hernández, and B. García-Villanova, Evolution of non-enzymatic browning during storage of infant rice cereal. *Food Chemistry*, 2003. 83(2): p. 219-225.

[24] Garcia-Villanova, B., et al., Liquid chromatography for the determination of 5-(hydroxymethyl)-2-furaldehyde in breakfast cereals. *J. Agric. Food Chem.*, 1993. 41(8): p. 1254-1255.

[25] Giudici, P., M. Gullo, and L. Solieri, *Traditional Balsamic Vinegar Vinegars of the World,* L. Solieri and P. Giudici, Editors. 2009, Springer Milan. p. 157-177.
[26] Lavelli, V., C. Pompei, and M.A. Casadei, Quality of nectarine and peach nectars as affected by lye-peeling and storage. *Food Chemistry*, 2009. 115(4): p. 1291-1298.
[27] Doner, L.W., Honey, in *Encyclopedia of Food Sciences and Nutrition*, T.L.C. Caballero B., Finglas P.M., Editor 2003, Academic Press: Amsterdam. p. 3125-3130.
[28] White, J.W., *Composition of American honeys1962*: US Dept. of Agriculture.
[29] Nozal, M.J., et al., High-performance liquid chromatographic determination of methyl anthranilate, hydroxymethylfurfural and related compounds in honey. *Journal of Chromatography* A, 2001. 917(1): p. 95-103.
[30] Spano, N., et al., An RP-HPLC determination of 5-hydroxymethylfurfural in honey: the case of strawberry tree honey. *Talanta,* 2006. 68(4): p. 1390-1395.
[31] Rufián-Henares, J.A., C. Delgado-Andrade, and F.J. Morales, Assessing the Maillard reaction development during the toasting process of common flours employed by the cereal products industry. *Food Chemistry*, 2009. 114(1): p. 93-99.
[32] Yuan, J.P. and F. Chen, Separation and identification of furanic compounds in fruit juices and drinks by high-performance liquid chromatography photodiode array detection. *J. Agric. Food Chem.*, 1998. 46(4): p. 1286-1291.
[33] Gaspar, E.M.S.M. and A.F.F. Lucena, Improved HPLC methodology for food control – furfurals and patulin as markers of quality. *Food Chemistry*, 2009. 114(4): p. 1576-1582.
[34] Mochizuki, N., et al., Identification of an Interfering Substrate in Apple Juice and Improvement for Determination of Patulin with High-Performance Liquid Chromatography Analyses. *Journal of Food Protection®*, 2009. 72(4): p. 805-809.
[35] Rada-Mendoza, M., et al., Formation of hydroxymethylfurfural and furosine during the storage of jams and fruit-based infant foods. *Food Chemistry*, 2004. 85(4): p. 605-609.
[36] Vorlová, L., et al., Hydroxymethylfurfural contents in foodstuffs determined by HPLC method. *Journal of Food and Nutrition Research*, 2006. 45(1): p. 34-38.
[37] Brenna, O.V., E.L.M. Ceppi, and G. Giovanelli, Antioxidant capacity of some caramel-containing soft drinks. *Food Chemistry*, 2009. 115(1): p. 119-123.
[38] Delgado-Andrade, C., J. Rufián-Henares, and F. Morales, Hydroxymethylfurfural in commercial biscuits marketed in Spain. *Journal of Food and Nutrition Research*, 2009. 48(1): p. 14-19.
[39] Ramírez-Jiménez, A., B. García-Villanova, and E. Guerra-Hernández, Hydroxymethylfurfural and methylfurfural content of selected bakery products. *Food Research International,* 2000. 33(10): p. 833-838.
[40] Cardenas Ruiz, J., E. Guerra-Hernandez, and B. García-Villanova, Furosine is a useful indicator in pre-baked breads. *Journal of the Science of Food and Agriculture*, 2004. 84(4): p. 366-370.
[41] Ramírez-Jiménez, A., B. García-Villanova, and E. Guerra-Hernández, Effect of toasting time on the browning of sliced bread. *Journal of the Science of Food and Agriculture,* 2001. 81(5): p. 513-518.
[42] Ramirez-Jimenez, A., E. Guerra-Hernández, and B. García-Villanova, Browning indicators in bread. *J. Agric. Food Chem.*, 2000a. 48(9): p. 4176-4181.

[43] Sensidoni, A., D. Peressini, and C.M. Pollini, Study of the Maillard reaction in model systems under conditions related to the industrial process of pasta thermal VHT treatment. *Journal of the Science of Food and Agriculture*, 1999. 79(2): p. 317-322.

[44] Murkovic, M. and M.A. Bornik, Formation of 5-hydroxymethyl-2-furfural (HMF) and 5-hydroxymethyl-2-furoic acid during roasting of coffee. *Molecular Nutrition & Food research*, 2007. 51(4): p. 390-394.

[45] Arribas-Lorenzo, G. and F.J. Morales, Estimation of dietary intake of 5-hydroxymethylfurfural and related substances from coffee to Spanish population. *Food and Chemical Toxicology*, 2010. 48(2): p. 644-649.

[46] Ho, P., T. Hogg, and M. Silva, Application of a liquid chromatographic method for the determination of phenolic compounds and furans in fortified wines. *Food Chemistry,* 1999. 64(1): p. 115-122.

[47] Spano, N., et al., Chemical characterization of a traditional honey-based Sardinian product: Abbamele. *Food Chemistry,* 2008. 108(1): p. 81-85.

[48] de Aquino, F.W.B., et al., Simultaneous determination of aging markers in sugar cane spirits. *Food Chemistry*, 2006. 98(3): p. 569-574.

[49] Bozkurt, H., F. Göğüş, and S. Eren, Nonenzymic browning reactions in boiled grape juice and its models during storage. *Food Chemistry,* 1999. 64(1): p. 89-93.

[50] Masino, F., et al., A study of the relationships among acidity, sugar and furanic compound concentrations in set of casks for Aceto Balsamico Tradizionale of Reggio Emilia by multivariate techniques. *Food Chemistry*, 2005. 92(4): p. 673-679.

[51] Masino, F., et al., A study on relationships among chemical, physical, and qualitative assessment in traditional balsamic vinegar. *Food Chemistry*, 2008. 106(1): p. 90-95.

[52] Morales, F.J. and G. Arribas-Lorenzo, The formation of potentially harmful compounds in churros, a Spanish fried-dough pastry, as influenced by deep frying conditions. *Food Chemistry,* 2008. 109(2): p. 421-425.

[53] Edris, A.E., M. Murkovic, and B. Siegmund, Application of headspace-solid-phase microextraction and HPLC for the analysis of the aroma volatile components of treacle and determination of its content of 5-hydroxymethylfurfural (HMF). *Food Chemistry,* 2007. 104(3): p. 1310-1314.

[54] Husøy, T., et al., Dietary exposure to 5-hydroxymethylfurfural from Norwegian food and correlations with urine metabolites of short-term exposure. *Food and Chemical Toxicology,* 2008. 46(12): p. 3697-3702.

[55] Jöbstl, D., et al., Analysis of 5-hydroxymethyl-2-furoic acid (HMFA) the main metabolite of alimentary 5-hydroxymethyl-2-furfural (HMF) with HPLC and GC in urine. *Food Chemistry*, 2010. 123(3): p. 814-818.

[56] Kreppenhofer, S., O. Frank, and T. Hofmann, Identification of (furan-2-yl)methylated benzene diols and triols as a novel class of bitter compounds in roasted coffee. *Food Chemistry*, 2011. 126(2): p. 441-449.

[57] FAO, Revised Codex standard for honey, R. *CODEX STAN* 12-1981, Rev.2 (2001). Editor 2001.

[58] Yang, X. and T. Peppard, Solid-phase microextraction for flavor analysis. *J. Agric. Food Chem.,* 1994. 42(9): p. 1925-1930.

[59] Jerković, I., J. Mastelić, and S. Tartaglia, A study of volatile flavour substances in Dalmatian traditional smoked ham: Impact of dry-curing and frying. *Food Chemistry,* 2007. 104(3): p. 1030-1039.

[60] Kumazawa, K. and H. Masuda, Investigation of the change in the flavor of a coffee drink during heat processing. *J. Agric. Food Chem.*, 2003. 51(9): p. 2674-2678.

[61] Yuan, J.P. and F. Chen, Simultaneous separation and determination of sugars, ascorbic acid and furanic compounds by HPLC—dual detection. *Food Chemistry*, 1999. 64(3): p. 423-427.

[62] de Bruijn, J.M., et al., Reactions of monosaccharides in aqueous alkaline solutions. *Sugar Technology Reviews*, 1986. 13((1/2)): p. 21-52.

[63] Brands, C.M.J. and M.A.J.S. van Boekel, Reactions of Monosaccharides during Heating of Sugar−Casein Systems: Building of a Reaction Network Model. *J. Agric. Food Chem.*, 2001. 49(10): p. 4667-4675.

[64] Moon, J.K. and T. Shibamoto, Formation of volatile chemicals from thermal degradation of less volatile coffee components: quinic acid, caffeic acid, and chlorogenic acid. *J. Agric. Food Chem.*, 2010. 58(9): p. 5465-5470.

[65] Golubkova, T., *Bildung von potentiell toxischen Furanderivaten in Lebensmitteln*, 2011: Diplomarbeit. Institut für Biochemie TU Graz. Austria. p. 38-40.

[66] Moon, J.K. and T. Shibamoto, Role of roasting conditions in the profile of volatile flavor chemicals formed from coffee beans. *J. Agric. Food Chem.,* 2009. 57(13): p. 5823-5831.

[67] Buttery, R.G., et al., Volatile Flavor Components of Rice Cakes. *J. Agric. Food Chem.,* 1999. 47(10): p. 4353-4356.

[68] Jensen, S., et al., Antioxidants and shelf life of whole wheat bread. *Journal of Cereal Science,* 2011. 53(3): p. 291-297.

[69] Vazquez, L., et al., Changes in physico-chemical properties, hydroxymethylfurfural and volatile compounds during concentration of honey and sugars in Alicante and Jijona turrón. *European Food Research and Technology*, 2007. 225(5): p. 757-767.

[70] Vázquez-Araújo, L., et al., Investigation of aromatic compounds in toasted almonds used for the manufacture of turron. *European Food Research and Technology*, 2008. 227(1): p. 243-254.

[71] Karagül-Yüceer, Y., K.R. Cadwallader, and M.A. Drake, Volatile flavor components of stored nonfat dry milk. *J. Agric. Food Chem.,* 2002. 50(2): p. 305-312.

[72] Park, D. and J.A. Maga, Identification of key volatiles responsible for odour quality differences in popped popcorn of selected hybrids. *Food Chemistry*, 2006. 99(3): p. 538-545.

[73] Buttery, R.G. and L.C. Ling, Additional Studies on Flavor Components of Corn Tortilla Chips. *J. Agric. Food Chem.*, 1998. 46(7): p. 2764-2769.

[74] Bonvehí, J.S., Investigation of aromatic compounds in roasted cocoa powder. *European Food Research and Technology,* 2005. 221(1-2): p. 19-29.

[75] Ho, C.W., et al., Changes in volatile compounds of palm sap (Arenga pinnata) during the heating process for production of palm sugar. *Food Chemistry*, 2007. 102(4): p. 1156-1162.

[76] Wang, Y. and S.J. Kays, Contribution of Volatile Compounds to the Characteristic Aroma of Baked `Jewel' Sweetpotatoes. *Journal of the American Society for Horticultural Science*, 2000. 125: p. 638-643.

[77] Castro-Vázquez, L., M.C. Díaz-Maroto, and M.S. Pérez-Coello, Aroma composition and new chemical markers of Spanish citrus honeys. *Food Chemistry*, 2007. 103(2): p. 601-606.

[78] Takeoka, G., C. Perrino Jr, and R. Buttery, Volatile constituents of used frying oils. *J. Agric. Food Chem.,* 1996. 44(3): p. 654-660.

[79] Munro, I. and B. Danielewska-Nikiel, Comparison of estimated daily intakes of flavouring substances with no-observed-effect levels. *Food and Chemical Toxicology,* 2006. 44(6): p. 758-809.

[80] Monien, B.H., et al., Metabolic activation of furfuryl alcohol: formation of 2-methylfuranyl DNA adducts in Salmonella typhimurium strains expressing human sulfotransferase 1A1 and in FVB/N mice. *Carcinogenesis,* 2011. 32(10): p. 1533-1539.

[81] Program, N.T., Toxicology and Carcinogenesis Studies of Furfuryl Alcohol (CAS No. 98-00-0) in F344/N Rats and B6C3F1 Mice (Inhalation Studies), N.T. Program, Editor 1999: *Program Tech. Rep. Ser. NTP* - Department of Health and Human Services. p. 1-248.

[82] Swasti, Y.R. and M. Murkovic, Characterization of the polymerization of furfuryl alcohol during roasting of coffee. *Food & Function*, 2012. 3: p. 965-969.

[83] Lee, S.M., B.C. Seo and Y. Kim, Volatile compounds in fermented and acid-hydrolyzed soy sauces. *Journal of Food Science*, 2006. 71(3): p. 146-156.

[84] Hollnagel, A., Beiträge zur Chemie der nichtenzymatischen Bräunung von oligomeren Kohlenhydraten, 2000: PhD Dissertation. Technische Universität Berlin. Berlin. Germany.

[85] Troyano, E., et al., Isolation and characterization of 3-deoxypentulose and its determination in heated milk. *Journal of Dairy Research*, 1992. 59: 507-515.

In: Chemical Food Safety and Health
Editors: F. Pedreschi Plasencia and Z. Ciesarová
ISBN: 978-1-62948-339-9

Chapter 4

TYPES OF PESTICIDES, THEIR TOXICOLOGICAL EFFECTS AND RESIDUAL PRESENCE IN THE FOOD CHAIN

M. T. Molina*
Departamento de Ingeniería Química y Bioprocesos,
Pontificia Universidad Católica de Chile, Santiago, Chile

ABSTRACT

This review has two main purposes: (i) to show the toxicological effects on people's health produced by the direct intake of pesticides, and to advance the possible existence of toxicological effects associated with the indirect intake of pesticide residues; and (ii) to review many studies (most of them published after 2000) that provide evidence of pesticide residues in food of vegetal and animal origin, and also in processed food, due to the pesticides' persistence in the food chain.

1. INTRODUCTION

Pesticides or plaguicides are chemical or natural substances that are used to eliminate pests which attack agricultural crops. Their main objective is to prevent the deterioration of these crops in any of their stages of growth, storage, transportation, or processing. Thus, such products can be safely consumed by humans and some other animals. The Environmental Protection Agency (EPA) defines a pesticide as "any substance or mixture of substances intended for preventing, destroying, repelling, or mitigating any pest, including weeds, insects, rodents, fungi, bacteria, or other organisms" [1]. There is a wide variety of pesticides, such as insecticides, fungicides, herbicides, nematicides, rodenticides, bactericides,

* Correspondence: María Teresa Molina Maydl, Departamento de Ingeniería Química y Bioprocesos, Pontificia Universidad Católica de Chile, Av. Vicuña Mackenna 4860, Santiago, Chile, Phone: +56-2-23544237, E-mail: mtmolin1@uc.cl,

acaricides, molluscicides, avicides, repellents, and others[1]. Each one acts on different kinds of pest.

Before the 1940s the use of organic and inorganic substances for controlling pests was extremely high, but they had the drawback of having to be applied to crops in large amounts to produce the desired effects, thus lacking selectivity and phitotoxicity. These reasons were strong enough for industries to create and use synthetic pesticides to meet the needs of farmers. Since 1940 the use of synthetic pesticides grew exponentially due to their effectiveness and low cost, especially after the discovery of pesticides such as DDT, BHC, aldrin, dieldrin, endrin, chlordane, parathion, captan, and 2,4-D [2]. Around the 1980s, there arose concerns about uncontrolled use of pesticides, which led to the formulation of codes and guidelines, based on toxicity risks, regarding the use, handling, distribution, and selection of pesticides [3, 4].

According to the EPA's Pesticides Industry Sales and Usage Report (2011), herbicides are the most commonly used pesticides worldwide (Figure 1.1), mainly in agriculture (Figure 1.2).

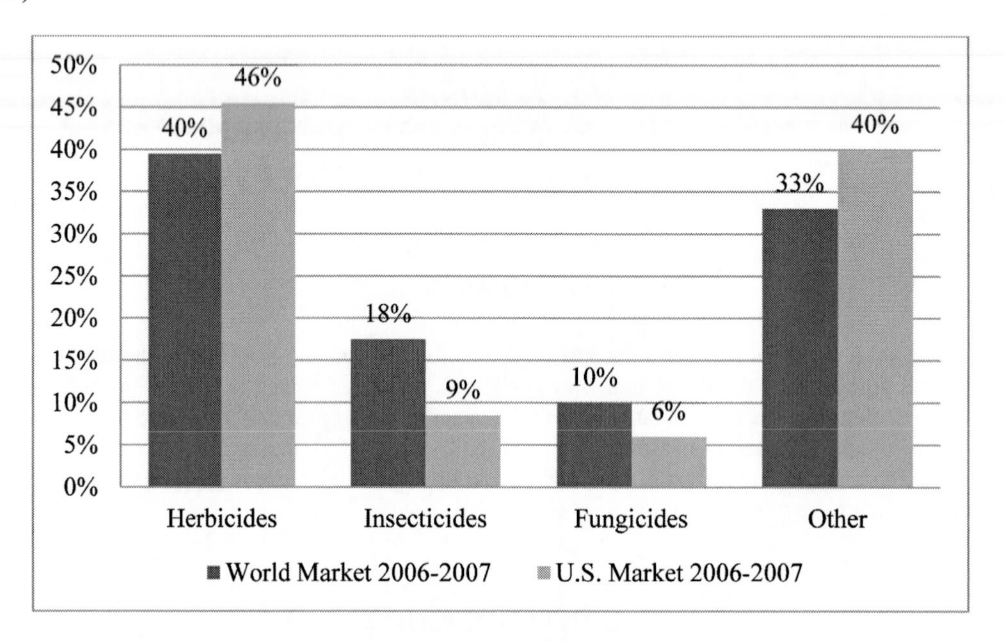

Figure 1.1. World and U.S. Amount of Pesticide Active Ingredient Used by Pesticide Type, 2006 and 2007 Estimates. *Herbicides* include herbicides and plant growth regulators. *Other* includes nematicides, fumigants, and other miscellaneous conventional pesticides, and other chemicals used as pesticides such as sulfur, petroleum oil, and sulfuric acid [5].

According to this information, there are three types of pesticide which are most commonly used in the agricultural sector: herbicides, insecticides, and fungicides. It is important to note that while both the United States and the European Union commercialize large amounts of pesticides used in agriculture [6], they have created severe monitoring programs in order to find pesticide residues in crops and thus ensure that consumers are not exposed to unacceptable levels of pesticide.

[1] For more information cf. The Book Pesticide and EPA, http://www.epa.gov/oppfead1/safety/spanish/healthcare/handbook/contents.htm.

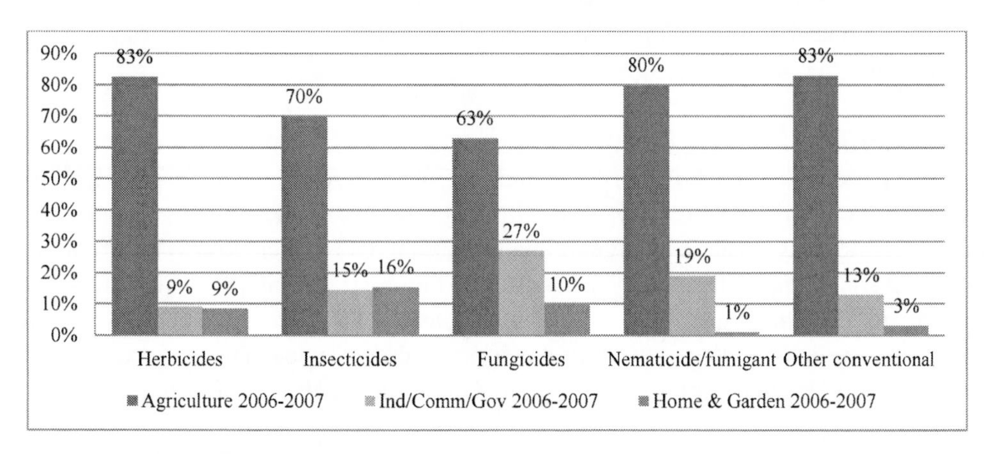

Figure 1.2. Amount of Conventional Pesticide Active Ingredient Used in the United States by Pesticide Type and Market Sector, 2006 and 2007 Estimates. *Other conventional* includes rodenticides and other miscellaneous conventional pesticides [5].

The presence of pesticide residues in agricultural crops has been demonstrated with the implementation of monitoring programs. This certainly affects both the products made from these crops and the animals fed with them. However, despite the fact that this has important effects on people's health, it is not thoroughly regulated by the competent organizations in these countries. Now, some significant questions arise: Why are pesticides found in cereals, animal products, and processed foods, if they are only applied in agricultural crops and the waiting period is respected? What pesticides and which of their physicochemical characteristics are relevant when assessing whether they are present in the products mentioned above? How does such persistence affect the possibility of finding pesticide residues in soils, freshwater, seawater, and groundwater, so that it could affect marine species and new crops? Are there pesticides persistent to degradation that remain in the environment and that may be bioaccumulated through the food chain? These questions are fundamental to know if and how certain types of pesticides affect human health.

In the next section, I will try to define those pesticides which are most commonly used worldwide according to their mode of action. In a third section, I will classify them into toxicity categories according to their doses and lethal concentrations. Finally, in Section 4, I shall present examples of their presence in food.

2. Types of Pesticides

There are four types of pesticide which are commonly used: insecticides, herbicides, fungicides, and nematicides. This section will define each of them according to their specific properties, modes of action, and their subgroups.

2.1. Insecticides

These are defined as pesticides designed to kill or control the growth of insects on plants, animals, and humans. The mechanism of action is the disruption of enzymatic and electrophysiological properties of the membranes of nerve cells [7]. There are four main types of insecticide.

Organochlorines

These insecticides contain chlorine in their chemical structure, which makes them highly liposoluble and poorly soluble in water (hydrophobic). This implies that organochlorines are easily stored in fatty tissue and organic matter. Furthermore, their low volatility and high chemical stability make them very persistent in the environment [8]. Their classification according to their structure is as follows: halogenated aromatic compounds (e.g. DDT); chlorinated cyclodiene (e.g. aldrin, dieldrin, endrin, endosulfan, mirex, chlordane, heptachlor); cycloalkanes chlorinated (e.g. lindane); and finally, chlorinated terpenes (e.g. toxaphene) [9].

Organophosphates

These insecticides are esters, derivatives of phosphoric acid, which are easily hydrolyzed. Moreover, their high vapor pressure, low solubility in water, and high solubility in organic solvents make them unstable in the environment. Additionally, they are highly toxic because they inhibit the enzyme acetylcholinesterase[2] (AChE) for a long period of time (hours or even several days) [11]. The most common organophosphate insecticides are acephate, chlorpyrifos, diazinon, dimethoate, fenitrothion, fenthion, malathion, methamidophos, monocrotophos, parathion, pirimiphos, profenofos, and temephos [12].

Carbamate

They are esters, derivatives of carbamic acid, which are easily hydrolyzed in the carbamate linkage. Moreover, their low solubility in water and high solubility in organic solvents make them unstable in the environment [10, 13, 14]. They also inhibit acetylcholinesterase action, but they are less toxic than organophosphates because their inhibitory effect is much lower (about 30 minutes) [11]. The most common carbamates are carbaryl, aldicarb, bendiocarb, carbofuran, carbosulfan, methiocarb, methomyl, pirimicarb, and thiodicarb [12].

Pyrethroids

These are substances synthesized from pyrethrin[3], whose chemical structure was improved to reduce their photolability. Moreover, they are highly liposoluble, and they have low vapor pressure, which make them a highly resistant pesticide in the environment [15, 16].

These pesticides may be classified into two groups according to their toxic effects. Type I pyrethroids are characterized by altering "startle" reflexes. Examples of these pesticides are the following: allethrin, bioallethrin, bifenthrin, permethrin, d-phenothrin, prallethrin, permethrin, bioresmethrin, tefluthrin, and tetramethrin [17].

---

[2] Acetylcholinesterase is an enzyme which regulates the passage of nerve impulses and hydrolyzes the neurotransmitter acetylcholine into two components, acetate and choline. But if this neurotransmitter is not hydrolyzed, then an over-accumulation of it would cause involuntary muscle contractions and even the death (due to laryngeal spasm). Cf. Guyton Physiology Treaty, Chapter 7, page 89.

[3] Pyrethrin, or pyrethrum extract is derived from Chrysanthemum cinerariaefolium as insectida was used in 1940s, but their instability to sunlight and therefore, low crop protection, led to the creation of pyrethroids [14].

Type II pyrethroids produce a syndrome characterized by convulsions, hyperactivity, and profuse salivation. Examples of this type are the following: cyfluthrin, cyhalothrin, lambda-cyhalothrin, cypermethrin, alpha-cypermethrin, deltamethrin, fenpropathrin, fenvalerate, esfenvalerate, flucythrinate, and tau-fluvalinate [17].

2.2. Herbicides

They are organic pesticides which control or eliminate undesired plants in agricultural crops. They can be classified according to five criteria [18, 19, 20]:

Selectivity: They act on a specific plant intended to be eliminated (*selective*), or they act over every type of weeds (*nonselective*, e.g. paraquat and glyphosate).

Time of Application: Depending on the period of sowing, the herbicides can act at three different stages:

Preplanting: The herbicide is applied several days or weeks after planting, sometimes on the soil.

Preemergence: The herbicide is applied after planting but before the crop and weed start to grow (e.g. terbacil, bromacil, imazapyr).

Emergence: The herbicide is applied after crops and unwanted herbs have grown (e.g. bromacil, imazapyr).

Mobility: These pesticides' mobility depends on their degree of penetration into the plant. If the herbicide only acts on those parts that had contact with the ground, their mobility is through *contact.* However, if the herbicide is absorbed by the roots or those parts of the plant that are above the soil surface, and travel through the conductive tissue of the plant, their mobility is *translocated.*

Mode of Action: The herbicides can act as growth regulators, namely by generating controlled growth (e.g. 2,4-D, MCPA, mecroprop, picloram, fluroxypyr); or they can act as inhibitors of any of the following:

- Production of amino acids: They generate foliage discoloration and deformation in new crops (e.g. glyphosate, glufosinate, chlorsulfuron, imazapyr).
- Photosynthesis: They inhibit the photosynthesis process (e.g. paraquat, diquat, triazines such as atrazine and simazine, terbacil, lenacil, propanil, bromoxynil, pyridate).
- Cell division: They inhibit the growth of roots or shoots.

Period of Residual Activity: Persistent herbicides remain for a long time in the environment, inhibiting the emergence and growth of weeds (e.g. atrazine, bromacil, tebuthiuron, imazapyr). But nonpersistent herbicides are quickly degraded, so their activity decreases with time. They enter the plant through the leaf's tissues (e.g. eptam or EPTC).

The persistence of herbicides in the soil depends mainly on three groups of factors: first, their microbiological, chemical, or photochemical degradation; second, their leaching through the soil, their volatilization, or absorption by plants; and third, the temperature or moisture of the soil, or the content of organic matter, for the increase of any of the latter decreases the herbicides' persistence [20].

2.3. Fungicides

They are chemicals highly used in industry, agriculture, and horticulture, in order to eliminate or stop the growth of unwanted fungi [21, 22]. They can be classified according to their chemical structure, as shown in Table 2.1 [22, 23].

Table 2.1. Classification of fungicides according to their chemical structure

Types	Fungicides (e.g.)
Substituted Benzenes	Chloromed, chlorothalonil, dicloran, hexachlorobenzene, pentachloronitrobenzene (PCNB)
Phenylamides	Metalaxyl, furalaxyl, benalaxyl, ofurace, cyprofuram, oxadixyl
Benzimidazoles	Benomyl, thiabendazole, carbendazim, thiophanate
Tiocarbamates	Thiram, ziram, ferbam
Ethylenebisdithiocarbamate (EBDC)	Maneb, zineb, nabam, mancozeb
Tiophtalamides	Captan, captafol, folpet
Carboxamides /Oxathiins	Carboxin, oxycarboxin
Dicarboxamides	Iprodione, procymidone, vinclozolin
Morpholines	Dodemorph, fenpropimorph, tridemorph, aldimorph
Imidazoles	Imazalil, triflumizole, prochloraz
Triazoles	Triadimenol, bitertanol, triadimefon, hexaconazole, penconazole, propiconazole, tetraconazole, tricyclazole
Copper Compounds	Organics: Copper acetate, copper hydroxide, copper oxychloride, cupric oxide, cuprous oxide, copper powder and lime, copper sulfate, copper silicate. Inorganics: copper phenylsalicylate, copper linoleate, copper naphthenate, copper oleate, copper quinolinolate, copper resinate.
Organomercury Compounds	Methyl mercury acetate, methoxyethyl mercury acetate, methoxyethyl mercury chloride, phenylmercuric acetate
Organotin Compounds	Phenyl tin acetate, phenyl tin chloride, triphenyltin, phenyl tin hydroxide.
Cadmium compounds	Cadmium chloride, cadmium succinate, cadmium sulfate.

Fungicides do not have the same kind of protective action in plants. They can be distinguished according to their level of penetration into plants. First, some fungicides are surface protectors, exerting their action before the fungi penetrate through the tissue (e.g. chlorothalonil, thiram, ziram, ferbam, zineb, maneb, mancozeb, captan, captafol, folpet, triphenyltin). And second, some fungicides are systemic protectors, which penetrate the surface of the plant to exert their fungicidal action (e.g. metalaxyl, furalaxyl, benalaxyl, ofurace, cyprofuram, oxadixyl, carboxin, oxycarboxin, dodemorph, fenpropimorph, tridemorph, aldimorph, benomyl, iprodione, cycloheximide). [21, 24]. But every fungicide has the same mode of action, regardless of their level of penetration. At the cellular level, fungicides act as metabolic inhibitors, specifically in the electron transport chain, nucleic acid synthesis, mitosis and cell division, protein synthesis, lipid and membrane synthesis, sterol biosynthesis, and multi-site processes [25].

2.4. Nematicides

These are chemicals used to eliminate nematodes. Nematodes are microscopic worms that live in the soil or in water [26]. Nematicides can be classified into two groups according to their volatility or movement in the soil: fumigant and non-fumigant.

Fugimant nematicides are highly volatile liquid pesticides, which pass to a gaseous phase when they enter into contact with the ground. They mainly consist of halogenated hydrocarbons and isothiocyanates, which are shown in table 2.2 [26, 27]. They are very harmful to plants and seeds. After spraying these nematicides, one should wait between 2 and 3 weeks before planting to avoid the harmful effect on plants and seeds [28]. The effectiveness of these pesticides depends on its vapor pressure, molecular weight, and soil conditions, such as porosity, moisture, temperature, and presence of organic matter [29-31]. Their mode of action consists in penetrating the nematode through its cuticle, affecting three of its systems : enzymatic, respiratory, and nervous [28].

Table 2.2. Examples of halogenated hydrocarbon and isothiocyanate nematicides

Fumigant	Examples
Halogenated hydrocarbons	Methyl bromide, chloropicrin, 1,3-dichloropropene (1,3-D), ethylene dibromide (EDB), ethylene dichloride (EDC), methyl iodide
Isothiocyanates	Dazomet, metam sodium, vorlex

Non-fumigant nematicides, on the other hand, are produced as liquids or granules that move through the ground when water (irrigated or in the form of rain) passes through their pores. These pesticides may be applied before or after planting [28]. The effectiveness of their penetration into the soil depends on the presence of moisture, organic matter, or soil type [30, 31]. Non-fumigant nematicides can be divided into organophosphates and carbamates (examples of them are shown in Table 2.3) [26, 27]. Their mode of action, as that of insecticides, consists in inhibiting the enzyme acetylcholinesterase produced by nematodes [27]. This means that some pesticides, such as carbamates (see table 2.3), act both as insecticides and as nematicides.

Table 2.3. Examples of organophosphate and carbamate nematicides

Non-fumigant	Examples
Organophosphates	Fenamiphos, cadusafos, disulfoton, ethoprophos, fosthiazate, isazofos, terbufos
Carbamates	Aldicarb, aldoxycarb, carbofuran, oxamyl

3. Toxicity as a Result From Exposure to Pesticides

Pesticides are widely used in agriculture, yet this use has been restricted over the years because it has been found that several of them are very persistent in the environment, highly toxic, and likely to produce damaging effects on people's health.

Although some pesticides may contain more than one active ingredient, each ingredient is individually tested according to its potential impact on human health. Thus, a pesticide's toxicity may be understood as "the ability of a substance to cause adverse effects develop rapidly, within a few hours or a day." (GBC - Government of British Columbia) [33].

The information needed to catalog their potential toxicity[4] is determined according to six points: (i) how the active ingredient is absorbed, metabolized, and excreted; (ii) the potential to cause eye or skin irritation or to cause allergic reactions on skin; (iii) the carcinogenic potential and toxicity associated when the ingredient is administered for long periods of time; (iv) the genotoxic potential; (v) the possibility that the active ingredient affects fetal development; and (vi) by means of tests that could better explain the effect of the active ingredient on systems, such as the nervous, immune and endocrine systems.

Based on these points, governamental food safety agencies throughout the world have established safety regulations that either prohibit the use of some pesticides involving potential risk for human health, or restrict the indiscriminate use of certain others. Moreover, they have established critical levels of exposure, such as ADI (Acceptable Daily Intake), ARfD (Acute Reference Dose), AOEL (Acceptable Operator Exposure Level), and MRLs (Maximum Residue Levels). Furthermore, pesticides have been classified according to their degree of toxicity, and their lethal doses have been defined for each category by taking into account how human beings can come into contact with pesticides[5] (orally, dermally, and / or by inhalation). Tables 3.1 and 3.2, extracted from the EPA [32], show the different categories into which pesticides are classified according to the toxicity and maximum dose (LD (x)[6] or LC (x)[7]) that need to be ingested to reach a degree of acute toxicity.

Table 3.1. Categories of pesticide's toxicity

Categories of Toxicity	
Category I	Danger, Poison
Category II	Warning
Category III	Caution
Category IV	Caution

The toxicity of pesticides depends on the dose which is ingested. Small doses of a highly toxic substance may produce serious symptoms of intoxication. In turn, large doses of a low-toxicity substance may generate acute symptoms of intoxication.

Based on this classification, two kinds of toxicity may be defined, acute and chronic. Acute toxicity refers to the adverse effects produced when exposure takes place for a long time (up to 24 hours). These effects may appear within the first 14 days after the exposure. Table 3.2 shows the required doses to generate acute toxicity depending on the kind of contact, i.e. oral, dermal, or by inhalation.

---

[4] See Committee on Toxicity (COT). Risk Assessment of Mixtures of Pesticides and Similar Substance. Available in http://cot.food.gov.uk/pdfs/reportindexed.pdf.

[5] For further information about classification of pesticides, see http://www.who.int/ipcs/ publications /pesticides_hazard_2009.pdf.

[6] Lethal Dose: It is considered lethal for 50% of animal population tested, measured in x mg / kg [31].

[7] Lethal Concentration: It is considered lethal for 50% of animal population tested, measured in x mg / l [31].

Chronic toxicity is defined as the adverse effects produced when an organism has had a continuous exposure. Its measurement is more complex than that of acute toxicity, since it does not immediately appear after exposure and it may take many years for any kind of symptom to appear. The adverse effects on human health are [33]:

- Carcinogenicity
- Mutagenicity
- Teratogenicity
- Oncogenicity
- Damage to the liver
- Reproductive system
- Nerve damage
- Allergic Sensitization

The existence of pesticides which are both lipophilic and highly persistent in the environment is indubitable. These two characteristics make it probable that they accumulate through the food chain for years; specifically, in animal and human tissues. Therefore, one should not discard the possibility that regular consumption of this kind of residues could produce chronic toxicity.

A summary table (Table 3.3) is shown below, which presents the toxicological effects of some types of pesticide, and examples of these that have been found as residues in food[8].

Table 3.2. Contact ways and lethal doses for acute toxicity

Study	Category I	Category II	Category III	Category IV
Acute Oral (LD 50)	Up to and including 50 mg/kg	>50 thru 500 mg/kg	>500 thru 5000 mg/kg	>5000 mg/kg
Acute Dermal (LD 50)	Up to and including 200 mg/kg	>200 thru 2000 mg/kg	>2000 thru 5000 mg/kg	>5000 mg/kg
Acute Inhalation (LC 50)	Up to and including 0.05 mg/kg	>0.05 thru 0.5 mg/liter	>0.5 thru 2 mg/liter	>2 mg/liter
Primary Eye Irritation	Corrosive (Irreversible destruction of ocular tissue) or corneal involvement or irritation persisting for more than 21 days	Corneal involvement or other eye irritation clearing in 8-21 days	Corneal involvement or other eye irritation clearing in 7 days or less	Minimal effects clearing in less than 24 hours
Primary Skin Irritation	Corrosive (tissue destruction into the dermis and/or scarring)	Severe irritation at 72 hours (severe erythema or edema)	Moderate irritation at 72 hours (moderate erythema)	Mild or slight irritation at 72 hours (no irritation or slight erythema)

[8] See http://www.epa.gov/oppfead1/safety/spanish/healthcare/handbook/contents.htm.

Table 3.3. Toxicological effects of some pesticides and examples of pesticide residues found in food

Type of Pesticide	Examples of Pesticides	Route of Absorption	Toxicology	Examples of pesticides found in food
Insecticides	Organophosphates	Inhalation, ingestion and dermal penetration	– Phosphorylation of the enzyme acetylcholinesterase, which allows accumulation of acetylcholine. – Induced delayed neuropathy. – Paralysis acute respiratory, muscle weakness, and paralysis of cranial nerves. – Inhibition of hepatic enzymes by malathion. – Deposition in fatty tissue, especially when more than two are absorbed at once.	Dioxathion, parathion, chlorfenvinphos, chlorpyrifos, demeton, diazinon, thiophos, famphur, methyl-parathion, trichlorfon, malathion, dichlorvos, fenitrothion, methamidophos, methidathion, pirimiphos-methyl, triaclorfon, tetraethyl, triazophos, dimethoate
Insecticides	Pyrethroids	High oral absorption, and low dermal and inhalation	– Central nervous system toxicity, causing seizures. – Paresthesia	Deltamethrin, permethrin, fenpropathrin, cyfluthrin, cypermethrin
Insecticides	N-methyl carbamate	Inhalation, ingestion, and some by dermal penetration.	- Reversible carbamylation of the enzyme acetylcholinesterase, allowing the accumulation of acetylcholine. Carbamyl-enzyme complex is dissociated faster than the phosphoryl-enzyme complex. - High concentrations of acetylcholine may cause: contractions and spasms, sensory disturbances, incoordination, and depressed motor function of the brain.	Aldicarb, carbofuran, methomyl, methiocarb, pirimicarb, thiodicarb, carbaryl, propoxur, bufencarb, oxamyl
Insecticides	Solid organochlorine	Dermal penetration	– Part of the absorbed dose is accumulated in fatty tissue. The metabolic distribution of some of these pesticides is so slow that they are stored in body fat. Studies have mentioned that these pesticides are released through breast milk. – Delayed fecal excretion due to the reabsorption of these pesticides executed by intestines. – Overexcitation of the brain, paresthesia, ataxia, hyperreflexia. – High concentrations of these pesticides promote tissue and cardiac arrhythmias. – Interaction with endocrine receptors, estrogen, and androgen could disrupt the endocrine system.	DDT, aldrin, dieldrin, endrin, heptachlor (HCH), lindane, hexachlorobenzene, dicofol, endosulfan

Type of Pesticide	Examples of Pesticides	Route of Absorption	Toxicology	Examples of pesticides found in food
Herbicides	Chlorophenolics	Gastrointestinal tract and low dermal	– High links to proteins. – Other pesticides can be generated in the production of these pesticides, such as CDD and CDF.	2,4 dichlorophenoxyacetic acid (2,4-D) 2,4 diclorofenoxipropiónico acid (2,4-B) 2,4,5 trichlorophenoxyacetic acid (2,4,5-T)
Herbicides	pentachlorophenol	Dermal, pulmonary and gastrointestinal absorption	– Increased cellular oxidative metabolism, producing hyperthermia. – The effect is embryotoxic and fetotoxic, causing malformations, abortion, and low birth weight.	PCP
Herbicides	Nitrophenolic and Nitrocresolic	Dermal, pulmonary and gastrointestinal absorption	– Highly toxic (25 mg / kg <LD50 <50 mg / kg). – Stimulation of oxidative metabolism in the mitochondria, generating hyperthermia, tachycardia, headache, dehydration, and reduction of carbohydrates and fats. – It affects the nervous system, kidney and liver.	Dinocap, dinoseb
Herbicides	Paraquat and Diquat	Pulmonary and dermal absorption (Paraquat) Systemic absorption, not selectively to the lungs (Diquat)	*Paraquat* – It affects the gastrointestinal tract, kidney, liver, and heart. – 3 mg / kg <LD50 <5 mg / kg. – It generates free radicals that oxidize the lung tissue, causing lipid peroxidation and cell damage. *Diquat* - Severe effects on the central nervous system: pathological changes in the brain.	
Fungicides	Substituted benzenes	High absorption through inhalation, and low dermal and gastrointestinal absorption (Chlorothalonil)	*Chlorothalonil* - Irritation of the skin and mucous membranes of the eyes. *Hexachlorobenzene* – In low doses, it produces mild irritant effects. In high doses, it may cause toxic porphyria. – People not occupationally exposed to this pesticide may have traces in blood due to residues presented in food.	Chlorothalonil, hexachlorobenzene (HCB)
Fungicides	Ethylene-bis-dithiocarbamates (EBDC Compounds)	Low oral absorption	– Maneb exhibits greater toxicity than the mancozeb and other EBDC (zineb, nabam) due to its high absorbency and water solubility. – There are not cholinesterase inhibitors or acetaldehyde dehydrogenase. – No test on poisoning.	Maneb, mancozeb

Table 3.3. (Continued)

Type of Pesticide	Examples of Pesticides	Route of Absorption	Toxicology	Examples of pesticides found in food
Fungicides	Tioftalamidas	Inhalation and dermal absorption	– No evidence of poisoning in humans. But Caltofol aggravates asthma after ocupational contact. – But in large doses applied to laboratory animals, Captan produces hypothermia, hyporeflexia and decreases urine production.	Captan, folpet, captofol
Fungicides	Organics	Dermal and oral absorption (dodine) Low oral and dermal absorption (iprodione, metalaxyl, triaforina)	– No reported poisoning in humans. – Studies in laboratory animals have a low acute toxicity via oral and dermal (iprodione, metalaxyl, triaforina). – The dodine presents severe toxicity in laboratory animals via oral and dermal.	Benomyl, iprodione, cycloheximide, dodine, metalaxyl, triaforina

4. PRESENCE OF PESTICIDE RESIDUES IN THE FOOD CHAIN

Let me first introduce the definition of two concepts that will be often used in this section: pesticide residue and maximum residue limit (MRL). The Codex Alimentarius defines pesticide residue as *any specified substance in food, agricultural commodities, or animal feed resulting from the use of pesticide. The term includes any derivatives of a pesticide, such as conversion products, metabolites, reaction products, and impurities considered to be of toxicological significance.* On the other hand, the Codex Alimentarius defines MRL *as the maximum concentration of a pesticide residue (expressed as mg / kg) to be legally permitted in or on food commodities and animal feeds.*

These two terms refer to the presence of pesticide residues in food of vegetal and animal origin that could affect or even jeopardize consumers' health. So the authorities were obliged to define regulations that establish a maximum of permissible residues.

Although each country controls pesticide use according to its own regulations, it is not rare to find foods with pesticide residues, some at very low concentrations but others above the MRL established by each country. However, it is unusual to find the presence of pesticides that have been banned (either because they hazard human health, or because they can persist in the environment for a long time). For instance, persistent organic pollutants (POPs) are chemical substances banned throughout the world because they can gravely affect people's health given that they are highly persistent in the environment and that they can bioacculumate in ecosystems. Here are some examples of POPs: aldrin, chlordane, dichlorodiphenyl, dieldrin, endrin, heptachlor, hexachlorobenzene, mirex, toxaphene, polychlorinated biphenyls (PCBs), polychlorinated dibenzo-p-dioxins (dioxins), and polychloronated dibenzofurans (furans) [34].

Below several studies are presented that confirm the presence of pesticide residues in food of animal and vegetal origin; processed foods; cereals; baby food; and food made for infants. While the levels detected by these studies were generally low, it should be noticed that, according to those studies, the presence of pesticide residues in the abovementioned foods is not only widespread, but is also above the established MRL.

4.1. Food of Animal Origin

In foods of this kind it is usual to find insecticide residues, such as organochlorines (OCs), organophosphates (OPs), carbamatos, and pyrethroids; and also fungicides, e.g. benzimidazoles and organophosphates. These types of pesticide are lipophilic, some of which are likely to be deposited in fat matrices. They can also be bioaccumulated through the food chain [35].

Granby et al. [36] mention that OCPs were detected in matrices with high fat content, such as butter, cheese, milk, and meat. In addition, the presence of these pesticides in fish could be related to water pollution. A study by Darko et al. [37] found residues of DDT and its metabolite DDE in tilapia fish, and also in sediment and water samples of Lake Bosomtwi, Ghana. Furthermore, analysis of 18 samples of fish made by Kalyoncu et al. [38] in Turkey, showed that DDT, its metabolites, and HCH were found mostly in the muscles of fish. Moreover, they found detectable levels of aldrin, heptachlor, and HCH in the majority of samples.

Several studies have researched the presence of pesticide residues in milk. The results have identified organochlorine residues; specifically, PCBs, *p,p'*-DDT and its metabolite *p,p'*-DDT, and OCPs. Because breast milk is the main baby food, the presence of such pesticides is particularly worrisome, especially when exceeding the MRLs [39-41].

Badia-Vila et al. [42] compared the butter sold in Spain and in other European countries (Germany, France, Poland, Denmark, Netherlands, and Ireland) in terms of the presence of several PCBs. They found high levels of lindane, hexachlorobenzene and hexachlorocyclohexane in samples of butter consumed in Spain, although none of them troubling.

Herrera et al. [43] studied the levels of organochlorine pesticides in 229 samples of meat and other Spanish meat products. The results showed that every sample had hexachlorobenzene (HCB) and hexachlorocyclohexane (HCH), especially lindane (100% detection on lamb and pork). Furthermore, 8%, 12%, and 15% of pork meat, cured pork sausage, and pork bologna samples, respectively, had dieldrin; and 83% of lamb meat samples had DDTs.

Mallatou et al. [44] analyzed 38 samples of cow milk and 28 samples of chesse, both from Greece. As for the samples of milk, 28.9% contained one or more residues of lindane, α-isomeric hexachlorocyclohexane (α-BHC), 1,1-bis [p-chlorophenyl] -2,2-dichloroethylene (pp'- DDE), and methyl parathion. Regarding the samples of cheese, 32.1% contained one or more residues of α-BHC, p, p'-DDE, lindane, aldrin, and dieldrin.

In the study carried out by Ahmad et al. [45], they analyzed 519 samples of eggs, chicken, lamb, and beef from Jordan. The results showed that 28%, 20%, and 49% of egg, chicken, and meat samples, respectively, had residues of organochlorine pesticides, where the HCH and DDT were the most prominent.

4.2. Food of Vegetal Origin

Fruits and vegetables represent a considerable proportion of the samples analyzed by monitoring programs for pesticide residues, since a wide range of them are used in agriculture [46]. Constant monitoring ensures that farmers are conforming to good agricultural practices, especially those related to the handling of pesticides.

Insecticide, acaricide, and fungicide residues are usually found in this kind of food. Their detection by means of analytical equipments depends on three molecular properties: polarity, volatility, and thermal ability [46]. The most commonly found pesticides by monitoring programs are: dithiocarbamates, imazalil, procymidone, group benomyl, iprodione, thiabendazole, orthophenylphenol, chlorpyriphos, chlormequat, and bromide [36]. Granby et al. mention an interesting case regarding chlormequat. Its use was regulated between 2001 and 2006 and diminished from that time on, but its systemic effect favored its retention in pear trees, so that each year within that time period chlormequat residues were detected in pear crops.

Poulsen, M. E. et al. [47] conducted a study in Denmark to examine fruits and vegetables, fresh and frozen. They analyzed 4,404 samples from Denmark (34%) and other countries (66%). The results surprisingly showed presence of the following pesticides: aldrin, binapacryl, dieldrin, DDT, and fenson. The 10 pesticides most frequently reported were: dithocarbamates, chlorpyriphos, carbedazim, imazalil, endosulfan, iprodione, procymidone, thiabendazole, captan, and brompropylate. Only 4% of the samples (which included apples, carrots, lemons, tangerines, melons, oranges, lettuces, and tomatoes) had residues that exceeded the maximum limits of the European Union. 60% of fruit samples contained pesticide residues, and 6% of them were over this maximum limit. 18% of vegetable samples contained residues of pesticides, and 2% of them contained residues that exceeded the maximum.

Hjorth et al. [48], in a collaborative project involving five countries (Denmark, Finland, Norway, Estonia, and Sweden), conducted a study focusing on the presence of pesticide residues in fruits and vegetables coming from South America. In general, these samples showed pesticide residues that exceeded the limits of permissibility, in contraposition to fruits and vegetables coming from European countries. Two additional reasons motivated this study: (i) the fact that control programs for pesticide residues are very limited due to lack of resources and stringent legislation on the subject; and (ii) that training programs for technical staff and the equipment used to monitor pesticide residues are very scarce. They analyzed 724 fruit and vegetable samples, which mostly came from Brazil, Chile, and Argentina. The majority of the samples had an amount of pesticide residues under the maximum level established by the European Union. The pesticides most frequently found were thiabendazole, imazalil, and chlorpyriphos. Of all the countries surveyed, the highest percentage of samples containing residues in relation to total samples analyzed was Chile, with 85%. Only 5% of samples from this country had pesticide residues over the maximum level. Moreover, Brazil was the country with the highest percentage (13%) of samples, in relation to the total samples, containing residues exceeding the maximum allowed. Overall, samples that actually exceeded the limits did it in more than 30% (there were samples that even exceeded the limit by 200% and 300%). The fruits which exceeded this limit the most were mainly apples, papayas, passion fruits, and table grapes.

Other studies have shown that pesticide residues in fruit and vegetables under commercial processing can be diminished significantly. This especially depends upon the pesticide's physicochemical properties; its location in food; the time it was in contact with the food; the nature of the latter; the unit operations (steps) of its processing; and the processing time [36].

Holland et al. [49] mention a number of unit operations and their effects on reducing the levels of pesticide residues. For a residue to be removed in the washing step, there are four key elements to be analyzed: the location of the residue, the age of the residue, the solubility of the pesticide in water, and the temperature and type of wash. In the steps of peeling, trimming, or hulling, pesticides that are better eliminated are insecticides or fungicides that have limited movement in the cuticle of the fruit. The juicing operation is characterized by having a low amount of highly lipophilic pesticide residues, but levels of these residues may be increased when making juice concentrate, due to water loss in the product. Finally, in the cooking step, the degradation and volatilization of residues are influenced by the time it takes to complete the process, the loss of moisture, the temperature, and whether the system is open or close.

Granby et al. affirm that the majority of pesticides are directly applied to crops. Some of them may be on the surface or skin of the products for human consumption. So if this skin or surface is removed, much of the pesticides in the product can be reduced. This is the case of citrus fruits, since research showed that over 90% of pesticide residues were on the skin.

Bonnechere et al. [50] study two varieties of melon treated with carbendazim, maneb, acetamiprid, cyromazin, imazalil, and thiamethoxam. The results, after the peeling step, showed that maneb, imazalil, and acetamiprid residues decreased by more than 90%. Moreover, residues of cyromazin, carbendazim, and thiamethoxam decreased by 50%.

Chavarri, M. J. et al. [51] analyze samples of tomatoes, peppers, asparagus, spinach, and peaches, which had been exposed to acephate, chlorpyriphos, cypermethrin, mancozeb, maneb, thiram, and propineb. In most samples, the washing and blanching steps allowed the removal of more than 50% of the residue; and mancozeb, maneb, and propineb were completely removed from tomatoes and spinach after the washing and blanching (using hot water) steps. Overall, the combined processes of canning (washing, blanching, peeling, pureeing, and cooking) made it possible to remove between 90% and 100% of the residues present in most samples.

4.3. Cereals

Cereal grains are stored for a period of 3 to 36 months at room temperature, in which pesticides are applied to the product [49]. Since grains should be protected against insects, stored grains are mainly sprayed with insecticides, fungicides, and herbicides [36]. The main insecticides found in cereal samples are malathion, pirimiphos-methyl, chlorpyrifos-methyl, deltamethrine, and dichlorvos. [36].

Degradation of pesticide residues in grains depends on the type of pesticide and on its affinity with the grain's lipophilic matter. It has been generally studied that residues of insecticide-treated grains degrade very slowly [49]. Pareja et al. [52] mention that the physicochemical characteristics of rice can explain the presence of pesticide residues. They assert that lipophilic pesticides are frequently found in brown rice, while carbendazim, malathion, iprodione, tebuconazole, quinclorac, and tricyclazole are found mainly in white rice.

A study by the European Commission in 2006 [53] analyzed 3,645 grain samples, of which 27% showed residues below MRL, and a 0.7% exceeded this limit. The most frequently found pesticides were pirimiphos-methyl, malathion, chlorpyrifos-methyl, chlormequat, deltamethrin, permethrin, chlorpyriphos, bromides, dichlorvos, and mepiquat.

Guler et al. [54] conducted a study in the region of Konya, Turkey. This research focused on different wheat samples of that region. The results showed that all of them had residues of organochlorine pesticides, some of them above the MRL established by the EU. The main pesticides found were chlordane isomers, methoxychlor, DDT and its metabolites, aldrin, β-HCH, heptachlor, and lindane.

Uygun et al. [55] conducted a study to investigate the presence of some organophosphate residues in samples of wheat bran, flour, and biscuits (with and without fiber). Samples of wheat were treated with malathion and chlorpyrifos-methyl and then stored for eight months. The results showed that this was not enough time to reduce the levels of residues below MRLs. Furthermore, the processing of cookies significantly reduced the concentrations of both pesticides, yet chlorpyrifos-methyl proved to be more persistent than malathion due to its physicochemical properties.

Conclusion

The previous sections presented the main problem associated with the presence of pesticide residues in agricultural crops, animal foods, and processed foods, namely: their persistence in the food chain and, as a consequence, the adverse effects they may have on people's health. A wide variety of pesticides is used mainly in agriculture, yet this has been subjected to regulations and, in many cases, restricted because they are highly persistent in the environment and toxic for people.

If pesticides are applied on vegetable, fruit, and cereal crops, how can we explain the presence of pesticide residues in products of animal origin, such as meat, fish, cheese, milk, and eggs, or in soil and water samples? It is possible that highly persistent pesticides did not degrade, which would explain their presence; however, one should not rule out the possibility that they have been mishandled.

Although it has been proved that direct intake of pesticides causes toxicological effects, this is not true of indirect intake. There are only a few studies on toxicological effects produced by indirect intake, so it should not be discarded that there exists a relation between the presence of pesticide residues in food and the possible adverse effects on people's health due to food consumption.

Because people's health could be at risk, new ways to control pests in crops have been explored to reduce their persistence in the environment and in the food chain. Biopesticides are products elaborated with bacterias, viruses, or fungi as active ingredients. They have the following advantages and disadvantages: (i) they do not pollute the environment and are safe for people; (ii) they act on the specific pest; (iii) it is difficult for pests to develop resistance to them; yet (iv) they are sensitive to environmental factors such as temperature, moisture, and radiation; and (v) it is difficult to produce them at an industrial level.

The presence of some biopesticides in the market indicates that they are already being used as an alternative to chemical pesticides to stop pests in crops. Future studies on biopesticides will certainly prove to be a great contribution to agriculture and the food markets.

REFERENCES

[1] Environmental Protection Agency (EPA). *Pesticides: Glossary*. Available in: http://www.epa.gov/pesticides/glossary/m-q.html#p

[2] International Union of Pure and Applied Chemistry (IUPAC). *History of Pesticide Use*. Available in: http://agrochemicals.iupac.org/index.php?option=com_sobi2&sobi2Task=sobi2Details&catid=3&sobi2Id=31

[3] World Health Organization (WHO) (2009). *The WHO recommended Classification of Pesticide by Hazard and Guidelines to Classification.* Available in: http://www.who.int/ipcs/publications/pesticides_hazard_2009.pdf

[4] Food and Agriculture Organization (FAO) (2003). *International Code of Conduct on the Distribution and Use of Pesticide*. Available in: ftp://ftp.fao.org/docrep/fao/005/y4544e/y4544e00.pdf

[5] Environmental Protection Agency (EPA). *Pesticide Industry Sales and Usage – 2006 and 2007 Market Estimates*. Available in: http://www.epa.gov/opp00001/pestsales/07pestsales/market_estimates2007.pdf

[6] Zhang, W., Jiang, F., Ou, J. (2011). Global pesticide consumption and pollution: with China as a focus. *Proceedings of the International Academy of Ecology and Environmental Sciences,* 1(2), 125-144. Available in: http://www.iaees.org/publications/journals/piaees/articles/2011-1(2)/Global-pesticide-consumption-pollution.pdf

[7] Thompson, C., Richardson, R. (2004). Insecticides. In *Pesticide Toxicology and International Regulation* (pp. 89-116). England: John Wiley & Sons Ltd.

[8] Verdes, A., et al (1990). General characteristics of organochlorine pesticides. *In organochlorine pesticides*. Retrieved from: http://www.bvsde.paho.org/bvsacd/eco/033965/033965-02-A1.pdf

[9] Pesticide Action Network and Alternatives for Latin America (RAP-AL). *Toxicity Classification of Pesticides*. Retrieved from: http://www.rap-al.org/index.php?seccion=4&f=toxicidad.php

[10] Vallejo, M. (1983). Chemistry of Pesticides. Ongoing Pesticides in Colombia (pp. 133-137). Available at: http://books.google.cl/books?id=PpS4UbdupKcC&printsec=frontcover&hl=es&source=gbs_ge_summary_r&cad=0#v=onepage&q=vallejo&f=false

[11] F, R. (1990). Mechanism of Action of Organophosphorus and Carbamate Insecticides. *Environmental Health Perspectives,* 87 (july), 245-254. Available in: http://www.ncbi.nlm.nih.gov/pmc/articles/PMC1567830/?page=1

[12] Bisset, J. (2002). Proper Use of Insecticides: resistance control. *Journal of Cuban Medicine*, 54 (3), 202-219. Available at: http://scielo.sld.cu/scielo.php?script=sci_arttext&pid=S0375-07602002000300005&lang=es

[13] Ware, G., Whitacre, M. (2004). Insecticides. In *The Book Pesticide* (6th edition, pp. 47-84). United States.
[14] International Programme on Chemical Safety (IPCS). *Carbamate Pesticides: A General Introduction.* Retrieved from: http://www.inchem.org/documents/ehc/ehc/ehc64.htm#PartNumber:2
[15] Casida, J. (1980). Pyrethrum flowers and pyrethroid insecticides. *Environmental Health Perspectives,* 34 (February), 189-202.
[16] Coats, J. (1990). Mechanisms of Toxic Action and Structure-Activity Relationships for Organochlorine and Synthetic Pyrethroid Insecticides. *Environmental Health Perspectives,* 87 (July), 255-262.
[17] International Programme on Chemical Safety (IPCS). *Pyrethroids.* Retrieved from: http://www.inchem.org/documents/ukpids/ukpids/ukpid75.htm
[18] Bussan, A. J. and W. E. Dyer. (1999). Herbicides and rangeland. In: R. L. Sheley and J. K. Petroff, eds. *Biology and Management of Noxious Rangeland Weeds* (pp. 116–132). Corvallis, OR: Oregon State University Press. Available in: http://teamarundo.org /control_manage/docs/herbicides_rangeland.pdf
[19] Causal Analysis/Diagnosis Decision Information System (CADDIS). *Sources, Stressors & Responses: Herbicides.* Available in: http://www.epa.gov/caddis/ssr_herb_int.html
[20] Kogan, M., Pérez, A. (2003). *Herbicidas. Fundamentos fisiológicos y bioquímicos del modo de acción* (1ra. ed, pp. 60-85; 168-205). Santiago de Chile: Ediciones Universidad Católica de Chile.
[21] Ware, G., Whitacre, M. (2004). Fungicides and Bactericides. In *The Book Pesticide* (6th edition, pp. 155-172). United States.
[22] Thompson, C., Richardson, R. (2004). Fungicides. En *Pesticide Toxicology and International Regulation* (pp. 193-292). England: John Wiley & Sons Ltd.
[23] Environmental Protection Agency (EPA). *Fungicidas.* Available in: http://www.epa.gov/oppfead1/safety
[24] Encyclopedia Access Science. *Fungistat and fungicide.* Available in: http://accessscience.com/content/Fungistat%20and%20fungicide/276000
[25] Ware, G., Whitacre, M. (2004). Mode of action for fungicides. In *The Book Pesticide* (6th edition, pp. 211-218). United States.
[26] Ware, G., Whitacre, M. (2004). Nematicides. In *The Book Pesticide* (6th edition, pp. 89-92). United States.
[27] Perry, R., Moens, M., Starr, J. (2009). Current and Future Management Strategies in Intensive Crop Production Systems. In Nyczepir, A., Thomas, S. *Root-Knot Nematodes* (pp. 414-416). Available in: http://books.google.cl/books?id=ACmHXeF8SHQC&pg=PA414&lpg=PA414&dq=fumigant+and+non+fumigant+classification+of+nematicide&source=bl&ots=2qPJd-g_W-&sig=IQ0UsFTRK9f_UPeMyfun8tIJKE8&hl=es&sa=X&ei=ahJFT4TQNYnrgQfv3PCZBA&ved=0CDAQ6AEwAQ#v=onepage&q=fumigant%20and%20non%20fumigant%20classification%20of%20nematicide&f=false
[28] Noling, J.W. 1997. Movement and Toxicity of Nematicides in the Plant Root Zone. Part 1. *Nematicides: Toxicity and Mode of Action.* Florida Coop. Ext. Serv. IFAS. Univ. of Florida. Available in: http://edis.ifas.ufl.edu/ng002
[29] Khanna, D. (2004). Nematod Control. In *Biology Of Helminthes* (pp. 416-427). Available in: http://books.google.cl/books?id=QZn2XbJl330C&printsec=frontcover&hl=es&source=gbs_ge_summary_r&cad=0#v=onepage&q&f=false

[30] Food and Agriculture Organization of the United Nations (FAO). *Chemical control of nematodes: efficiency and side-effects*. Available in: http://www.fao.org/docrep/V9978E/v9978e08.htm

[31] Brown, R., Kerry, B. (1987). Factors affecting the efficacy of nematicides .In *Principles and Practice of Nematode Control in Crops* (pp. 142-148). United Kingdon: Academic Press.

[32] Environmental Protection Agency (EPA). Precautionary Labeling (2007). In *Label Review Manual.* Available in: www.epa.gov/oppfead1/labeling

[33] Government of British Columbia. *Toxicity and Hazard*. Pesticide Wise. Available in: www.agf.gov.bc.ca/pesticides/b_1.htm#3

[34] EPA's International Programs. Persistent Organic Pollutants: A Global Issue, A Global Response. In *Reducing Exposure to Toxic Chemicals.* Available in: http://www.epa.gov/oia/toxics/pop.html

[35] Garrido Frenich, A., Martinez, J. L., & Covaci, A. (2008). Determination of Pesticides in Food of Animal Origin. En J. Tadeo (Ed), *Analysis of Pesticides in Food and Environmental Samples* (pp. 1-34). EE.UU.: CRC Press.

[36] Granby, K., Petersen, A., Herrmann, S., & Poulsen M. E. (2008). Levels of Pesticides in Food and Food Safety Aspects. En J. Tadeo (Ed), *Analysis of Pesticides in Food and Environmental Samples* (pp. 1-34). EE.UU.: CRC Press.

[37] Darko, G., Akoto, O., & Oppong, C. (2008). Persistent organochlorine pesticide residues in fish, sediments and water from Lake Bosomtwi, Ghana. *Chemosphere, 72*(1), 21-24.

[38] Kalyoncu, L., Agca, I., & Aktumsek, A. (2009). Some organochlorine pesticide residues in fish species in Konya, Turkey. *Chemosphere, 74*(7), 885-889.

[39] Dillon, J. C., Martin, G. B., & O'Brien, H. T. (1981). Pesticide residues in human milk. *Food and Cosmetics Toxicology, 19*, 437-442.

[40] Dahmardeh Behrooz, R., Esmaili Sari, A., Bahramifar, N., & Ghasempouri, S. M. (2009). Organochlorine pesticide and polychlorinated biphenyl residues in human milk from the Southern Coast of Caspian Sea, Iran. *Chemosphere, 74*(7), 931-937.

[41] Bergkvist, C., Aune, M., Nilsson, I., Sandanger, T., Derakhshani Hamadani, J., Tofail, F. Vahter, M. (2012). Occurrence and levels of organochlorine compounds in human breast milk in Bangladesh. *Chemosphere, 88*(7), 784-790.

[42] Badia-Vila, M., Ociepa, M., Mateo, R., & Guitart, R. (2008). Comparison of residue levels of persistent organochlorine compounds in butter from Spain and from other European countries. *Journal of Environmental Science and Health, Part B: Pesticides, Food Contaminants, and Agricultural Wastes, 35*(2), 201-210, doi: 10.1080/03601230009373264

[43] Herrera, A., Ariño, A., Conchello, M. P., Lazaro, R., Bayarri, S., & Perez, C. (1994). Organochlorine Pesticide Residues in Spanish Meat Products and Meat of Different Species. *Journal of Food Protection, 57*(5), 441-444.

[44] Mallatou, H., Pappas, C.P., Kondyli, E., & Albanis, T.A. (1997). Pesticide residues in milk and cheeses from Greece. *Science of The Total Environment, 196*(2), 111-117.

[45] Ahmad, R., Salem, N., & Estaitieh, H. (2010). Occurrence of organochlorine pesticide residues in eggs, chicken and meat in Jordan. *Chemosphere, 78*(1), 667-671.

[46] Schenck, F. J., & Wong, J. W. (2008). Determination of Pesticides in Food of Vegetal Origin. En J. Tadeo (Ed), *Analysis of Pesticides in Food and Environmental Samples* (pp. 1-34). EE.UU.: CRC Press.

[47] Poulsen, M. E., & Andersen, J. H. (2003). Results from the monitoring of pesticide residues in fruit and vegetables on the Danish market, 2000-01. *Food Additives and Contaminants, 20*(8), 742-757.

[48] Hjorth, K., Johansen, K., Holen, B., Andersson, A., Christensen, H. B., Siivinen, K., & Toome, M. (2011). Pesticide residues in fruits and vegetables from South America – A Nordic Project". *Food Control, 22,* 1701-1706.

[49] Holland, P. T., Hamilton, D., Ohlin, B., & Skidmore. M. W. (1994). Effects of Storage and processing on pesticide residues in plant products. *International Union of Pure and Applied Chemistry, 66*(2), 335-356.

[50] Bonnechère, A., Hanot, V., Bragard, C., Bedoret, T., & van Loco, J. (2012). Effect of household and industrial processing on the levels of pesticide residues and degradation products in melons. *Food Additives & Contaminants: Part A, 29*(7), 1058 – 1066.

[51] Chavarri, M. J., Herrera, A., & Ariño, A. (2005). The decrease in pesticides in fruit and vegetables during comercial processing. *International Journal of Food Science and Technology, 40*, 205-211.

[52] Pareja, L., & Fernández-Alba, A. R. (2011). Analytical methods for pesticide residues in rice. *TrAC Trends in Analytical Chemistry, 30*(2), 270-291.

[53] Commission of the European Communities (2006). Monitoring of Pesticide Residues in products of Plant Origin in the European Union, Norway, Iceland and Liechtenstein.

[54] Guler, G. O., Cakmak, Y. S., Dagli, Z., Aktumsek, A., & Ozparlak, H. (2010). Organochlorine pesticide residues in wheat from Konya region, Turkey. *Food and Chemical Toxicology, 48*(5), 1218-1221.

[55] Uygun, U., Senoz, B., Öztürk, S., & Koksel, H. (2009). Degradation of organophosphorus pesticides in wheat during cookie processing. *Food Chemistry, 117*(2), 261-264.

In: Chemical Food Safety and Health
Editors: F. Pedreschi Plasencia and Z. Ciesarová
ISBN: 978-1-62948-339-9

Chapter 5

Polyphenols as Food Antioxidants

M. A. Fellenberg *

Departamento de Ciencias Animales, Facultad de Agronomía e Ingeniería Forestal,
Pontificia Universidad Católica de Chile, Santiago, Chile

Abstract

Polyphenols (Pp) are molecules that occur in the plant world. They have captured a lot of attention in the last 15 years because they have multiple positive functions for human health. Currently, different research projects are being conducted describing new molecules of polyphenols and discovering new functions. One interesting function of this kind of molecules is the antioxidant capacity. Because they have at least one aromatic ring, they can donate one electron (ē), or one hydrogen (H) or chelating metals, decreasing oxidation of different substances. Two interesting matrices where polyphenols can act are foods and beverages. In fact, rosemary extract has been used as an antioxidant for many years, and currently, research is providing new polyphenols that may be added to food to prevent the oxidative process.

This chapter describes topics such as oxidative damage, polyphenols, and the mechanisms used by antioxidants, and give some examples where polyphenols have been successfully used as antioxidants.

1. Introduction

1.1. Pro-Oxidants and Oxidative Damage

One of the main causes of food deterioration in general and meat deterioration specifically is oxidative rancidity (OR) [1-5]. This process is oxidative damage affecting lipids present in food. The damage generally starts with the action of reactive oxygen species (ROS), such as free radicals (FR). There are species which present great biological reactivity

* Corresponding author: Dr. María Angélica Fellenberg. Departamento de Ciencias Animales, Facultad de Agronomía e Ingeniería Forestal, Pontificia Universidad Católica de Chile. Address: Av. Vicuña Mackenna 4860, Santiago, Chile. Phone:+56-2-354 4147. Fax:+56-2-552 9435. E-mail: mafellen@uc.cl.

as a result of one, or more, unpaired electrons in the most external (atomic or molecular) orbital. ROS, even though they are not radicals, are able to promote the oxidation of susceptible substratum (pro-oxidants).

Free radicals may be generated by the interaction of the O_2 molecule with trace concentrations of redox-active transition metals (Me^{n+}) like Fe^{2+} y Cu^{1+} (Eq. 1). Despite the low reactivity of $O_2^{\cdot-}$, this species undergoes a fast dismutation, leading to the production of hydrogen peroxide (H_2O_2) (Eq. 2).

$$O_2 + Me^{n+} \rightarrow O_2^{\cdot-} + Me^{n-\bar{e}+} \quad \text{(Eq. 1)}$$

$$2O_2^{\cdot-} + 2\,H^+ \rightarrow O_2 + H_2O_2 \quad \text{(Eq. 2)}$$

Although H_2O_2 is not a FR (since it doesn't have unpaired ē) it is an important generator of hydroxyl species (HO·) (Eq. 3). HO· is considered to be one of the most reactive radical species to biological substratum [6, 7]. The mono-reduction of H_2O_2 to HO· is easily catalyzed by redox active metals (Eq. 4 – Fenton reaction).

$$H_2O^{2+\bar{e}} \rightarrow (HO^{\cdot}) \quad \text{(Eq. 3)}$$

$$H_2O_2 + Me^{n+} \rightarrow Me^{n-\bar{e}+} + (HO^{\cdot}) + (HO^{-}) \quad \text{(Eq. 4)}$$

Lipids are a substratum particularly susceptible to oxidative damage, because of their double bonds which positively correlated with the degree of unsaturation. The FR attack on a lipid begins by the removal of a H atom (generally near a double bond), transforming it into a lipid radical (L·). During the lipid oxidative process (Figure 1), in aerobic conditions, the radical L· generates FR LOO.

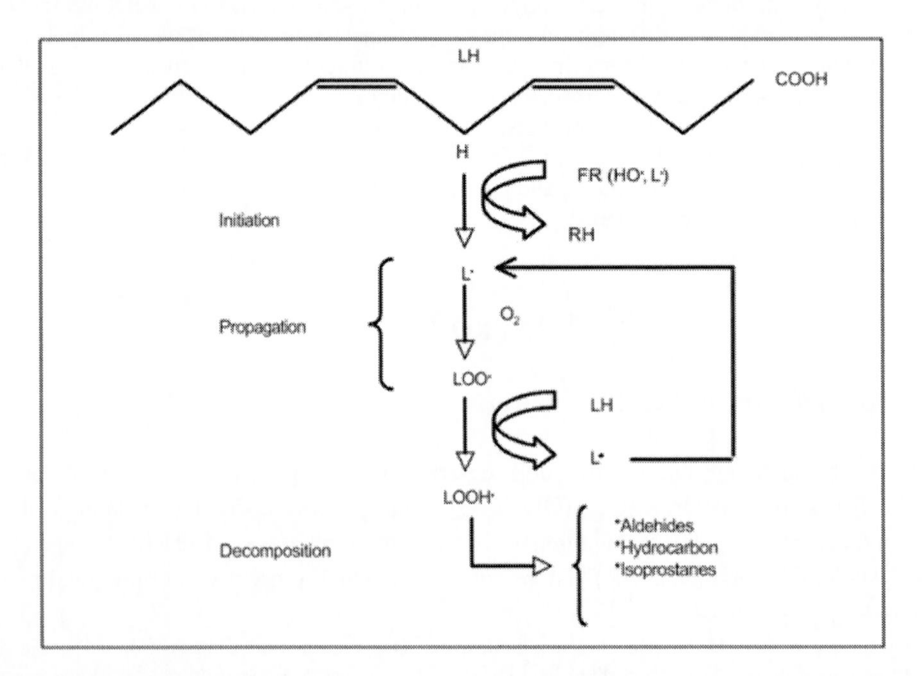

Figure 1. Lipid oxidation scheme [13].

The latter is able to remove a new atom of H from another nearby fatty acid. As a result, LOO· loses its radical character, becoming a lipidhydroperoxide (LOOH) and generating a new radical L·. This process represents an oxidative chain reaction, which in the absence of antioxidants (AOX) becomes autopropagative, leading to the production of LOOH [8]. These LOOH are easily decomposed in aldehydes, ketones, alcohols, and lactones [9], and if accumulating in food they can affect its organoleptic characteristics [10-12]

Oxidative rancidity begins when animals are slaughtered, however live animal oxidative balance is the baseline for these chemical reactions. OR described above when occurring in foods has the following consequences:

1) High value lipids or fatty acid is lost. It is well known that Poly Unsaturated Fatty Acids (PUFAs), especially those from the omega 3 family, act as health protectors in: different cardiac diseases [14], inflammatory diseases [15], Krohn Disease [16] and certain kinds of cancers [17]. It is important to note that PUFA are more susceptible to suffering OR due to the double bond present in their chemical structure.
2) Oxidation residues are present in flesh. Lipid oxidation generates hydroperoxids, which turn into aldehydes, ketones, alcohols and lactones, all of them potentially toxic for human health [9]. Additionally, during the cooking process, peroxidized fat and free radicals (oxidation initiators) are strongly correlated with increased production of heterocyclic amines, all of them dangerous for human health [18, 19].
3) Sensorial characteristics are lost. It is important to notice that OR and lipids deteriorates produce an accumulation of oxidation products, which change the characteristic flesh flavor and odor, perceived by customers as rancid or off-flavor flesh [10, 11, 20].

1.2. Antioxidants

The food industry, worried about this situation, delays OR by adding antioxidants (AOX) to food. Depending on its origin, antioxidants can be classified as synthetic or natural. Synthetic AOX have been widely used as food preservatives, because of their effectiveness and relative low cost.

The most used antioxidants are those derived from phenolic structures, such as butylated hydroxyanisole (BHA), butylated hydroxytoluene (BHT), tert-butylhydroxiquinone (TBHQ) and dodecyl, propyl and octyl gallate (Figure 2). All of them have an admissible daily ingest (ADI). Ethoxyquin (ETOX) is another synthetic AOX with a non-phenolic structure. In contrast to the others, its consumption by humans is not allowed, so it is only used in animal diets [21].

On the other hand, natural AOX generally are molecules present in plant parts (e.g. leaves, bark, seeds and/or its fruits). Among the most important natural AOX are tocopherols (or Vitamin E, liposoluble) (Figure 3) and ascorbic acid (Vitamin C, hydrosoluble) (Figure 4). While the first one represents an essential nutrient (it must be consumed in the diet), the second is biosynthesized [22]. Other natural molecules with antioxidant characteristics are polyphenols (Pp) such as carotenes (i.e. β-carotene, lycopene, lutheine, asta-, zea- y casta-xanthine), flavonoids (i.e. catechins, epigallocatechins, quercetin, rutin, morin among others), and non-flavonic phenols (i.e. rosmanol and rosmaridiphenol).

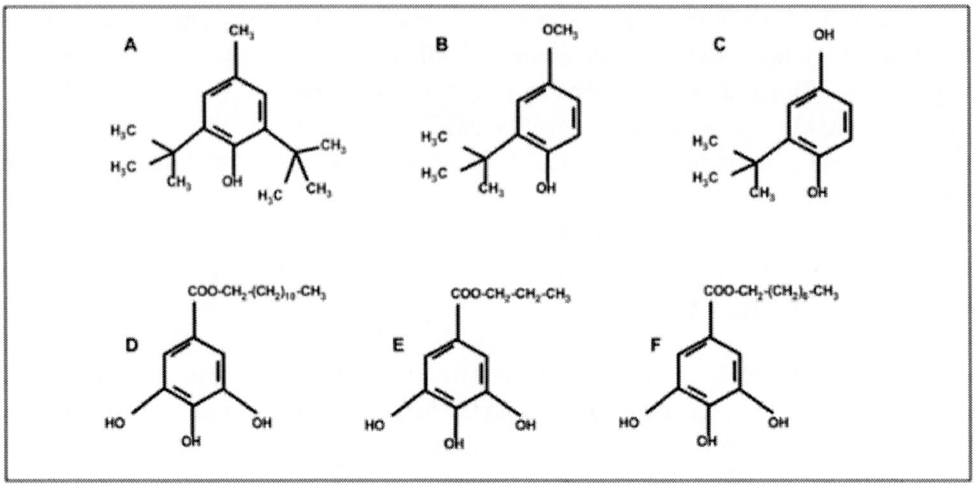

Figure 2. Synthetic antioxidants. A: BHT; B: BHQ; C: t-BHQ; D: dodecyl gallate; E: propyl gallate; F: octyl gallate [13].

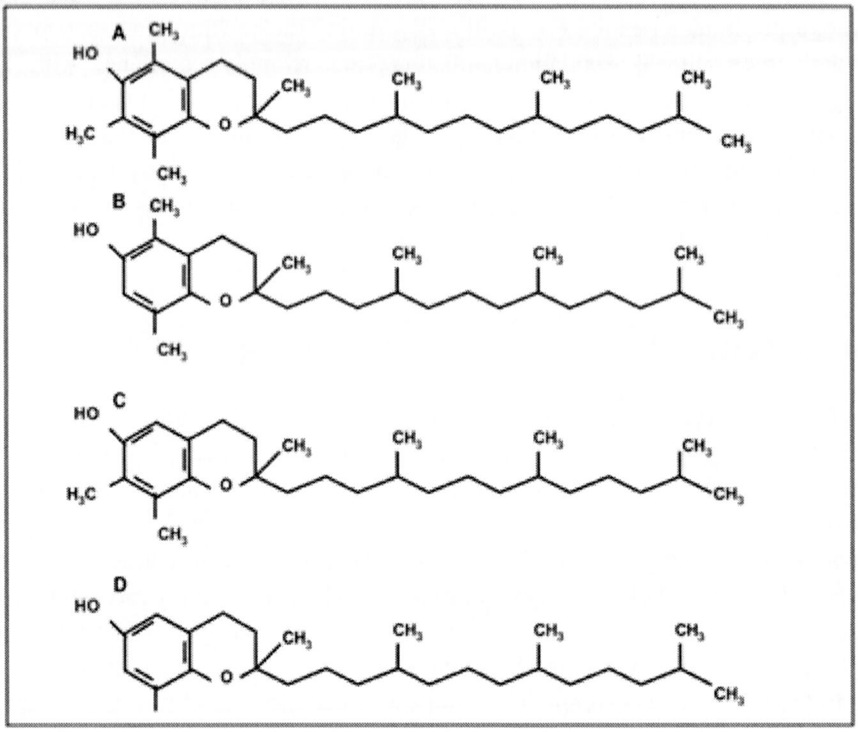

Figure 3. Natural antioxidants: Tocopherols. A: α-tocopherol; B: β-tocopherol; C: γ-tocopherol; D: δ-tocopherol.

Most of the AOX compounds have synthetic origins, but although they are very effective, up to this time they cannot be guaranteed safe [23-28]. For this reason, the most recent scientific research in this field has focused on natural AOX and within this group, polyphenols (Pp) have received a lot of attention, because of their multiple functions that have the potential to produce human health benefits [29-31].

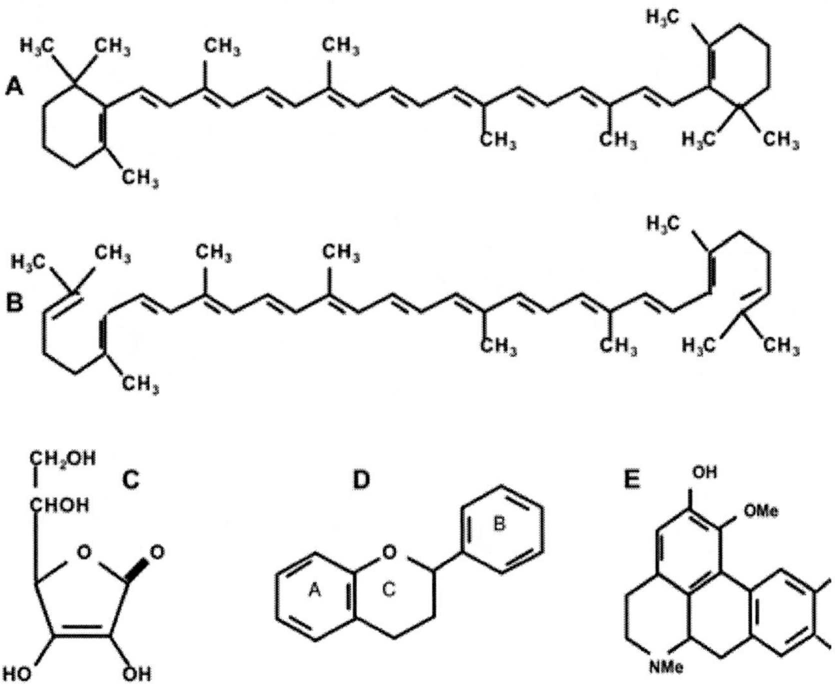

Figure 4. Natural antioxidants: A: β-carotene; B: Lycopene; C: ascorbic acid; D: Flavonoids (basic scheme); E: Boldine.

Pp are molecules produced by the secondary metabolism of plants [32]. Most of them are produced by a shikimic acid pathway[33], where 4-P-eritrose and phosphoenol piruvic acids produce phenylalanine, and then produce the different basic structures. About 8,000 different molecules of Pp have been described [34].However in spite of this diversity, a common characteristic of all of them is to have at least one aromatic ring in their chemical structure, which has one or more hydroxyls residues. In this way, Pp covers the range from simple phenols with simple structures to tannins with complex structures and heavy molecular weight [31, 33, 35].

Depending on their basic chemical structure, it is possible distinguish to three large groups of Pp, derivates of: gallic acid, flavones and cinnamic acid (Figure 5).

Within the gallic acid group, are found hydrolysable tannins, which are formed when different gallic acid units link one sugar molecule. In the flavones group are found flavonoids and condensed tannins. The former, have a wide variety of molecules depending on substitutions in R1 and R2 positions, while the latter are polymerizations of flavones, generating both more complex and larger molecules. Finally, in the cinnamic acid group are lignins, which are insoluble Pp, which occurs in the woody part of plants.

Polyphenols are related to different functions of plants (pigmentation, flavor, growth, reproduction and protection against pathogens and predators). Additionally they are omnipresent in the plant world, where they may be found in fruits, vegetables, beverages (tea, wine), and oils, among others. That implies Pp are incorporated in human food every day [29, 37, 38]. According to Scalbert et al. [30] Pp are the most abundant AOX in human alimentation. In fact, it is possible to eat approximately 1 g of Pp per day, ten times more than Vitamin C and 100 times more than Vitamin E and carotenoids.

Gallic acid 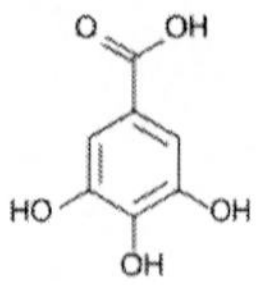	Hydrolysable tannins	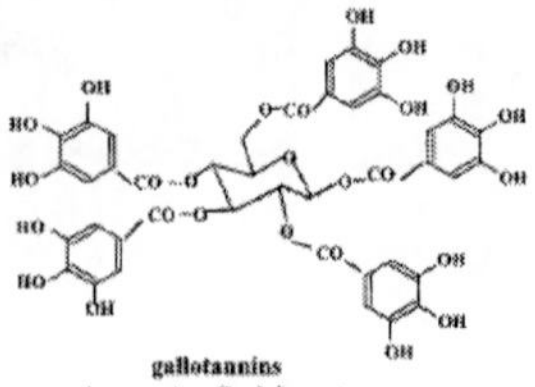 gallotannins (e.g. pentagalloylglucose)
Flavones 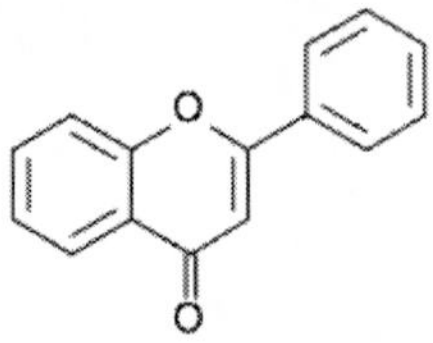	Flavonoids	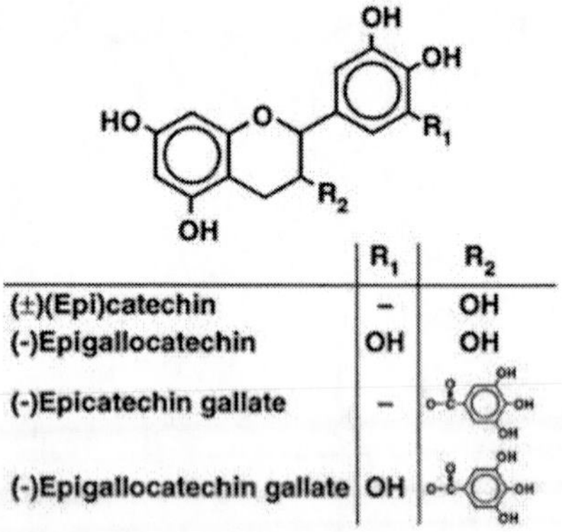 R₁ / R₂: (±)(Epi)catechin: – / OH (-)Epigallocatechin: OH / OH (-)Epicatechin gallate: – / galloyl (-)Epigallocatechin gallate: OH / galloyl
	Condensated tannins	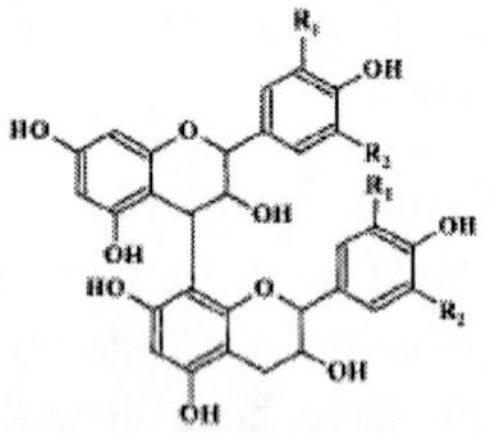 Proanthocyanidins (R_1, R_2 =H, OH) e.g. B-type procyanidin dimer: R_1=OH, R_2=H
Cinnamic acid 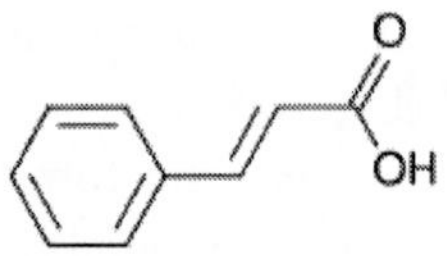	Lignins	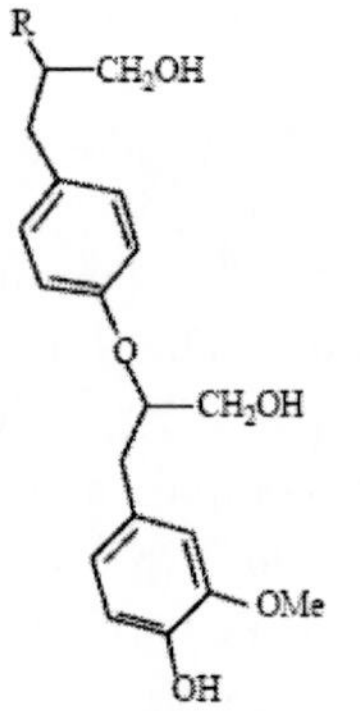 Lignin polymer

Figure 5. Polyphenols [29, 36].

Absorption and metabolism of Pp are determined by their chemical structure [29]. The wide variety of these molecules has hampered research about bioavailability and both their physiological and nutritional effect [33]. Vaya and Aviram [34] reported that Pp's bioavailability mainly depends on both, Pp liberation from food and also on Pp stability to avoid modifications that may be produced by intestinal microorganisms.

Polyphenols may act as anti-inflammatories, anti-allergics, anti-microbials, anti-thrombotics and AOX, among others functions [31, 33, 39, 40].

1.3. Antioxidant Mechanism of Polyphenols

The antioxidant effect of Pp may be produced by two different mechanisms. The first, also called the primary mechanism, is the scavenging or neutralizing of FR, either at the beginning of oxidative reactions, or generated in the lipid oxidation chain. This mechanism is considered as an oxidative-chain-breaker, since it can stop oxidative processes from ocurring [34]. In this case, Pp AOX transfer one electron (reducing capacity) (Eq. 5) or one H (scavenging capacity) (Eq. 6) to a radical molecule, thereby stabilizing it [34]. In this way, FR is inactivated and Pp molecule becomes a low reactivity FR because its unpaired electron is stabilized by resonance with double bonds present in Pp molecule.

$$M^{(n)} + \bar{e}\,(AOX) \rightarrow AOX^{\cdot} + M^{(n-1)} \quad \text{(Eq. 5)}$$

$$ROO^{\cdot} + AOXH \rightarrow ROOH + AOX^{\cdot} \quad \text{(Ec. 6)}$$

In vitro reducing capacity of an extract may be assessed by different analytical techniques such as: FRAP (Ferric ion Reducing Antioxidant Parameter) [41], DPPH (Diphenyl -1-picrylhydrazyl) [42], Indice Folin-Cicolteau (IFC) [43] y TEAC (Trolox Equivalent Antioxidant Capacity) [44] among others. *In vitro* scavenging capacity (hydrogen transfer) of an extract may be evaluated through: ORAC (Oxygen Radical Absorvance Capacity) [45], TRAP (Total Radical traping Antioxidant Parameter) [46], IOU (Inhibited Oxygen Uptake) [47], among others.

Different chemical-structural criteria may explain major or minor AOX capacity of Pp. In phenolic acids, AOX capacity depends on the quantity and position of OH groups in relation to carboxyl functional group [48, 49]. In this way, monobenzoic acids show low capacity to transfer an electron when the OH group is in *orto* or *para* position (Table 1).

In dihydroxybenzoic acids, 2,3 dihydroxybenzoic acid (*orto-meta* substitution) has more TEAC than 3,4 dihydroxybenzoic acid (*meta-para* substitution), and 3,5 dihydroxibenzhoic acid (*meta-meta* substitution) has the largest capacity of dihydrobenzoic acids to transfer one H (largest antioxidant capacity). Gallic acid (3,4,5 trihydroxybenzoic acid, *meta-para-meta* substitution) has the best TEAC activity, because it has three hydroxilic groups [48].

Table 1. Total Antioxidant Activity (mM) relating to Trolox of Hydroxybenzoic acids [48]

OH position	TEAC
2 (salicylic acid)	0,04 ± 0,01
3	0,84 ± 0,05
4	0,08 ± 0,01
2,3	1,46 ± 0,01
3,4 (protocatechuic acid)	1,19 ± 0,03
2,5	1,04 ± 0,03
3,5	2,15 ± 0,05
4-hydroxi,3-metoxy	1,43 ± 0,05
3,4,5 (gallic acid)	3,01 ± 0,05
Pirogallic acid	1,91 ± 0,02
Gallic acid and y metylester	2,40 ± 0,03
3,5 dimethoxy,4-hydroxy (syringic acid)	1,36 ± 0,01

In flavonoids, the largest group of Pp present in the plant world [Balasundram et al., 2006] with more than 4,000 molecules described [50]. Chemical criteria that relate their structure with AOX capacity are (Figure 6):

- Presence of *o*-dihydroxy structure in B-ring (OH groups in 3' and 4' positions in B-ring) [36, 48, 51-53].
- Double bond between 2 and 3 ring positions conjugated with 4 position carboxyl group in C ring [36, 48, 50].
- Presence of OH groups in 3 and 5 positions in C and A rings respectively conjugated with carboxyl group in 4 position of C ring [36, 48].
- Insaturation of C ring [48].

The presence of functional groups (described above) allows a maximun capacity to tranfer one H atom or one electron, because double bonds will permit resonance of unpaired electrons, thereby stabilizing this molecule.

On the other hand, a secondary AOX mechanism is throught the capacity of the Pp to chelate the transitions metals out of the solution [34]; they are therefore not available to generate FR [32], and oxidative processes do not begin. All Pp do not have the same chelating capacity. In flavonoids, the more efficient chelating structures are:

- *Orto*-dihydroxilic group (3'- 4' dihydroxil) [32, 34, 54].
- *Orto*-dihydroxilic group (7- 8 dihydroxil) [32].
- OH group in position 5 conjugated with a keto group in 4 position (ej: quercetin) [32, 54].
- OH group in 3 position conjugated with a keto group in 4 position [32].
- Large numbers of OH groups (Ej. Tartaric acid) [32, 50]

Chelating capacity of an extract may be assessed mainly by two methods: Ferrozin method [55, 56] and FASR (ferric ammonium sulfate reagent) [32], among others.

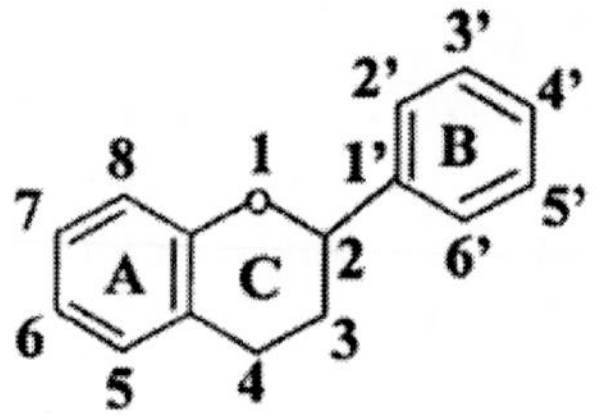

Figure 6. Flavonoid structure [50].

1.4. Polyphenols as Antioxidants in Meats Products

The addition of AOX to meat may be done by two methods. One of them is by adding AOX to animal feed, with the intention that AOX will be incorporated in muscle and fat tissue and from there exert their action once the animal is slaughtered [13]. In this method, dietary addition of vitamin E, in doses of more than 200 mg/kg of poultry feed, has demonstrated to be a most effective natural antioxidant [3, 57-59] in poultry. Other natural AOX (with Pp) which have been added to poultry feed and have demonstrated the ability to protect poultry meat against lipid oxidation are: β-carotene [20], rosemary extract [57], sage extract [57], dry tomato pulp (281 mg/kg of lycopene plus 24,3 mg/kg de β-carotene) [60], tea catechins [61] and green tea powder [62]. However, not all trials have been successful [63] evaluated boldo extract (*Peumus boldo*, Mol) with a high content of Pp, adding it to broiler feed. Results did not show any protection of flesh against lipid oxidation, although this extract showed good antioxidant activity *in vitro* studies. Pp in foods must be absorbed and metabolized [64, 65] before they can reach fat tissues. In blood molecules can be found that are derived from the originals Pp but not necessarily maintain the same AOX properties and the same effectiveness.

The second way of adding AOX to meat for protection is by the marinade process that the food industry uses for most kinds of meat. Marinade is incorporated by steeping, mixing or injection, a water solution, salts or other ingredients to the chicken meat [66], with the main objective of improving sensorial characteristics such as texture, flavor and tenderness, among others. This approach has been less studied than the first, but some research conducted in chicken showed it is successful in protecting meat against lipid oxidation [63].

Conclusion

The use of Pp as a natural AOX has become in an interesting research field because of the multiple benefits that Pp can contribute to human health. Due to their natural origin and the fact that they are consumed primarily in plant foods, they are perceived as safe for consumers. Nevertheless, their natural origin is not a guarantee of safety; it is absolutely necessary that the food industry conduct all the research that is needed to assure that Pp are safe for consumption. The next step is to understand if and how adding Pp to food can contribute in a functional way to human health beyond the nutritional level. How the cooking process modifies Pp and at what levels, is another field that needs more research.

Acknowledgments

To Ms. Marsha Vonduerckheim for her kind support.

References

[1] Pearson, A., J.D. Love, and F. Shorland, "Warmed-Over" Flavor in Meat, Poultry, and Fish. *Advances in Food Research,* 1977. 23: p. 1-74.

[2] Sheehy, P.J.A., P.A. Morrissey, and A. Flynn, Influence of heated vegetable oils and α-tocopheryl acetate supplementation on α-tocopherol, fatty acids and lipid peroxidation in chicken muscle. *British poultry science*, 1993. 34(2): p. 367-381.

[3] De Winne, A. and P. Dirinck, Studies on vitamin E and meat quality. 2. Effect of feeding high vitamin E levels on chicken meat quality. *J. Agric. Food Chem.*, 1996. 44(7): p. 1691-1696.

[4] Frankel, E.N., Antioxidants in lipid foods and their impact on food quality. *Food Chemistry*, 1996. 57(1): p. 51-55.

[5] Morrissey, P.A., et al., Tissue content of α-tocopherol and oxidative stability of broilers receiving dietary α-tocopheryl acetate supplement for various periods pre-slaughter. *British poultry science*, 1997. 38(1): p. 84-88.

[6] Halliwell, B., Reactive oxygen species in living systems: source, biochemistry, and role in human disease. *The American journal of medicine*, 1991. 91(3): p. S14-S22.

[7] Kehrer, J.P., Free radicals as mediators of tissue injury and disease. *CRC critical reviews in toxicology,* 1993. 23(1): p. 21-48.

[8] Speisky C, H. and I. Jiménez T, Radicales libres y antioxidantes en la prevención de enfermedades: I mecanismos de generación de radicales libres; Free radicals and antioxidants in disease prevention: I free radical generating mechanisms. *Rev. chil. nutr.,* 2000. 27(1): p. 48-55.

[9] Esterbauer, H., Cytotoxicity and genotoxicity of lipid-oxidation products. *The American journal of clinical nutrition*, 1993. 57(5): p. 779S-785S.

[10] Pearson, A., et al., Safety implications of oxidized lipids in muscle foods. *Food Technology*, 1983. 37.

[11] Higgins, F., Effects of alpha-tocopheryl acetate supplementation and salt addition on the oxidative stability (TBARS) and warmed-over flavour (WOF) of cooked turkey meat. *British poultry science*, 1999. 40(1): p. 59-64.

[12] Ruiz, J., et al., Descriptive sensory analysis of meat from broilers fed diets containing vitamin E or beta-carotene as antioxidants and different supplemental fats. *Poultry Science,* 2001. 80(7): p. 976-982.

[13] Fellenberg, M.A. and H. Speisky, Antioxidants: their effects on broiler oxidative stress and its meat oxidative stability. *World's Poultry Science Journal*, 2006. 62(1): p. 53-70.

[14] Lavie, C.J., et al., Omega-3 polyunsaturated fatty acids and cardiovascular diseases. *J. Am. Coll. Cardiol.*, 2009. 54(7): p. 585-594.

[15] Kremer, J.M., et al., Effects of high-dose fish oil on rheumatoid arthritis after stopping nonsteroidal antiinflammatory drugs clinical and immune correlates. *Arthritis & Rheumatism*, 2005. 38(8): p. 1107-1114.

[16] Belluzzi, A., et al., Polyunsaturated fatty acids and inflammatory bowel disease. *The American Journal of Clinical Nutrition*, 2000. 71(1): p. 339s-342s.

[17] Jacobsen, C., Enrichment of foods with omega-3 fatty acids: a multidisciplinary challenge. *Annals of the New York Academy of Sciences,* 2010. 1190(1): p. 141-150.

[18] Cheng, K.W., F. Chen, and M. Wang, Heterocyclic amines: chemistry and health. *Molecular nutrition & Food research*, 2006. 50(12): p. 1150-1170.

[19] Smith, J., F. Ameri, and P. Gadgil, Effect of marinades on the formation of heterocyclic amines in grilled beef steaks. *J. Food Sci.,* 2008. 73(6): p. T100-T105.

[20] Ruiz, J.A., A.M. Pérez-Vendrell, and E. Esteve-García, Effect of β-carotene and vitamin E on oxidative stability in leg meat of broilers fed different supplemental fats. *J. Agric. Food Chem.*, 1999. 47(2): p. 448-454.

[21] Bailey, C.A., L.J. Srinivasan, and R.B. McGeachin, The effect of ethoxyquin on tissue peroxidation and immune status of single comb White Leghorn cockerels. *Poultry Science,* 1996. 75(9): p. 1109-1112.

[22] Pardue, S. and J.P. Thaxton, Ascorbic acid in poultry: a review. *World's Poult. Sci. J.,* 1986. 42: p. 107-123.

[23] Ito, N., et al., Carcinogenicity of butylated hydroxyanisole in F344 rats. *Journal of the National Cancer Institute*, 1983. 70(2): p. 343-352.

[24] Ito, N., S. Fukushima, and H. Tsuda, Carcinogenicity and modification of the carcinogenic response by BHA, BHT, and other antioxidants. *CRC critical reviews in toxicology,* 1985. 15(2): p. 109-150.

[25] Ito, N., et al., Studies on antioxidants: their carcinogenic and modifying effects on chemical carcinogenesis. *Food and Chemical Toxicology*, 1986. 24(10): p. 1071-1082.

[26] Masui, T., et al., Sequential changes of the forestomach of F344 rats, Syrian golden hamsters, and B6C3F1 mice treated with butylated hydroxyanisole. *Japanese Journal of Cancer Research: Gann*, 1986. 77(11): p. 1083.

[27] Kahl, R. and H. Kappus, Toxicology of the synthetic antioxidants BHA and BHT in comparison with the natural antioxidant vitamin E. *Zeitschrift fur Lebensmittel-untersuchung und-forschung*, 1993. 196(4): p. 329.

[28] Iverson, F., Phenolic antioxidants: health protection branch studies on butylated hydroxyanisole. *Cancer letters,* 1995. 93(1): p. 49-54.

[29] Manach, C., et al., Polyphenols: food sources and bioavailability. *The American Journal of Clinical Nutrition,* 2004. 79(5): p. 727-747.

[30] Scalbert, A., I.T. Johnson, and M. Saltmarsh, Polyphenols: antioxidants and beyond. *The American Journal of Clinical Nutrition*, 2005. 81(1): p. 215S-217S.

[31] Balasundram, N., K. Sundram, and S. Samman, Phenolic compounds in plants and agri-industrial by-products: Antioxidant activity, occurrence, and potential uses. *Food Chemistry*, 2006. 99(1): p. 191-203.

[32] Khokhar, S. and R.K. Owusu Apenten, Iron binding characteristics of phenolic compounds: some tentative structure–activity relations. *Food Chemistry*, 2003. 81(1): p. 133-140.

[33] Bravo, L., Polyphenols: chemistry, dietary sources, metabolism, and nutritional significance. *Nutrition reviews*, 1998. 56(11): p. 317-333.

[34] Vaya, J. and M. Aviram, Nutritional antioxidants mechanisms of action, analyses of activities and medical applications. *Current Medicinal Chemistry-Immunology, Endocrine & Metabolic Agents,* 2001. 1(1): p. 99-117.

[35] Urquiaga, I. and F. Leighton, Plant polyphenol antioxidants and oxidative stress. *Biological Research*, 2000. 33(2): p. 55-64.

[36] Salah, N., et al., Polyphenolic Flavanols as Scavengers of Aqueous Phase Radicals and as Chain-Breaking Antioxidants. *Archives of Biochemistry and Biophysics*, 1995. 322(2): p. 339-346.

[37] Cheynier, V., Polyphenols in foods are more complex than often thought. *The American Journal of Clinical Nutrition,* 2005. 81: p. 223S-229S.

[38] Wolfe, K.L. and R.H. Liu, Cellular antioxidant activity (CAA) assay for assessing antioxidants, foods, and dietary supplements. *J. Agric. Food Chem.,* 2007. 55(22): p. 8896-8907.

[39] Miura, Y., et al., Green tea polyphenols (flavan 3-ols) prevent oxidative modification of low density lipoproteins: an ex vivo study in humans. *The Journal of Nutritional Biochemistry*, 2000. 11(4): p. 216-222.

[40] Perron, N. and J. Brumaghim, A Review of the Antioxidant Mechanisms of Polyphenol Compounds Related to Iron Binding. *Cell Biochemistry and Biophysics*, 2009. 53(2): p. 75-100.

[41] Benzie, I.F.F. and J.J. Strain, The Ferric Reducing Ability of Plasma (FRAP) as a Measure of "Antioxidant Power": The FRAP Assay. *Analytical Biochemistry*, 1996. 239: p. 70-76.

[42] Huang, D., B. Ou, and L. Ronald, The chemistry behind antioxidant capacity assays. *J. Agric. Food Chem.,* 2005. 53(6): p. 1841-1856.

[43] Singleton, V.L., R. Orthofer, and R.M. Lamuela-Raventos, Analysis of total phenols and other oxidation substrates and antioxidants by means of folin-ciocalteu reagent. *Methods Enzymol.*, 1999. 299: p. 152-178.

[44] Miller, N., et al., A novel method for measuring antioxidant capacity and its application to monitoring the antioxidant status in premature neonates. *Clinical science* (London, England: 1979), 1993. 84(4): p. 407.

[45] Cao, G., H.M. Alessio, and R.G. Cutler, Oxygen-radical absorbance capacity assay for antioxidants. *Free Radical Biology and Medicine*, 1993. 14(3): p. 303-311.

[46] Wayner, D., et al., Quantitative measurement of the total, peroxyl radical-trapping antioxidant capability of human blood plasma by controlled peroxidation: the important contribution made by plasma proteins. *FEBS letters*, 1985. 187(1): p. 33-37.

[47] Burton, G.W. and K.U. Ingold, Autoxidation of biological molecules. 1. Antioxidant activity of vitamin E and related chain-breaking phenolic antioxidants in vitro. *J. Am. Chem. Soc.,* 1981. 103(21): p. 6472-6477.

[48] Rice-Evans, C.A., N.J. Miller, and G. Paganga, Structure-antioxidant activity relationships of flavonoids and phenolic acids. *Free Radical Biology and Medicine,* 1996. 20(7): p. 933-956.

[49] Robards, K., et al., Phenolic compounds and their role in oxidative processes in fruits. *Food Chemistry*, 1999. 66(4): p. 401-436.

[50] Heim, K.E., A.R. Tagliaferro, and D.J. Bobilya, Flavonoid antioxidants: chemistry, metabolism and structure-activity relationships. *The Journal of Nutritional Biochemistry*, 2002. 13(10): p. 572-584.

[51] Ratty, A.K. and N.P. Das, Effects of flavonoids on nonenzymatic lipid peroxidation: Structure-activity relationship. *Biochemical Medicine and Metabolic Biology*, 1988. 39(1): p. 69-79.

[52] Mora, A., et al., Structure-activity relationships of polymethoxyflavones and other flavonoids as inhibitors of non-enzymic lipid peroxidation. *Biochemical Pharmacology*, 1990. 40(4): p. 793-797.

[53] Dugas Jr, A.J., et al., Evaluation of the total peroxyl radical-scavenging capacity of flavonoids: structure-activity relationships. *Journal of Natural Products*, 2000. 63(3): p. 327-331.

[54] Cheng, I.F. and K. Breen, On the ability of four flavonoids, baicilein, luteolin, naringenin, and quercetin, to suppress the Fenton reaction of the iron-ATP complex. *Biometals,* 2000. 13(1): p. 77-83.

[55] Carter, P., Spectrophotometric determination of serum iron at the submicrogram level with a new reagent (ferrozine). *Analytical Biochemistry*, 1971. 40(2): p. 450-458.

[56] Lopes, G.K.B., H.M. Schulman, and M. Hermes-Lima, Polyphenol tannic acid inhibits hydroxyl radical formation from Fenton reaction by complexing ferrous ions. *Biochimica et Biophysica Acta (BBA)-General Subjects*, 1999. 1472(1): p. 142-152.

[57] Lopez-Bote, C., et al., Effect of dietary administration of oil extracts from rosemary and sage on lipid oxidation in broiler meat. *British poultry science*, 1998. 39(2): p. 235-240.

[58] Maraschiello, C., C. Sárraga, and J.A. García Regueiro, Glutathione Peroxidase Activity, TBARS, and α-Tocopherol in Meat from Chickens Fed Different Diets. *J. Agric. Food Chem.,* 1999. 47(3): p. 867-872.

[59] Grau, A., et al., Oxidative stability of dark chicken meat through frozen storage: influence of dietary fat and alpha-tocopherol and ascorbic acid supplementation. *Poultry Science*, 2001. 80(11): p. 1630-1642.

[60] Botsoglou, N., et al., Effect of dietary dried tomato pulp on oxidative stability of Japanese quail meat. *J. Agric. Food Chem.*, 2004. 52(10): p. 2982-2988.

[61] Tang, S., et al., Dietary tea catechins and iron-induced lipid oxidation in chicken meat, liver and heart. *Meat science*, 2000. 56(3): p. 285-290.

[62] Biswas, A.H. and M. Wakita, Effect of Dietary Japanese Green Tea Powder Supplementation on Feed Utilization and Carcass Profiles in Broilers. *The Journal of Poultry Science*, 2001. 38(1): p. 50-57.

[63] MA, F., et al., Antioxidant and Bacteriostatic Effects of the Addition of Extract of Quillay Polyphenols (Quillaja saponaria) in the Marinade of Broiler Chicken. *Brazilian Journal of Poultry Science*, 2011. 13(1): p. 71-79.

[64] Barrington, R., et al., Absorption, conjugation and efflux of the flavonoids, kaempferol and galangin, using the intestinal CaCo-2/TC7 cell model. *Journal of Functional Foods,* 2009. 1(1): p. 74-87.

[65] Kay, C.D., P.A. Kroon, and A. Cassidy, The bioactivity of dietary anthocyanins is likely to be mediated by their degradation products. *Molecular Nutrition & Food Research,* 2009. 53(S1): p. S92-S101.

[66] D.P., S. and A. J.C, *Marination, cooking, and curing of poultry products, in Poultry Meat Processing*, S. AR, Editor 2001: CRC Press, Boca Raton (FL).

In: Chemical Food Safety and Health
Editors: F. Pedreschi Plasencia and Z. Ciesarová

ISBN: 978-1-62948-339-9

Chapter 6

SELENIUM AND HEALTH: DISCOVERING NUTRITIONAL BIOMARKERS

A. Mahn*
Departamento de Ingeniería Química, Universidad de Santiago de Chile, Santiago, Chile

ABSTRACT

Selenium (Se) was for long time investigated because of its supposed toxic and carcinogenic effects, however hitherto only selenium sulphide has been recognized as a carcinogen. In the middle of the 20th century it was discovered that Se is an essential micronutrient for mammals, microorganisms and other eukaryotes. In the 1970's Se was identified as an essential micronutrient for humans, and it was shown that it must be included in the human diet. Recently, it was demonstrated that Se is a powerful anticarcinogenic compound. Se metabolism, and consequently Se toxicity and anticarcinogenic effect, depends on the chemical form in which it has been incorporated in the organism. The traditional metabolic Se indexes do not distinguish between the different chemical forms of this element. Then, new biomarkers of Se status are necessary to contribute in nutritional diagnosis and counseling.

In this chapter, Se metabolism and the effects of Se intake on human health are reviewed and discussed. Besides, advances in new Se status biomarkers are presented. Finally, some new potential biomarkers are proposed and compared with traditional Se indexes.

1. INTRODUCTION

There is strong evidence of the chemoprotective effect of selenium (Se) against some cancer types, such as colon cancer [1], breast cancer [2], skin carcinoma [3], prostate cancer [4] and lung cancer [5]. Despite the chemoprotection mechanism by selenium is not fully

* Corresponding author: Dr. Andrea Mahn, Departamento de Ingeniería Química, Universidad de Santiago de Chile, Av. Libertador Bernardo O'Higgins 3363, Casilla 10233, (Correo Central-Santiago), Zip Code 9170019, Santiago, Chile, Phone: +56-2-2718 1803; Fax:+56-2-2681 7135; e-mail:andrea.mahn@usach.cl.

understood, it has been demonstrated that selenoproteins and low molecular weight selenium compounds play an important role [6]. The chemoprotective effect of selenium strongly depends on its chemical form. Selenomethylselenocysteine (SeMSeC) offers the highest chemoprotection, as compared to selenite, selenate and selenomethionine [7].

Selenium bioavailability in mammals has been usually determined by measuring selenium saturation concentration in tissues, total selenium concentration in blood, and also by determining glutathione peroxidase activity. Despite these methods rely on general approval; recent findings about selenium health benefits make it necessary to develop alternative methods to detect the intake of organic selenium compounds. This interest relies on the fact that selenium chemoprotective capacity seems to have no relationship with glutathione peroxidase activity or with residual selenium concentration in tissues.

2. SELENIUM AS AN ESSENTIAL MICRONUTRIENT

Se is the 34th element in the periodic table, and it was discovered in the early 19th century by the Swedish chemist Jöns Jakob Berzelius (1779-1848). This element was investigated for a long time because of its toxic effects and possible carcinogenic properties. Hitherto only one chemical form of Se, selenium sulphide, has been recognized as a carcinogen [8]. In the middle of the 20th century it was discovered that Se is an essential micronutrient for mammals, microorganisms and other eukaryotes [9, 10]. In the 1970's Se was identified as an essential micronutrient for humans, and it was shown that Se has to be included in the human diet. Selenium participates in some of the key metabolic pathways, such as thyroid hormone metabolism [11 – 13], oxidative stress defense [14 – 16], and immune system [17], as it is present in the active site of the selenoenzymes that control these pathways. The effect of Se in mammals' health is exerted mainly through its incorporation into selenoproteins (i.e. proteins that contain Se as an integral part of the active site) as the amino acid selenocysteine, the 21st amino acid.

In humans, there have been identified 25 genes that encode selenoproteins [18], which were broadly classified as antioxidant enzymes, despite their exact function is not known for all of them [16]. The most studied selenoproteins in mammals are glutathione peroxidases (GPx), thioredoxin reductases (TR), and iodothyronin deiodinases (ITD). Additionally, other mammalian selenoproteins have been identified, such as selenoproteins H, M, T, V, W, K, S, O, and I [19], whose function has not been established so far.

Glutathione peroxidase (GPx) was the first human selenoezyme discovered [20]. This enzyme is responsible for oxygen metabolism and detoxification at cellular level. The GPx isoforms are well known to be the major components of the antioxidant defense [15], as they catalyze the destruction of hydrogen peroxide and lipoperoxides [10]. They can be found mainly in the cytosol (GPx1), gastro-intestinal mucosa (GPx2), plasma (GPx3), liver and kidney (GPx4), and olfactory epithelium and embryonic tissues (GPx6). This enzyme was the first functional biomarker of Se in mammal organisms, and it is still considered as a reliable index of Se status in humans and animals [21, 22]. Thioredoxin reductase is able to reduce oxidized thioredoxin. It is involved in the repair of methionine sulfoxide oxidized proteins, and also in redox signaling via hydrogen peroxide [15]. Additionally, TR participates in several cell signaling pathways through controlling the activity of transcription factors such as

NF-kβ and p53 [23]. Therefore, TR plays a crucial role in the control of cell proliferation, viability and apoptosis [15], and thus, it would be implicated in cancer prevention and cure. This group of selenoproteins can be found in cytosol and in nucleus (TR1), mitochondria (TR2) and testis (TR3).

Iodothyronine deiodinases (ITD1 and ITD2) catalyze the deiodination of thyroxine (T4, the major thyroid hormone) into its active form (T3), while IDT3 catalyzes the conversion of T4 into reverse-T3, thus maintaining the homeostasis of the thyroid hormones [14].

There is another group of selenoproteins whose biological roles have not been established yet. Selenoprotein P (SelP) is the most abundant selenoprotein in the blood plasma. SelP has 10 selenocysteine residues per molecule, and its main function would be the transport and delivery of Se to the tissues, and also to act as heavy metal chelator [15]. It is believed that its function is related to selenium homeostasis and oxidant defense [24]. Selenoprotein 15 (Sep15) belongs to the thioredoxin-like fold superfamily of proteins, and it is believed to be involved in glycoprotein folding in endoplasmic reticulum [25].

Selenoprotein R (SelR) reduces methionine-R-sulfoxides [15]. Selenoprotein W (SelW) is expressed in the nervous system, heart and muscles, and its functions would be related to muscle growth and differentiation by protecting the cells from oxidative stress [26].

In summary, Se plays crucial roles in different cellular metabolic processes such as oxidative stress defense, cell growth and proliferation, by means of selenoproteins.

3. Selenium Metabolism

Se metabolism depends on the chemical form in which it has been incorporated in the organism. Plants can take up Se from soil, mainly as selenite or selenate salts, depending on the redox equilibrium in the soil, and also on other factors [27], and convert it to organic selenium compounds, such as seleno-amino-acids. Despite Se is not recognized as essential for plants, it has been demonstrated that Se fertilization produces antioxidant effects [28 – 30]. Selenium is metabolized by the incorporation pathway of sulfate, through the action of sulfate permease found in roots. Se (IV) is accumulated without suffering any transformation, while Se (VI) is transformed into seleno-amino-acids through the non-enzymatic reduction by glutathione. The seleno-amino-acids are finally incorporated in proteins [30], which contributes to Se toxicity in non-accumulator plants.

Some plants have the capacity to accumulate Se, thus representing an important source of Se through the mammalian diet. Some of these plants belong to *Brassicae*, which are recognized as Se hyper-accumulators [8]. In these plants, selenocysteine is transformed into non-proteinogenic amino acids, such as Se-methylselenocysteine (SMSeC), by the action of the enzyme selenocysteine methyltransferase [31]. These forms are accumulated without producing toxic effects for the plant [32]. The accumulation of Se in the form of non toxic compounds has been postulated as the basis of Se tolerance in Se-accumulator plants, as a protection mechanism [33]. *Brassicae* can accumulate SMSeC up to a concentration of 2.8 mmol /g dry weight, when grown in Se enriched medium [34, 35].

In mammals, inorganic forms of Se may produce toxic effects, unlike some organic Se compounds, which can be excreted thus minimizing toxicity. Some forms of Se are preferably incorporated specifically in selenoproteins; other forms are incorporated in common proteins in a non-specific way, whereas other Se compounds are preferentially excreted [36, 37]. Selenocysteine is preferentially used in the synthesis of selenoproteins, as it is encoded as amino acid in the genetic code. Selenomethionine is incorporated in Se-containing proteins (i.e. proteins that have Se in their primary structure but not in the active site) by randomly replacing the amino acid methionine in a non-specific way. This non-specific incorporation of selenomethionine produces a great Se accumulation [35]. Inorganic forms of Se can be methylated to give low toxicity compounds [38] such as methylselenol, dimethylselenide, and trimethylselenonium ion. These Se compounds are excreted in urine and breathe [20, 39]. Seleno-amino-acids can also be methylated. SMSeC, a non-proteinogenic amino acid, serves as a precursor of methylselenol or methylseleninic acid [40], and then it exhibits a low body accumulation [41]. Some of these monomethylated forms of Se have proven anticarcinogenic effects, especially SMSeC and methylselenol [42 – 44].

4. Selenium and Human Health

Selenium is a scarce element that can be found naturally in soil, and it enters the food chain through plants. Se can be supplemented in water and in food, in different chemical forms, organic and/or inorganic ones. Most common inorganic forms are selenite and selenate salts, while organic forms correspond mainly to seleno-amino-acids such as selenomethionine and selenocysteine, where the sulfur atom has been replaced by selenium [14]. The Se level in foods is determined by many factors, such as geochemical, geological and climatic characteristics of the soil where plants are grown and further eaten by cattle, poultry, and other animals, all of them entering in the food chain, as do the plants. Se concentration in plants varies depending on the bioavailability of Se in the soil where they were grown, and also on the plant species [27]. In mammals, Se status depends on a continuous supply of this element, because these organisms have a limited Se storage capacity [9].

The effects of Se to human health strongly depend on its dose and chemical form. The concentration range in which Se is considered toxic or beneficial is very narrow [30]. It was estimated that the intake of foods containing more than 1 mg Se Kg^{-1} result in toxicity, while a concentration lower than 0.1 mg Se Kg^{-1} may result in Se deficiency. The dietary recommended allowance of Se for humans depends on region, sex and age; however it is estimated in average as 55 mg (Subcommittee on the tenth Edition of the RDAs, Food and Nutrition Board, National Research Council, 1989).

Se toxicity depends on its chemical form, oxidation state, and dose, and it is manifested as acute or chronic selenosis. Acute exposure to Se may result mainly in bronchitis, pulmonary edema and pneumonia. Chronic exposure to Se instead, results in discoloration of the skin, hair loss, and deformation of nails, weakness and a lack of mental alertness [30]. In general, the health injuries caused by excess of Se are much lower than those caused by Se deficiency.

Selenium deficiency decreases selenoprotein expression, and then it alters the metabolic processes mediated by them [30]. Since Se intake is related to the geographic location, some endemic diseases have been reported in low-Se regions (China and Eastern Siberia): Keshan disease (a cardiomiopathy) and Kashin-Beck disease (a deforming arthritis). Additionally, a form of cretinism associated with hypothyroidism has been attributed to low Se status.

Low Se status has been related to immune dysfunction, cardiovascular diseases, low male fertility, and development of some types of cancer [45, 46] It has been demonstrated that increased levels of Se intake produce an enhancement of both cell-mediated and humoral immune responses [17]. Besides, Se deficiency would result in less robust immune responses in experimental animals. The existence of a strong correlation between the risk of cardiovascular disease and a low Se status in humans was shown. Selenium also plays an important role in male fertility, since it is essential for testosterone synthesis [47]. Structural abnormalities and low motility in sperm have been reported in rats fed a Se-depleted diet [48]. In human trials, it has been shown that Se supplementation increases sperm motility and fathering [49].

5. Selenium as Chemoprotective Agent

In the last twenty years, the main interest has been set on the anticarcinogenic properties of Se [3, 4, 50 – 55]. In 1991 it was carried out the first human intervention trials for cancer prevention with Se [56], resulting in a significant reduction of liver cancer. Later, Clark et al. [3] showed that the supplementation of free-living people with Se (as selenomethionine) resulted in a decrease of 50% in the overall cancer morbidity and mortality. Se supplementation was found to be related with a reduced risk of colorectal cancer, prostate cancer, and lung cancer [57]. In 2001 it began SELECT, the **SEL**enium and vitamin **E C**ancer prevention **T**rial, funded by the National Cancer Institute (NCI), U.S.A. The aim of this study was to determine whether selenium, vitamin E, or both could prevent prostate cancer and other diseases in healthy men [58], based on epidemiological and preclinical data that showed the potential of Se and vitamin E in the prevention of prostate cancer [59]. Oral selenium (200 mg/d from L-selenomethionine) and vitamin E (400 IU/d of all rac-alpha-tocopheryl acetate) were administered to >50 years old healthy men, during 7 years. Recently, in September 2008, the partial results of SELECT were analyzed, and no decline in prostate cancer could be detected [60]. This unexpected result was attributed to the chemical form of the Se supplement (selenomethionine), and the relatively high initial levels of selenium in the enrolled men. However, the neutral results of the SELECT study do not discredit the hypothesis of cancer prevention by Se [61]. Since selenomethionine did not give the expected results, Se-methylselenocysteine, a naturally occurring selenocompound, seems to be a promising alternative.

Organic Se compounds are the most effective in cancer chemoprotection, especially SMSeC [50]. In human interventions it was demonstrated that at 1 – 3 mg Se/Kg, SMSeC is a more powerful chemoprotective agent that other Se compounds, such as sodium selenite and selenomethionine [42]. The chemoprotective action of SMSeC has been attributed to the generation of monomethylated Se compounds. Since SMSeC is a non-proteinogenic amino acid, it would be totally available for cancer chemo protection [9]. SMSeC exerts its anticarcinogenic properties by serving as precursor of methylselenol and methylseleninic acid, which would be the active anticarcinogenic compounds [62, 63].

Current investigations about the relationship between Se intake and cancer prevention have focused mainly on the chemical form of Se: Se-enriched food and *in vitro* effect of monomethylated forms of Se. It has been reported that dietary supplementation with selenized vegetables, such as garlic and broccoli grown in Se-enriched soil, results in a much higher chemoprotective effect, in comparison with selenite and selenomethionine [50, 64]. These vegetables are capable to store inorganic forms of Se and convert them to an organic form, mainly SMSeC. Additionally, it was shown that the health benefits of Se are achieved when supranutritional doses of this element are administered [65], ranging from 100 up to 200 mg Se/d for humans. A dose of 400 mg Se/d is considered as a safe upper limit. As a consequence, most of the recent interest in Se nutrition has been focused on over-supplementation several times beyond the Recommended Dietary Allowance [37].

6. Biomarkers of Selenium Status

Nutritional biomarkers reflect the nutritional status regarding the consumption or the metabolism of a nutrient. They can be clinical, functional or biochemical indexes. Metabolic biomarkers provide useful information about the nutritional status of the organism [66, 67]. Biological activity of Se is reflected as the presence of different selenium compounds, rather than as a change in the total Se content [68]. Selenium bioavailability has been traditionally determined as total Se concentration in tissues and by measuring the Gpx activity. While these methods count on general acceptance, recent findings about the health benefits of Se intake have revealed the need for alternative measurements. The mayor interest has been focused on the cancer protective ability of Se [3]. Ip et al. [7] reported that this effect would not be related with Gpx synthesis or with total concentration of Se in tissues. Finley and Davis [1] showed that no correlation exists between prevention of colon cancer in rats and total Se concentration or Gpx activity. Accordingly, those indexes are indicative of Se intake but not of its functional or metabolic status in the organism.

Some alternative indexes to assess Se bioavailability have been proposed based on the activity or concentration of other selenoproteins [69], such as iodothyronin deiodinase and selenoprotein P. However, the use of these proteins as Se indexes has not been validated so far, probably because of analytical requirements and low reproducibility of the results. Despite of these difficulties, Thomson [22] postulated that the assessment of metabolic status of Se should be based on individual selenoproteins, and not on total Se concentration in blood or tissues. Besides, the recent discovery of new isoforms of Gpx and other selenoenzymes opens the possibility of finding new biomarkers of Se status [18].

New approaches to investigate and discover new biomarkers have arisen, such as nutrigenomics, nutritional metabolomics and nutritional proteomics [67]. A genomic approach has been used to investigate the *in vitro* effect of different forms of selenium on gene expression of cancer cell lines [70]. Genes implicated in apoptosis and molecular mechanisms of cancer prevention were identified as induced by selenium; however complementary approaches such as proteomics and metabolomics are needed in order to validate these results.

The study of whole patterns or changes in protein expression due to a nutritional stimulus is known as "nutriproteomics" or nutritional proteomics. Biomarkers discovery approaches based on proteomics have gained popularity because they allow a global view of protein changes attributed to a certain stimulus. Besides it makes it possible to characterize proteins involved in a physiological state or a disease process [71 – 73].

7. New Potential Biomarkers of the Intake of Organic Seleno-Compounds

Seleno amino acids offer important health benefits, including cancer prevention. The effect of dietary supplementation with selenomethylselenocysteine (SMSeC) on the protein profile of rat blood plasma was investigated by Mahn et al. [74], in order to identify a protein profile that could be proposed as biomarker of nutritional status of selenium. Four experimental groups and six control groups consisting of six rats each were fed with base diet supplemented with SMSeC or sodium selenate in different concentrations for different periods of time. A proteomic approach was used to quantify protein expression differences in blood plasma, consisting in two-dimensional gel electrophoresis and mass spectrometry. Statistically significant differences in expression of some proteins were detected in all experimental groups. Four proteins responded to the experimental factors. Apolipoprotein E, haptoglobin and α-1-antitrypsin expressions varied with supplementation time, while transthyretin responded to SMSeC dose in a directly proportional way. Apolipoprotein E and transthyretin were not differentially expressed when sodium selenate was administered instead of SMSeC. Then the authors speculated that these proteins would have potential as chemoprotective selenium intake biomarkers.

In a later study, Mahn et al. [75] showed that haptoglobin, apolipoprotein E and transthyretin increased their abundance after diet supplementation with either SMSeC or sodium selenate in equivalent doses. Besides, the protein HNF6 was responsive only to dietary supplementation with SMSeC, whereas fibrinogen and alpha-1-antitrypsin responded only to sodium selenate administration. The authors proposed that these protein patterns could be considered as new selenium indexes to assess the metabolic status of this element.

8. Statistical Analysis of Protein Expression Pattern

In order to identify the proteins whose abundance was affected by dietary supplementation with selenium, in this chapter the proteomic data reported by Mahn et al. [74, 75] is statistically analyzed. For each protein, the statistical effects (i.e. the magnitude of the change in a protein's abundance when each factor moved from the low to the high level) of the following factors: selenium dose, extent of dietary supplementation period, the interaction between them and the interaction of selenium dose with itself were calculated. Table 1 shows the calculated effects, and its significance was determined using the Pareto Diagram with a confidence level of 95%, and the results are shown in Figure 1.

The following group of 13 proteins was significantly affected by selenium supplementation: alpha–1-antitrypsin (isoforms 1 and 2), apolipoprotein A-IV (isoform 1), fibrinogen (isoforms 1 and 2), apolipoprotein A-I (isoform 2), alpha-1-antitrypsin precursor, cyclin H, immunoglobulin light chain, apolipoprotein E (isoform 1), haptoglobin, transthyretin, and zinc finger protein 108. Seven of these proteins showed an increment in abundance directly proportional to selenium dose: alpha-1-anitrypsin precursor, cyclin H, apolipoprotein E, haptoglobin, transthyretin, zinc finger protein 108, and alpha-1-antitrypsin (isoform 2). No protein exhibited a reduction in abundance due to an increment in selenium dose.

Table 1. Calculated effects of experimental factors on protein synthesis. Statistically significant effects are highlighted with shadow

Protein	Effect			
	Extent of supplementation period	Dose	Dose * time	Dose * dose
Onecut1 protein	14.60 ± 72.70	143.62 ± 102.8	110.60 ± 102.8	138.60 ± 178.06
Contrapsin-like protease inhibitor	-24.29 ± 164.06	-328.73 ± 200.93	349.91 ± 200.93	-427.44 ± 348.02
Alpha-1-antitrypsin (isoform 1)	-0.20 ± 77.09	-73.88 ± 94.41	290.69 ± 94.41	-288.96 ± 163.53
Apolipoprotein A-IV (isoform 1)	51.97 ± 9.98	-21.58 ±12.22	31.71 ± 12.22	-56.76 ± 12.17
Fibrinogen (isoform 1)	21.59 ± 19.55	-3.07 ± 23.95	11.24 ± 23.95	9.53 ± 41.48
Fibrinogen (isoform 2)	47.31 ± 16.39	-41.79 ± 20.07	47.54 ± 20.07	325.34 ± 34.78
Fibrinogen (isoform 3)	-20.54 ± 6.67	6.29 ± 8.17	-3.55 ± 8.17	42.63 ± 14.16
Apolipoprotein A-I (isoform 1)	72.71 ± 74.99	72.25 ± 91.85	-133 87 ± 91.85	133.12 ± 159.08
Apolipoprotein A-I (isoform 2)	-334.20 ± 96.99	121.44 ± 118.78	-144.51 ± 118.78	79.91 ± 205.74
Alpha-1-antitrypsin precursor	-13.83 ± 6.02	22.96 ± 7.38	-22.96 ± 7.38	11.19 ± 12.78
Cyclin H	-4.85 ± 1.66	7.27 ± 2.03	-8.38 ± 2.03	8.38 ± 3.51
Immunoglobulin light chain	82.96 ± 12.88	34.28 ± 15.77	-73.12 ± 15.77	17.15 ± 23.31
Apolipoprotein E (isoform 1)	3.28 ± 12.36	44.45 ± 15.14	-13.32 ± 15.14	-13.24 ± 26.22
Apolipoprotein E (isoform 2)	-4.72 ± 2.82	7.08 ± 3.45	-7.08 ± 3.45	7.08 ± 5.98
Haptoglobin	10.40 ± 5.57	20.18 ± 6.82	1.52 ± 6.82	-7.96 ± 11.81
Rat Transthyretin	-1.79 ± 11.67	66.01 ± 14.30	1.70 ± 14.30	30.17 ± 24.76
Apolipoprotein A-IV (isoform 2)	-3.62 ± 2.83	5.43 ± 3.46	-6.80 ± 3.46	6.80 ± 5.99
Zinc finger protein 108	-5.46 ± 1.64	8.19 ± 2.00	-8.19 ± 2.00	8.19 ± 3.47
Alpha-1-antitrypsin (isoform 2)	-4.47 ± 4.97	15.53 ± 6.09	-9.38 ± 6.09	7.44 ± 10.54
Alpha-1-antitrypsin (isoform 3)	-3.51 ± 4.14	10.61 ± 5.07	-9.34 ± 5.07	2.47 ± 8.79
Gelsolin	14.27 ± 7.61	4.06 ± 9.33	4.25 ± 9.33	21.59 ± 16.15

Another group of proteins was significantly affected by the extent of the dietary supplementation period: apolipoprotein A-IV (isoform 1), fibrinogen (isoform 2), and immunoglobulin light chain showed an abundance increment with this factor, while fibrinogen (isoform 3), apolipoprotein A-I (isoform 1), cyclin H and zinc finger protein 108 reduced their abundance. The effect of selenium dose was directly proportional for all the proteins that were affected significantly, while the extent of the supplementation period increased the abundance of three proteins, and decreased the abundance of other four proteins, making its global effect on blood plasma proteome not so clear. Another group of proteins was significantly affected by the combined effect of dose and period extent. This effect produced an abundance increment of alpha-1-antitrypsin (isoform 1) and apolipoprotein A-IV (isoform 1), while it negatively affected the abundance of alpha-1-antitrypsin precursor, cyclin H, immunoglobulin light chain and zinc finger protein 108. The second order effect of dose produced an abundance reduction of apolipoprotein A-IV (isoform 1), and an increment of fibrinogen (isoforms 2 and 3). No protein was significantly affected by all factors in the same direction.

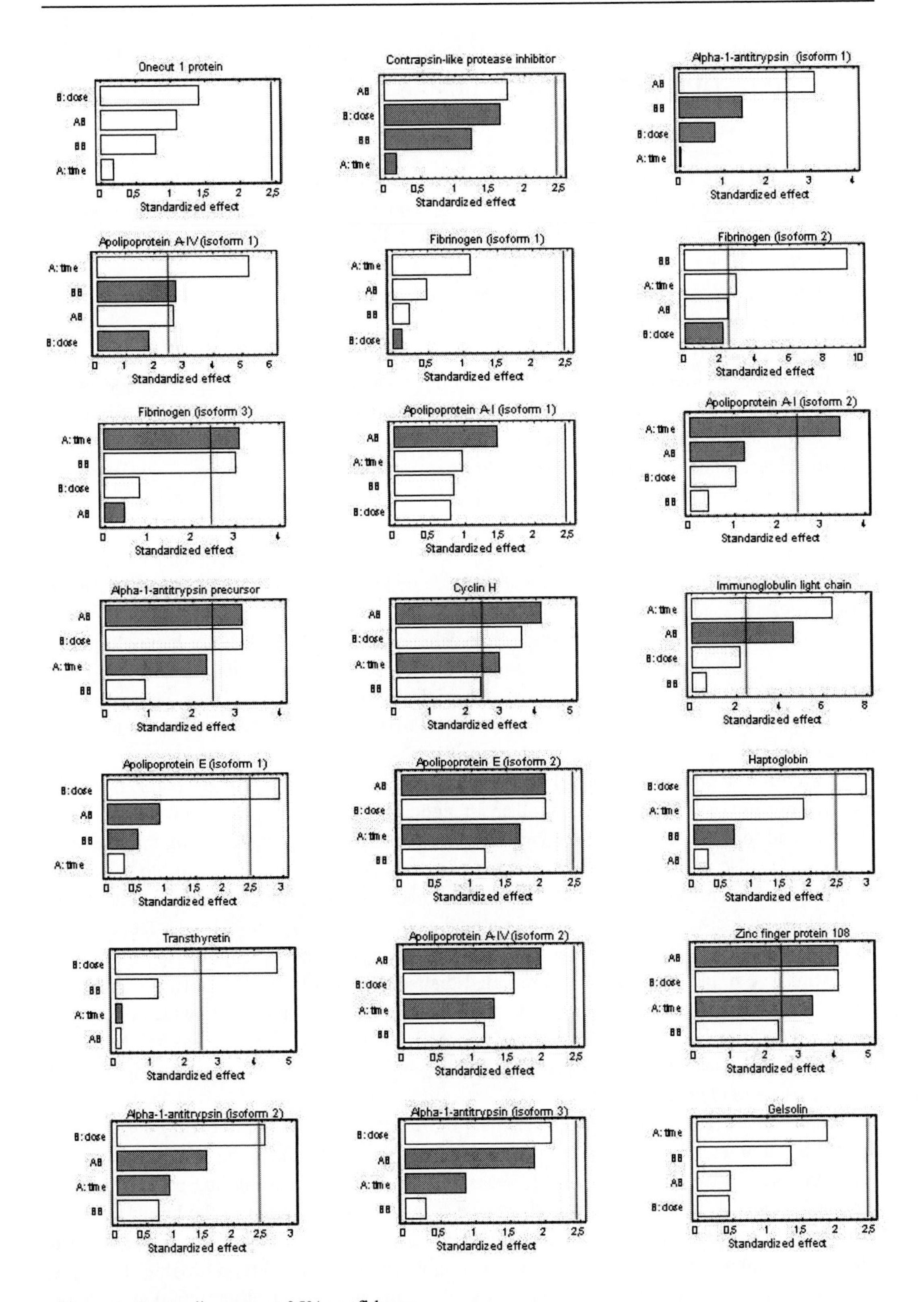

Figure 1. Pareto diagrams at 95% confidence.

9. DIFFERENTIAL PROTEIN EXPRESSION WITH SUPRANUTRITIONAL SELENIUM DIETARY SUPPLEMENTATION AS COMPARED TO MINIMUM SELENIUM DOSE

Given that the selenium dose had a clear effect on protein expression pattern; it was decided to investigate if this factor was able to produce a significant difference in protein abundance that could reflect supranutritional SMSeC dietary supplementation with respect to a base diet.

Protein abundance in plasma from animals fed with 1.9 μg Se /g diet (supra nutritional dose) was compared to those fed with a 0.15 μg Se /g diet (minimum dose), in order to determine which proteins increased their abundance due to supranutritional SMSeC dietary supplementation. Three proteins were detected only when SMSeC was supplemented in the diet in a supra nutritional dose, and they were not detected in animals fed with the minimum selenium dose: apolipoprotein E (isoform 1), haptoglobin, and α-1-antitrypsin (isoform 2). Additionally, a statistically significant difference in transthyretin abundance was detected when a supranutritional selenium dose was fed (p-value equal to 0.035 at a 95% confidence interval). Then, it can be assumed that these four proteins reflect SMSeC intake in a supranutritional dose as a significant increment in their abundance in rat blood plasma.

The lineal association between the abundance of these proteins in plasma and selenium dose was established. Relatively high R^2 values were obtained: 74% for transthyretin (p-value equal to 0.0007), 55% for apolipoprotein E (p-value equal to 0.009), 47% for haptoglobin (p-value equal to 0.020) and 45% for alpha-1-antitrypsin (p-value equal to 0.036). Then, selenium dose could explain 45% to 74% of variability in protein abundance, demonstrating that a higher abundance of these four proteins reflects SMSeC intake in a supranutritional dose.

Two of these proteins can be related to selenium metabolism. Apolipoprotein E mediates the binding, internalization and catabolism of lipoproteins. It serves as ligand for the LDL receptor and for the specific apo-E receptor of hepatic tissues. It is worth noting that the apo-E receptor is also a selenoprotein P receptor, the main selenoprotein found in blood plasma [76]. It was demonstrated that apo-E receptor mediates selenium uptake by the mouse testis [77]. Then, an increase in Apolipoprotein abundance could be explained by the fact that the apo-E receptor binds preferably selenoprotein P and, thus, a higher amount of Apolipoprotein E remains free in plasma. It has been reported that selenium deficiency resulted in increased levels of apolipoprotein E in rat plasma; however, the mechanism by which selenium deficiency affects lipoprotein metabolism is poorly understood. This mechanism has been related to the housekeeping selenoproteins, which would have a role in regulating lipoprotein biosynthesis and metabolism [78].

The inverse relationship between selenium deficiency and apolipoprotein E abundance is in contradiction with the results presented in this work, probably due to the different source of selenium used by Sengupta et al. [78]. Transthyretin is a hormone binding protein, rich in aromatic amino acids, that transports thyroxine from the blood stream to the brain, and it is synthesized in liver and in choroid plexus [79]. This protein is involved in the thyroid hormone metabolism, and selenium exerts major control function on thyroid hormone homeostasis [80]. This control is performed through the antioxidative action of several selenoenzymes synthesized in the thyroid gland [81]. These selenoenzymes can be produced only if the seleno amino acid selenocysteine is available, and SMSeC would be the source of bioavailable selenium in this case. Then, transthyretin would indirectly reflect the overexpression of selenoenzymes in thyroid gland.

Finally, here it is proposed that transthyretin, apolipoprotein E, haptoglobin and alpha-1-antitrypsin belong to a group of proteins whose incremented abundance in rat blood plasma reflects the intake of SMSeC in a supranutritional dose.

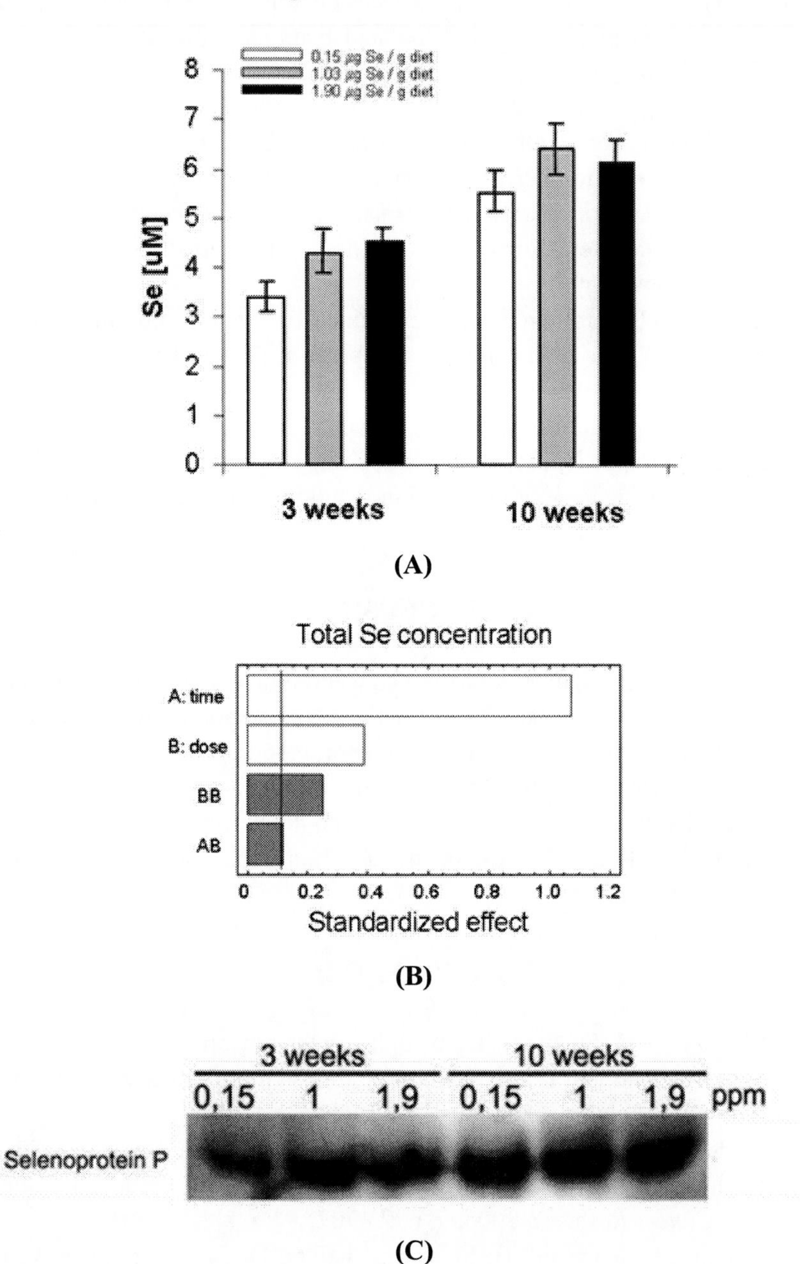

Figure 2. Selenium status assessment through traditional indexes. (a) Total Se concentration in blood plasma; (b) Pareto diagram for Se concentration; (c) SelP concentration in plasma determined by western blot.

10. Selenium Status Assessment through Traditional Indexes

The selenium status was assessed by measuring two commonly used indexes: total Se-concentration and selenoprotein-P abundance in plasma. The Se concentration was determined analytically by atomic absorption spectrophotometry. A Pareto Diagram at a 95% confidence level was used in order to find the statistically significant effects of the factors time and dose on this widely used selenium index. The results are shown in Figures 2(a) and 2(b).

The total selenium concentration was significantly affected by the SMSeC dose and by the extent of the supplementation period, in a directly proportional way. As expected, dietary supplementation with SMSeC increased the plasmatic selenium concentration. The interaction between the factors and the interaction of selenium dose with itself showed significant effects, in an inversely proportional way.

The abundance of selenoprotein P was determined by western blot analysis. The results are shown in Figure 2(c). The abundance of this protein increased with selenium dose and with the extent of the supplementation period, in a directly proportional way. As a consequence, these two selenium indexes, Se concentration and selenoprotein-P abundance, responded in a directly proportional way to SMSeC supplementation, as it was expected, and are not able to distinguish between organic and inorganic selenium compounds.

Conclusion

The traditional selenium indexes, selenium concentration and abundance of selenoprotein P in plasma, responded proportionally to SMSeC supplementation. Dietary supplementation with SMSeC significantly affected protein profile in rat blood plasma.

A characteristic protein profile was found, through a nutriproteomics approach, composed by transthyretin, apolipoprotein E, haptoglobin and alpha-1-antitrypsin. This pattern will probably help to characterize an adequate nutritional status related to the intake of seleno-amino-acids in the future.

References

[1] Finley, JW; Davis, C. Selenium from high - selenium broccoli is utilized differently than selenite, selenate and selenomethionine, but is more effective in inhibiting colon carcinogenesis. *BioFactors* 2001, 14, 191 - 196.

[2] Unni, E; Koul, D; Young, WK; Sinha, R. Se-methylselenocysteine inhibits phosphatidylinositol 3-kinase activity of mouse mammary epithelial tumor cells in vitro. *Breast Cancer Research* 2005, 7, 699 - 707.

[3] Clark, J; Combs, G; Turnbull, B; Slate, E; Chalker, D; Chow, J; Davis, L; Glover, R; Graham, G; Gross, E; Krongard, A; Lesher, J; Park, H; Sanders, B; Smith, C; Taylor, J. Effects of selenium supplementation for cancer prevention in patients with carcinoma of the skin. *Journal of the American Medical Association* 1996, 276, 1957 - 1963.

[4] Clark, LC; Dalkin, B; Krongrad, A; Combs, GF; Turnbull, W. Decreased incidence of prostate cancer with selenium supplementation: results of a double-blind cancer prevention trial. *British Jpurnal of Urology* 1998, 81, 730 - 734.

[5] Li, L; Xie, Y; El-Sayed, WM; Szakacz, JG; Franklin, MR; Roberts, J.C. Chemopreventive activity of selenocysteine prodrugs against tobacco-derived nitrosamine (NNK) - induced lung tumors in the A/J mouse. *Journal of Biochemistry and Molecular Toxicology* 2006, 19, 396 - 405.

[6] Irons, R; Carlson, B; Hatfield, D; Davis, C. Both selenoproteins and low molecular weight selenocompounds reduce colon cancer risk in mice with genetically impaired selenoprotein expression. *Journal of Nutrition,* 2006, 136, 1311 - 1317.

[7] Ip, C; Birringer, M; Block, E; Kotrebai, M; Tyson, J; Uden, P; Lisk, D. Chemical Speciation Influences Comparative Activity of Selenium-Enriched Garlic and Yeast in Mammary Cancer Prevention. *Journal of Agriculture and Food Chemistry*, 2000, 48, 2062 - 2070.

[8] Ellis, DR; Salt, DE. Plants, selenium. *Current Opinion in Plant Biology* 2003, 6, 273-279.

[9] Wachowicz, B; Zbikowska, K; Nowak, P. Selenium compounds in the environment: their effect on human health. *Cellular and Molecular Biology Letters*, 2001, 6, 375 - 381.

[10] Birringer, M; Pilawa, S; Flohe, L. Trends in selenium. *Natural Product Reports* 2002, 19, 693-718.

[11] Combs, GE. Food system-based approaches to improving micronutrient nutrition. *Biofactors* 2000, 12, 39-43.

[12] Combs, GF Jr.; Midthune DN; Patterson KY. Effects of selenomethionine supplementation. *American Journal of Clinical Nutrition* 2009, 89, 1808-1814.

[13] Gaertner, R. Selenium and thyroid. *Journal of Trace Elements in Medicine and Biology* 2009, 23, 71-74.

[14] Brown, KM; Arthur, JR. Selenium, selenoproteins and human health: a review. *Publics Health Nutrition* 2001, 4, 593 - 599.

[15] Lu, J; Berndt, C; Holmgren, A. Metabolism of selenium. *Biochimica et Biophysica Acta-General Subjects* 2009, 1790, 1513-1519.

[16] Reeves, MA; Hoffmann, PR. The human. *Cellular and Molecular Life Sciences* 2009, 66, 2457-2478.

[17] Hoffmann, PR; Berry, MJ. The influence of selenium. *Molecular Nutrition & Food Research* 2008, 52, 1273-1280.

[18] Kryukov, GV; Castellano, S; Novoselov, SV; Lobanov, AV; Zehtab, O; Guilo, R; Gladyshev, VN. Characterization of mammalian selenoproteomes. *Science* 2003, 300, 1439 – 1443.

[19] Lobanov, AV; Hatfield, DL; Gladyshev, VN. Eukaryotic selenoproteins and selenoproteomes. *Biochimica et Biophysica Acta-General Subjects* 2009, 1790, 1424-1428.

[20] Suzuki, KT. Metabolomics of selenium: Se metabolites based on speciation studies. *Journal of Health Science* 2005, 51, 107 – 114.

[21] Sunde, RA; Evenson, JK; Thompson, KM. Dietary selenium. *Journal of Nutrition* 2005, 135, 2144-2150.

[22] Thomson, C.D. Selenium speciation in human body fluids. *Analyst* 1998, 123, 827 - 831.

[23] Lillig, CH; Holmgren, A. Thioredoxin and related molecules. *Antioxidants & Redox Signaling* 2007, 9, 25-47.

[24] Burk, FR; Hill KE. Orphan selenoproteins. BioEssays 1999, 21, 231 - 237.

[25] Gromer, S; Eubel, JK; Lee, BL. Human selenoproteins at a glance. *Cellular and Molecular Life Sciences* 2005, 62, 2414-2437.

[26] Loflin, J; Lopez, N; Whanger, PD. Selenoprotein W during development and oxidative stress. *Journal of Inorganic Biochemistry* 2006, 100, 1679-1684.

[27] Haug, A; Eich-Greatorex, S; Bernhoft, A. Effect of dietary selenium. *Lipids in Health and Disease* 2007, 6, Art. 29.

[28] Cartes, P; Gianfreda, L; Mora, ML. Uptake of selenium. *Plant and Soil* 2005, 276, 359-367.

[29] Mora, ML; Pinilla, L; Rosas, A. Selenium uptake and its influence on the antioxidative system of white clover as affected by lime and phosphorus *Plant and Soil* 2008, 303, 139-149.

[30] Pedrero, Z; Madrid, Y. Novel approaches for selenium. *Analytica Chimica Acta* 2009, 634, 135-152.

[31] Wang, XL. Assessment of biomarker selection in selenium-deficiency disease. *American Journal of Clinical Nutrition* 2005, 81, 829–834.

[32] Neuhierl, B; Thanbichler, M; Lottspeich, FA. Family of S-methylmethionine-dependent thiol/selenol methyltransferases - Role inselenium tolerance and evolutionary relation. *Journal of Biological Chemistry* 1999, 274, 5407-5414.

[33] Pedrero, Z; Elvira, D; Camara, C. Selenium transformation. *Analytica Chimica Acta* 2007, 596, 251-256.

[34] Whanger, PD; Ip, C; Polan, CE. Tumorigenesis, metabolism. *Journal of Agricultural and Food Chemistry* 2000, 48, 5723-5730.

[35] Whanger, PD. Selenocompounds in plants. *Journal of the American College of Nutrition* 2002, 21, 223-232.

[36] Standtman, TC. Selenocysteine. *Annual Reviews of Biochemistry* 1996, 65, 83 - 100.

[37] Finley, JW. Selenium accumulation in plant foods. Nutrition Reviews 2005, 63, 196-202.

[38] Ip, C; Ganther, HE. Activity of methylated forms of selenium. *Cancer Research* 1990, 50, 1206-1211.

[39] Janghorbani, M; Xia, Y; Ha, P; Whanger, PD; Butler, JA; Olesik, JW; Daniels, L. Qualitative significance of measuring trimethylselenonium in urine for assessing chronically high intakes of selenium in human subjects. *British Journal of Nutrition* 1999, 82, 291 - 297.

[40] Ganther, HE. Selenium metabolism. *Carcinogenesis* 1999, 20, 1657-1666.

[41] Lyi, SM; Heller, LI; Rutzke, M. Molecular and biochemical characterization of the selenocysteine Se-methyltransferase gene and Se-methylselenocysteine synthesis. *Plant Physiology* 2005, 138, 409-420.

[42] Abdulah, R; Miyazaki, K; Nakazawa, M. Chemical forms of selenium. Journal of Trace Elements in Medicine and Biology 2005, 19, 141-150.

[43] Last, K; Maharaj, L; Perry, J. The activity of methylated and non-methylated selenium. *Annals of Oncology* 2006, 17, 773-779.

[44] Brigelius-Flohe, R. Selenium, glutathione. *Free Radical Research* 2008, 42, S28-S28.
[45] Pagmantidis, V; Meplan, C; van Schothorst, EM. Supplementation of healthy volunteers with nutritionally relevant amounts of selenium. *American Journal of Clinical Nutrition* 2008,87, 181-189.
[46] Koyama, H; Abdulah, R; Ohkubo, T. Depressed serum. *Nutrition Research* 2009, 29, 94-99.
[47] Behne, D; Gessner, H; Kyriakopoulos, A. Information on the selenium. *Journal of Trace Elements in Medicine and Biology* 1996, 10, 174-179.
[48] Hardy, G; Hardy, I. Selenium: The Se-XY nutraceutical. Nutrition 2004, 20, 590-593.
[49] Scott, R; Macpherson, A; Yates, RWS. The effect of oral selenium. *British Journal of Urology* 1998, 82, 76-80.
[50] Finley, JW; Davis, C; Feng, Y. Selenium from high selenium broccoli protects rats from colon cancer. *Journal of Nutrition* 2000,130, 2384 - 2389.
[51] Rayman, M. Selenium in cancer prevention: a review of the evidence and mechanism of action. *Proceedings of the Nutrition Society* 2005, 64, 527 - 42.
[52] Zhuo, H; Smith, AH; Steinmaus, C. Selenium and lung cancer: a quantitative analysis of heterogeneity in the current epidemiological literature. *Cancer Epidemiology Biomarkers and Prevention* 2004,13, 771-118.
[53] Bhattacharyya, RS; Husbeck, B; Feldman, D. Selenite treatment. *International Journal of Radiation Oncology Biology Physics* 2008, 72, 935-940.
[54] Gundimeda, U; Schiffman, JE; Chhabra, D. Relevance to selenium. *Journal of Biological Chemistry* 2008, 283, 34519-34531.
[55] Rayman, MP; Infante, HG; Sargent, M. Food-chain selenium. *British Journal of Nutrition* 2008, 100, 238-253.
[56] Yu, SY; Zhu, YJ; Li, WG. A preliminary-report on the intervention. *Biological Trace Element Research* 1991, 29, 289-294.
[57] Combs, GF. Status of selenium. *British Journal of Cancer* 2004, 91, 195-199.
[58] Lippman, SM; Klein, EA; Goodman, PJ. Selenium and Vitamin E Supplementation for Cancer Prevention Reply. *JAMA-Journal of the American Medical Association* 2009, 301, 1877-1877.
[59] Nadiminty, N; Gao, AC. Mechanisms of selenium. *Molecular Nutrition & Food Research* 2008, 52, 1247-1260.
[60] Hatfield, DL; Gladyshev, VN. The Outcome of Selenium and Vitamin E Cancer Prevention Trial (SELECT) Reveals the Need for Better Understanding of Selenium Biology. *Molecular Interventions* 2009, 9, 18-21.
[61] El-Bayoumy, K. The Negative Results of the SELECT Study Do Not Necessarily Discredit the Selenium-Cancer Prevention Hypothesis. *Nutrition and Cancer-An International Journal* 2009, 61, 285-286.
[62] Vadhanavikit, S, Ip, C, Ganther, H. Metabolites of sodium selenite and methylated selenium compounds administered at cancer chemoprevention levels in the rat. *Xenobiotica* 1993, 23, 731 - 745.
[63] Medina, D; Thompson, HT; Ganther, H; Ip, C. Se-methylselenocysteine: A new compound for chemoprevention of breast cancer. *Nutrition and Cancer* 2001; 40, 12 - 17.
[64] Yamanoshita, O; Ichihara, S; Hama, H. Chemopreventive effect of selenium. TOHOKU *Journal of Experimental Medicine* 2007, 212, 191-198.

[65] Fleming, J; Ghose, A; Harrison, P. Molecular mechanisms of cancer prevention by selenium compounds. *Nutrition and Cancer* 2001, 49, 42-49.

[66] Potischman, N; Freudenheim, JL. Biomarkers for nutritional exposure and nutritional status: An overview. *Journal of Nutrition* 2003, 133, 873S – 874S.

[67] Maruvada, P; Srivastava, S. Biomarkers for cancer diagnosis: Implications for nutritional research. *Journal of Nutrition* 2004, 134, 1640S – 1645S.

[68] Milner, J; McDonald, SS; Anderson, DE; Greenwald, P. Molecular targets for nutrients involved with cancer prevention. Nutrition and Cancer 2001, 41, 1 – 16.

[69] Sheehan, TM; Halls, DJ. Measurement of selenium in clinical specimens. *American Clinical Biochemistry* 1999, 36, 301 - 315.

[70] El-Bayoumi, K; Sinha, R. Molecular chemoprevention by selenium: a genomic approach. *Mutation Research* 2005, 591, 224 - 236.

[71] Sironi, L; Tremoli, E; Miller, I; Guerrini, U; Calvio, A; Eberini, I; Gemeiner, M; Asdente, M; Paoletti, R; Gianazza, E. Acute-phase proteins before cerebral ischemia in stroke-prone rats: identification by proteomics. *Stroke* 2001, 32, 753 – 760.

[72] van Eijk, H; Deuts, N. Plasma protein synthesis measurements using a proteomics strategy. *Journal of Nutrition* 2003, 133, 2084S – 2089S.

[73] Barnes, S; Kim, H. Nutriproteomics: Identifying the molecular targets of nutritive and non-nutritive components of the diet. *Journal of Biochemistry and Molecular Biology* 2004, 37, 59 - 74.

[74] Mahn, A; Toledo, H; Ruz, M. Organic and inorganic selenium compounds produce different protein patterns in the blood plasma of rats. *Biological Research* 2009, 42, 163 – 173.

[75] Mahn, A; Toledo, H; Ruz, M. Dietary supplementation with selenomethyl selenocysteine produces a differential proteomic response. Journal of Nutritional Biochemistry 2009, 20, 791–799.

[76] Burk, RF; Hill, KE; Olson, GE; Weeber, EJ; Motley, AK; Winfrey, VP; Austin, LM. Deletion of apolipoprotein E receptor-2 in mice lowers brain selenium and causes severe neurological dysfunction and death when a low-selenium diet is fed. *Journal of Neuroscience* 2007, 27, 6207-6211.

[77] Olson, GE; Winfrey, VP; NagDas, SK; Hill, KE; Burk, RF. Apolipoprotein E Receptor-2 (ApoER2) Mediates Selenium Uptake from Selenoprotein P by the Mouse Testis. *Journal of Biological Chemistry* 2007, 282, 12290-12297.

[78] Sengupta, A; Carlson, BA; Hoffmann, VJ; Gladyshev, VN; Hatfield, DL. Loss of housekeeping selenoprotein expression in mouse liver modulates lipoprotein metabolism. *Biochemistry and Biophysics Research Communication* 2008, 365, 446-452.

[79] Navab, M; Mallia, A; Kanda, Y; Goodman, D. Rat plasma prealbumin. Isolation and partial characterization. Journal of Biological Chemistry 1977, 252, 5100-5106.

[80] Kohrle, J. The trace components -selenium and flavonoids- affect iodothyronine deiodinases, thyroid hormone transport and TSH regulation. *Acta Medica Austriaca* 1992, 19, 13-17.

[81] Schmutzler, C; Mentrup, B; Schomburg, L; Hoang-Vu, C; Herzog, V; Kohrle, J. Selenoproteins of the thyroid gland: expression, localization and possible function of glutathione peroxidase 3. *Biological Chemistry* 2007, 388, 1053-1059.

In: Chemical Food Safety and Health
Editors: F. Pedreschi Plasencia and Z. Ciesarová
ISBN: 978-1-62948-339-9

Chapter 7

EFFECT OF FOOD MICROSTRUCTURE ON NUTRIENT BIOAVAILABILITY AND HEALTH

***J. Parada*[1*] *and J. M. Aguilera*[2]**
[1]Instituto de Ciencia y Tecnología de los Alimentos,
Universidad Austral de Chile Valdivia, Chile
[2]Departamento de Ingeniería Química y Bioprocesos, Facultad de Ingeniería,
Pontificia Universidad Católica de Chile, Macul, Santiago, Chile

ABSTRACT

An important property of the nutrients in food is its bioavailability, which is the fraction really available for action or storage in the consumer's body. It has been seen that the food microstructure (or food matrix) plays a major role in the release, transformation, and consequent absorption of several nutrients during digestion, affecting finally their bioavailability. Several microstructural characteristics can act in a food and to affect the nutrient bioavailability, and therefore a real understanding of each one is needed to an adequate management of processing in order to improve nutritional quality of food products. This chapter reviews basic concepts about the effect of food microstructure on nutrients bioavailability, summarizes relevant *in vivo* and *in vitro* methods used to assess the bioavailability, and gives some examples (polyphenols, starch, etc.) to understand the actual implications of microstructural changes during processing in relation with bioavailability.

1. INTRODUCTION

The available scientific evidence suggests a relationship among food consumption, health, and well-being. There have been observed that several illnesses as cardiovascular diseases, diabetes, and some types of cancers can be related with the excess or lack of specific

[*] Corresponding author: Dr. Javier Parada, Instituto de Ciencia y Tecnología de los Alimentos, Universidad Austral de Chile,Av. Prof. Julio Sarrazín s/n, Campus Isla Teja, Valdivia, Chile, Phone: +56-63-221 302, Fax:+56-63-221 355; e-mail:javier.parada@uach.cl.

nutrients in the diet. So, the amount of nutrient that effectively acts in the consumer's body is the key factor to be controlled by modern food industry and considered by consumers, rather than the total nutrient in the food. Although the total quantity of a nutrient may be obtained from composition tables or standard analysis, its "availability" for absorption in the gastrointestinal tract is in many cases quite uncertain or varies for the same food depending on processing conditions, presence of other components, and so on. Some factors which affect the nutrient availability are the chemical state of the nutrient, its release from the food matrix, possible interactions with other food components, presence of suppressors or cofactors, and formation of stable compounds that are slowly metabolized, among others. The objective of this chapter is to present some available evidence that food microstructure may affect the final uptake of nutrients in the gastrointestinal tract, hence, their presence in the blood plasma.

2. Nutrient Bioavailability and Its Importance

Food composition can be measured by analytical methodologies or found in food composition databases (FCDs) which provide values for the amount of energy, protein, fat, vitamins, minerals, and some other specific nutrients present in a food item. For FCDs the values are normally determined by standard chemical analyses (for example, "Official Methods") or sometimes derived, in the case of complex foods, from the nutrient composition of ingredients [1]. This information is generally used to assess the nutrient content of diets and to derive nutrition guidelines. It is also often utilized in food policy recommendations and in nutrition monitoring. However, the problem when use these data is that information is related to the amount of nutrients present in foods prior to ingestion but gives no clue of the actual amount that becomes available for physiological activity after absorption in the gastrointestinal tract. So, the bioavailability concept takes great relevance.

2.1. Definitions of Bioavailability and Bioaccessibility

The FDA has defined *bioavailability* as the rate and extent to which the active substances or therapeutic moieties contained in a drug are absorbed and become available at the site of action [2]. This definition also applies to active substances (nutrients) present in foods. However, even today nutrient bioavailability is an important but often nebulous concept associated with the efficiency of absorption and metabolic utilization of an ingested nutrient [3]. Another term that is commonly used is *bioaccessibility*, which is defined as the amount of an ingested nutrient that is available for absorption in the gastrointestinal tract after digestion [4]. Thus, it is not equivalent to speak of bioavailability or bioaccessibility. If the amount of recovered nutrient after digestion is of relevance then the term to use is bioaccessibility. On the other hand, bioavailability of nutrients is usually measured in the blood plasma of humans (*in vivo* assay) so factors such as the individual variability, physiological state, dose, and presence of other meal components come into play, as described by Faulks and Southon [5]. These authors established that although a nutrient can be potentially bioaccessible, almost any one is totally converted during digestion into a potentially absorbable form. In almost every case, bioaccessibility and bioavailability of a nutrient are governed by the physical properties of the food matrix, which affect the efficiency of the physical, enzymatic, and chemical digestion processes [6]. Summarizing, bioavailability and bioaccessibility can be defined as:

- *Bioavailability*: the fraction of ingested nutrient that is available for utilization in normal physiologic functions and for storage.
- *Bioaccessibility*: fraction that is released from food matrix and is available for intestinal absorption.

Methods to Determine Bioavailability/Bioaccessibility

Methods for determining bioavailability and/or bioaccessibility of nutrients involve human (*in vivo*) or simulated experiments performed in a laboratory (*in vitro*). *In vivo* methods provide direct data of bioavailability and have been used for a great variety of nutrients and foods. Usually a response is measured after consumption of a pure nutrient (natural or synthetic) by living beings, either humans (most common) or animals, and compared to an equivalent nutrient dose found in a food source [7]. Ethical restrictions and abiding to severe protocols when humans and/or animals are used in biological research are severely limiting this type of studies [8, 9]. Most commonly, *in vivo* bioavailability studies imply the consumption of certain dose of a nutrient and following changes of its concentration (measured by standard analytical procedures) in the blood plasma compared with time (for example, postprandial period, or the time after the meal). Metabolic mechanisms transport the nutrients from gastrointestinal tract to blood and then to tissues, being possible to observe an increasing in the nutrient blood concentration followed by a decreasing until return to the basal levels. So, three parameters can be derived from the kinetics: the area under curve (AUC; area between the concentration curve and the base line), the maximal plasma concentration (C_{max}; maximal concentration achieved before to return to the basal concentration), and the time to reach C_{max}, t_{max}. AUC is a measure of the absorption intensity, whereas C_{max} and t_{max} give an idea of the rate of absorption [10, 11]. Another method to assess bioavailability is to measure the plasma concentration of a nutrient through an extended period (days, weeks) of constant consumption of a specific food [12, 13]. Relevant parameters in this case are C_{sat} (value at which the concentration remains constant in the time) and the t_{sat} (time at which C_{sat} is attained). The main drawbacks of *in vivo* data are the variability in physiological state of individuals and the possible interaction of the nutrient with other components in the diet.

In vitro methods are being extensively used at present since they are rapid, safe, and do not have the ethical restrictions of *in vivo* methods. *In vitro* methods either simulate the digestion and absorption processes (for bioavailability) or only the digestion process (for bioaccessibility) and the response measured is the concentration of a nutrient in some kind of final extract. The digestion process is simulated under controlled conditions using commercial digestive enzymes (for example, pepsin, pancreatin, and so on) while the final absorption process is commonly assessed using Caco-2 cells cultures. "Caco-2 cells" is the short name of polarized human colon carcinoma cells line [14]. Figure 1 shows the basic elements in a digestion Caco-2 cell assay, where exact conditions of time, pH, temperature, and so on, depend on the compound to be analyzed and the type of food matrix. The amount of a nutrient present in the extract (after the Caco-2 cell step) is assumed as the final amount bioavailable [15]. Several protocols following the scheme of Figure 1 have been adapted to assess the bioavailability of specific nutrients. A major problem to be resolved is that nutrients in foods may be transformed from the gastrointestinal tract into metabolites (for example, by colonic bacteria) that are the active form in which they are absorbed (thus "bioavailable").

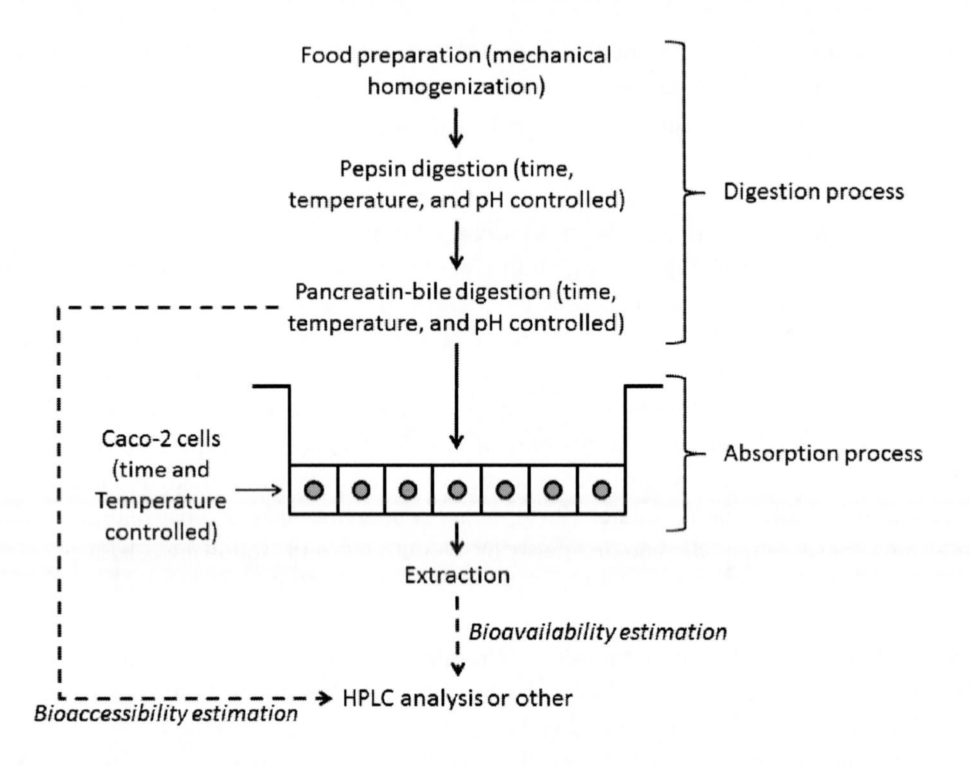

Figure 1. Diagram of an *in vitro* method to determine bioavailability involving a digestion/absorption step using a Caco-2 cell culture. If the absorption step is omitted, bioaccessibility can be estimated.

In regard with *in vitro* procedures, methods that simulate the gastrointestinal digestion process under laboratory conditions are commonly known as gastrointestinal models (GIMs). They are used as a suitable alternative to *in vivo* assays to determine bioavailability, in spite of their limitations regarding the significance of data generated. GIMs try to reproduce the physiological conditions in the mouth, stomach, and small intestine during mastication, digestion, and absorption. In general, GIMs fall into 2 broad categories: *static models*, where the products of digestion remain largely immobile and do not mimic physical processes such as shear, mixing, hydration, etc, whereas *dynamic models* try to include physical and mechanical processes and temporal changes in luminal conditions to mimic conditions *in vivo*. The latter are particularly useful where the physical condition of the digesta (mixture of ingested food particles and fluids released during digestion) changes over time (for example, particle size and viscosity) and take into account some temporal effects not considered otherwise (mixing, diffusion, formation of colloidal phases, and so on).

In vitro procedures using GIMs have been used in a wide rank of research related with bioavailability of nutrients and effect of food matrix, and can include some variations as water-jacketed glass tubes internally lined with flexible walls in order to simulated peristaltic movements [16]. Some examples are: the release of phenolic compounds from the matrix of orange juice, strawberries, and strawberry jam [17], determination of potential antimutagenic activity of extracts of black tea and green tea [18], digestion kinetics of carbohydrates and proteins of bread under mouth and stomach conditions [19], release of antioxidants from wholegrain foods with a GIM having enzymatic and fermentation steps [20], screening of carotenoids bioavailability from plant foods [21, 22], etc. At least 1 commercial GIM is now available in the market: TNO's gastrointestinal model, widely used in pharmacological and food testing for human and animal trials [23].

3. Food Microstructure

3.1. Definition

Food microstructure significantly affects the "macro properties" of products, including sensorial, physical, and even chemical properties, and therefore is important for consumer preference and nutritive quality. Foods produced by nature are generally organized hierarchically from molecules into assemblies and organelles that are later compartmentalized into cells and tissues. "Natural" food structures may be classified into 4 broad categories:

1) fibrous structures assembled hierarchically from macromolecules into tissues for specific functionality (for example, muscles) and held together at different levels by specific interfacial interactions;
2) fleshy materials from plants that are hierarchal composites of hydrated cells that exhibit turgor pressure and are bonded together at the cell walls (for example, tubers, fruits, and vegetables);
3) encapsulated embryos of plants that contain a dispersion of starch, protein, and lipids assembled into discrete packets (for example, in grains and pulses); and
4) a unique complex fluid called milk, intended for nutrition of the young mammal containing several nutrients in a state of dispersion.

Most fruits, vegetables, meat, fish, grains, and tubers are eaten around the world with minor processing; thus their edible microstructure has been largely imparted by nature. Processed foods (for example, baked and confectionery products, dried pasta, processed meats, and so on), on the other hand, are multicomponent structured matrices where the individual components (proteins, fats, carbohydrates, and so on) have been reassembled as colloidal dispersions, emulsions, amorphous or crystalline phases, or gel networks by heating and/or cooling and the application of shear. By food microstructure we understand the spatial arrangement of identifiable elements in a food and their interactions at levels below 100 μm [24]. Typical microstructural elements in foods are cell walls, starch granules, proteins, water and oil droplets, fat crystals, gas bubbles, etc. The concept of a "food matrix" points to the fact that nutrients are contained into a larger continuous medium that may be of cellular origin (in fruits and vegetables) or a microstructure produced by processing, where they may interact at different length scales with the components and structures of the medium. For example, nutrients may be found as individual molecules bound to plant organelles (for example, carotenoids in carrots) or entrapped in a complex macromolecular matrix of swollen starch granules and protein (for example, isoflavones in baked products). As pointed out by Cuvelier et al. [25] the molecular structure of a nutrient is the smallest structural level relevant for its biological role and activity (for example, *cis* or *trans* conformation, number of hydroxyl groups or chelating sites in phenolic antioxidants). The most common microscopy techniques to study the food microstructure are light microscopy in its many versions, scanning electron microscopy (SEM), transmission electron microscopy (TEM), and, recently, the confocal laser microscope and atomic probe microscopes. These techniques are now being routinely used by food scientists to characterize food microstructures and food matrices, providing qualitative information about their physical state [26].

3.2. Effect of Microstructure on Nutrient Bioavailability

As stated before, nutrients are often located in natural cellular compartments or within assemblies produced during processing. In either case, they need to be released during digestion so they can be absorbed in the gastrointestinal tract. For example, Ellis et al. [27] studied the role of plant cell walls in the bioaccessibility of lipids in almond seeds (where almond seeds and fecal samples were examined by microscopy to identify cell walls and intracellular lipids). They successfully identified intact almond tissue in fecal material collected from healthy subjects fed an almond-rich diet, showing that the main structures of almond tissue were found to be preserved even after chewing and digestion. In particular, cell walls that remained intact hindered the release of intracellular lipid.

Even if complete disruption of cellular structure is effected, full absorption of a particular nutrient is not ensured and may depend on the presence and interactions with other food components. For example, while Brown et al. [28] indicated that food matrix components such as fiber could decrease carotenoid absorption, Rondini et al. [29] found good bioavailability of ferulic acid in the presence of bran. Additionally, there is extensive evidence that the food matrix is also of considerable influence in the bioavailability of some minerals [30, 31]. Even though work still needs to be done in characterizing food microstructure, there is ample evidence that the physical state of the matrix plays a key role in the release, mass transfer, accessibility, and biochemical stability of many food components [32].

Changes on microstructure occur throughout all period of digestion, including, for example, the physical transformation of food matrices in the mouth during eating, where the mastication is considered the initial step in the digestion of foods. Mastication consists of grinding the food into small pieces and impregnating these pieces with saliva to form a swallowable bolus.

Decreasing the particle size enlarges the surface area available for the attack by digestive enzymes, thus increasing the overall digestion efficiency and the gastrointestinal absorption of nutrients [33, 34]. So, mastication is crucial to determine the final changes of microstructure and in nutrient bioavailability.

3.3. Changes on Nutrient Bioavailability in Foods

3.2.1. Importance of Processing

The bioavailability of nutrients and bioactive compounds present in plant products (fruits and vegetables) is presently an extremely important area of food and nutrition research. The objective of these studies is to determine the real contribution of actual foods as sources of specific nutrients (for example, antioxidants) and to establish processing conditions that maximize the health benefits. Although several phytochemicals are known to be important in promoting human health, only some of those with evidence that microstructure affects their bioavailability will be reviewed here. For example, food microstructure seems to be quite relevant in the bioavailability of several antioxidants.

Food processing such as grinding, fermentation, and/or mild heating may improve bioavailability, most likely as a result of disruption of the cell walls of plant tissues, dissociation the nutrient-matrix complexes, or transformation into more active molecular structures. The scheme in Figure 2 depicts the case where the total amount of a nutrient may decrease in the food chain due to chemical degradation during storage and physical losses in processing, while at the same time the bioavailability may increase by the aforementioned processes. Additionally, Table 1 shows some examples where bioavailability (or bioaccessibility) of nutrients is affected by food microstructure.

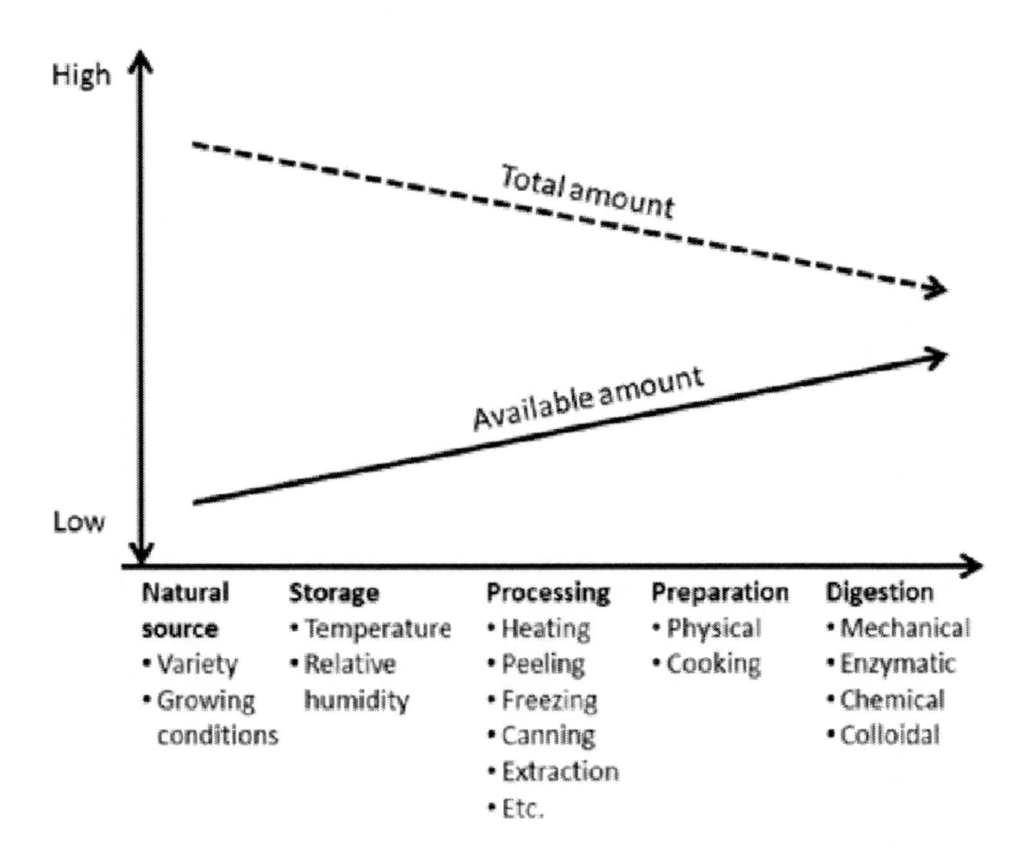

Figure 2. Example of a food where the total amount of a nutrient diminishes through the food chain, but the amount bioavailable increases due to suppression of food matrix effects.

Table 1. Selected examples showing the effect of matrix state on measured bioavailability/bioaccessibility of nutrients. There should be noted that each prcessing implicates a different state of the food matrix

Nutrient	Food (Matrix)	Processing	Bioavailability, bioaccessibility	Method and units	Reference
β-carotene	Spinach	Whole leaf	5.1	*In vivo* relative bioavailability as compared to bioavailability of the carotenoid supplement; percent	Castenmiller and others (1999)
		Minced leaf	6.4		
		Liquefied leaf	9.5		
Lycopene	Tomato	No homogenization	63.9 ± 16.5	Postprandial TRL response; μmol×h/L	van het Hof and others (2000a)
		Mild homogenization	82.6 ± 16.5		
		Severe homogenization	118 ± 16.5		
		Minimal heat treatment	78.6 ± 15.4		
		Extensive heat treatment	97.9 ± 15.4		
α-tocopherol	Fresh broccoli	Before cooking	0.32 ± 0.05	HPLC-method; mg/100g	Bernhardt and Schlich (2006)
		Boiling	1.54 ± 0.16		
		Stewing	1.61 ± 0.07		
		Steaming	1.58 ± 0.16		
		Pressure steaming	1.70 ± 0.08		
Starch	Cooked dough (starch/gluten)	Low mixing degree before cooking	48.3	*In vitro* rapidly available glucose; g/100 g	Parada and Aguilera (2011)
		High mixing degree before cooking	60.3		

3.3.2. Examples of Nutrient Bioavailability Affected by Microstructure

In theory, bioavailability of any nutrient can be affected by food microstructure, but detailed information is still limited. In this section, some examples of nutrients are shown in order to support the idea that microstructure affect the bioavailability. These examples include some phytochemicals and starch, like example of bioactive compounds and macronutrient, respectively.

Carotenoids

Carotenoids are a family of fat-soluble plant pigments that provide red and orange colors to fruits and vegetables. Their function is to absorb light in photosynthesis, protecting plants against photosensitization. Dietary carotenoids are considered to be beneficial in the prevention of a variety of diseases, including certain cancers and eye disorders. The 5 principal carotenoids found in human plasma as a result of ingestion of plants are α-carotene and β-carotene, cryptoxanthin, lutein, and lycopene, but over 600 carotenoids have been identified to date. Carotenoids present in a wide variety of plants are partially concentrated in chromoplasts or chloroplasts in different ways. The extent of release from the food matrix is highly variable depending on whether carotenoids are noncovalently bound to protein or fiber, dissolved in oil (as in corn and palm oil), or in crystalline form (carrots), making their optimal absorption difficult to achieve [7, 35, 36]. In general, the bioavailability of carotenoids has been estimated to vary from 10% in raw, uncooked vegetables to 50% in oil and commercial products [35]. Even when extracted from the food matrix, the bioavailability of carotenoids may be very low as revealed by *in vivo* studies of capsanthin and capsorubin from paprika oleoresin [37]. Since carotenoids are hydrophobic their absorption depends not only on the release from the food matrix but also on the subsequent solubilization by bile acids and digestive enzymes, culminating in their incorporation into micelles. For this reason dietary lipids have been considered to be important cofactors for carotenoids bioavailability, particularly in carotenoids-rich fruits that are low in lipids.

In general, the release of carotenoids from plant foods occurs only when the cells in the food matrix are disrupted, as is usually the case during food preparation, processing, and/or mastication, but not during digestion, at least in the ileum of humans [5, 8, 9, 12, 38]. In addition Zhou et al. [39] suggested that the food matrix, probably pectin-like fibers, and the crystalline form of carotenoids in carrot chromoplasts were the primary factors that reduced the relative bioavailability of carotenoids from carrot juice (so-called "incomplete release"). Serrano et al. [40] concluded that the proportion of β-carotene (and lutein) released by the sole action of digestive enzymes from spinach, chaya (*Cnidoscolus aconitifolius*), and macuy (*Solanum americanum*) ranged from 22% to 77%. Following release from the food matrix, the major limiting factor governing the extent of absorption of carotenoids is their solubilization in digesta [5]. It is well known that cooking can increase the extractability of β-carotene from the plant matrix, thereby improving its bioavailability. Daily consumption of processed carrots and spinach by women over a 4-wk period produced an increase in plasma β-carotene concentration that averaged 3 times that associated with consumption of the same amount of β-carotene from the raw vegetables [41]. Livny et al. [42] concluded that significantly more of the β-carotene was absorbed from cooked and pureed carrots (65.1% $\pm$ 7.4%) than from the raw vegetable (41.4% $\pm$ 7.4%). One conclusion is that providing cooked and pureed vegetables rather than raw vegetables would appear to be a better approach to providing bioavailable β-carotene from carotenoid-rich foods, which may be applicable for populations who rely on these foods to meet vitamin A requirements.

Lycopene

Lycopene, a carotenoid responsible for the distinctive red color of ripe tomatoes, is usually located within cell membranes and its release is determinant on the bioavailability. Epidemiological studies have suggested that consumption of lycopene may protect against cardiovascular diseases and reduce the risk of several types of cancer, most notably those of the prostate, breast, lung, and digestive tract [43].

Food processing like cooking or heating may improve lycopene bioavailability by breaking down cell walls, which weakens the bonding forces between lycopene and the tissue matrix, thus making it more accessible. Moreover, *cis*-isomerization is enhanced in free lycopene with the advantage that *cis*-isomers are more soluble in bile acid micelles and may be preferentially incorporated into chylomicrons. Shi and Le Maguer [2] and Re et al. [44] concluded that the matrix may contribute to the stability of all *trans*-forms of lycopene in tomatoes, thus preventing the isomeric equilibrium from occurring. During digestion the prevailing food matrix is further disrupted and lycopene may be incorporated into micelles prior to absorption. It is plausible that once this disruption occurs, further isomerization of *trans*-lycopene may occur. The practical result is that lycopene is 2.5 times more bioavailable in humans when present in tomato paste than in fresh tomatoes [43].

Folates

Folate and folic acid are forms of B vitamin that are necessary for the production and maintenance of new cells, especially important during periods of rapid cell division and growth, such as throughout infancy and pregnancy. Inadequate folate intake has been associated with development of birth defects [45]; esophageal, gastric,andpancreatic cancers [46]; and brain disorders such as depression [47]. Leafy green vegetables such as spinach and turnip greens, dry beans and peas, and some other fruits and vegetables are rich natural sources of folate [48]. In nature, folates are covalently bound to macromolecules. Results obtained by Verwei et al. [14, 49] showed that folate-binding proteins decrease the bioavailability of folate (especially pteroylmonoglutamic acid [PGA], a synthetic folic acid) in fortified milk products; this observation was confirmed by human studies. The food matrix itself and its individual components can also influence folate bioavailability by entrapment, thereby hindering diffusion to the absorptive surface during digestion [12, 50]. Also simple entrapment in the food bolus during digestion is a possible mechanism for incomplete absorption of food folates. In the absence of food matrix effects, the various folates are absorbed effectively and to an approximately equivalent extent [3].

Polyphenols

Polyphenols represent a wide variety of compounds belonging to several classes, for example, hydroxybenzoic and hydroxycinnamic acids, anthocyanins, proanthocyanidins, flavonols, flavones, flavanols, flavanones, isoflavones, stilbenes, and lignans [11]. Phenolic compounds (or polyphenols) are secondary metabolites of the pentosephosphate, shikimate, and phenylpropanoid pathways in plants. These compounds, one of the most widely occurring groups of phytochemicals, are of considerable physiological and morphological importance in plants [51]. Polyphenols are abundant micronutrients in our diet and alleged to play several roles in the prevention of degenerative diseases, acting as anti-allergenic, antiatherogenic, anti-inflammatory, antimicrobial, antioxidant, antithrombotic, cardioprotective, and vasodilatory agents. Derivatives of phenolic acids account for about one-third of the total intake of polyphenols in our diet and flavonoids account for the remaining two-thirds. They have been associated with the health benefits derived from consuming high levels of fruits, vegetables, and wine, mainly as antioxidants [51].

Reported bioavailability of polyphenols is highly variable depending on their structure and conjugation (for example, to sugars): <0.1% for most anthocyanins (colored flavonoids in berries and red wine), 1% to 5% for quercetin (red wine, apples, and onions), 10% to 30% for flavanones (citrus) and flavanols (red wine, tea, and cocoa), and 30% to 50% for isoflavones (soya products) and gallic acid (red wine, tea, and various fruits) [52]. A major part of the polyphenols ingested (75% to 99%) is not found in urine. This implies they have either not been absorbed through the gastrointestinal tract barrier, absorbed and excreted in the bile, or metabolized by the colonic microflora or our own tissues. Polyphenols are highly sensitive to the mild alkaline conditions in the small intestine and a good proportion of these compounds can be transformed before absorption [53]. This has been shown in a recent *in vitro* study using a digestion Caco-2 cell model by Laurent et al. [54], who obtained evidence that only pancreatic digestion plays a determining role in the bioavailability of phenolic compounds from grape seed extracts. Salivary and gastric digestion had no effect on polyphenol stability, because interactions between proteins (for example, digestive juice proteins and/or brush border cell proteins or enzymes) and phenolic compounds occurred mainly during the intestinal step and decreased their bioavailability. As a consequence, the most abundant polyphenols in our diet are not necessarily those leading to the highest concentrations of active metabolites in target tissues [11]. The bioavailability of phenolic compounds can be also affected by differences in concentration within plant tissues, variations in cell wall structure, location of glycosides in cells, and binding of phenolic compounds within the food matrix [51]. Methods of culinary preparation have also a marked effect on the polyphenols content of foods. For example, simple peeling of fruit and vegetables can eliminate a significant portion of polyphenols because these substances are often present in higher concentrations in the skin than in the pulp. Interestingly, Manach et al.[55] commented that the effect of the food matrix on the bioavailability of polyphenols had not been examined in much detail. In a later review by these authors, an extensive variability in the bioavailability and bioefficacy of polyphenols in humans was observed with up to 10-fold variation in the C_{max} values for most phenolic compounds. Among several factors that could explain this variability were the food matrix and the background diet [11]. Milbury et al. [56] also concluded that the information on the bioavailability of different flavonoid groups is limited. These authors suggested that anthocyanins appear to be absorbed in their unchanged glycosylated forms by humans and provided measurements of the pharmacokinetic parameters of dietary anthocyanins absorption. In their review, Aherne and O'Brien [57] concluded that flavonol content in processed foods (canned, glass jars, frozen) from onion, kale, apple, bean, and so on can be significantly lower (approximately 50%) than levels found in fresh products. However, processing of food such as tomatoes may increase flavonol availability (free form flavonol) due to hydrolysis and extraction from food matrix [58]. The accumulation of quercetin or release of the aglycone form in processed foods can occur during digestion as a consequence of enzymatic hydrolysis of quercetin that has become conjugated during pasteurization and fermentation. Simonetti et al. [59] have shown that flavonoid glucosides such as rutin were absorbed from tomato puree even at low amounts of intake, suggesting that this food was probably a good vehicle for these polyphenolic compounds.

Polyphenols from wine, in particular resveratrol, anthocyanins, catechins, and quercetin, have attracted a great deal of attention. Tannins (complex polyphenols) in the grape berry are located in specialized tissues of the skin and seed, and because of their differential extraction from these matrices during pressing and fermentation (especially in red wines) their presence in wine may not necessarily reflect their relative abundance in the fruit at harvest. This is important when invoking health-related benefits from wines. However, most of the major solutes present in the grape berry at harvest contribute to wine composition. This is the case of resveratrol where higher concentrations are found in red grapes rather than in white varieties, and in red wines (fermented with the skins) rather than in white wines [60]. Tannins are tightly bound to cellulose and hemicellulose in the cell walls of fresh grapes, but not to pectin [61]. It was found that only a fraction of the tannin was extracted during winemaking and some of the nonextracted tannin was tightly bound to the insoluble matrix of the grape berry. The capacity of the insoluble matrix to capture tannin can amount to more than 22% of the tannin present in the fruit. This result indicates that tannin binding to the insoluble matrix of grape berries may be an important factor in the ability to extract tannin from fruit during fermentation [62]. In addition, new polyphenols may be formed during processing [63]. Once extracted, the absorption of quercetin, catechin, and resveratrol in humans was almost equivalent in white wine, grape juice, and vegetable juice.

Berries that accumulate large quantities of anthocyanins, pigments associated with the red and blue colors of plant organs (fruits, flowers, and leaves), have been proposed to have important health related benefits apart from their antioxidant activity. Anthocyanins are composed of 6 anthocyanidin aglycones linked to sugar groups. However, the bioavailability of anthocyanins is very low and their metabolism is still not fully understood [64]. Felgines et al. [65] suggested that anthocyanins in fresh strawberries were glucuro- and sulfo- conjugated in humans and that their absorption was probably affected by the food matrix. On the other hand, in a study by Mazza et al. [66] the absorption of anthocyanins in humans was investigated after the consumption of a high-fat meal with a freeze-dried blueberry powder containing 25 individual anthocyanins. Nineteen of the 25 anthocyanins were detected in blood serum and their presence was directly correlated with an increase in serum antioxidant capacity. These results appear to indicate that anthocyanins can be absorbed in their intact glycosylated and possibly acylated forms in human subjects. *In vitro*, the exposure to differences in pH, oxygen, and heating combines to greatly reduce raspberry (extracts) anthocyanin availability to the serum fraction, but codigestion with common foodstuffs (such as bread, breakfast cereal, ice cream, and cooked minced beef) may help protect the labile anthocyanins and certainly does not markedly decrease the level of serum bioavailability polyphenols. Results suggests that polyphenols transiently bind to food matrices during digestion, which protects the more labile anthocyanins from degradation; however, the details about the components involved in the process require further attention [67]. Based on the limited knowledge available on absorption and metabolic fate of phytochemicals found in berries and conflicting results of bioavailability studies, Beattie et al. [68] in their comprehensive review have recommended that ". . . it would be unwise to ascribe additional health promoting benefits from berries beyond those recognized for fruits and vegetables in general."

Isoflavones (subclass of polyphenols) are phenolic compounds strikingly similar in chemical structure to mammalian female estrogens and occur naturally in plants, predominantly in soybeans, and thus are known as "phytoestrogens." They are currently heralded as offering potential alternative therapies for a range of hormone-dependent conditions, including some cancers, menopausal symptoms, cardiovascular disease, and osteoporosis [69, 70]. Isoflavones occur in different chemical forms: aglycones, ß-glucosides, manolyl-, and acetyl-glucosides. Although in soy foods the predominant form is as glucosides, the concentration and composition vary according to the part of the seed where the isoflavones are found (seed coat, cotyledon, and axis). Food processing can alter the ratio of glucosides and fermentation processes may result in an increase in the levels of aglycones in commercial soy products [69, 71]. In addition, isoflavone glycosides are not absorbed intact across the enterocytes of healthy adults, but require the hydrolysis of the sugar moiety by intestinal ß-glucosidases [72].

There is little information about the effect of the food matrix (and its changes along the digestion process) on the bioavailability of isoflavones. Low recovery of isoflavones after *in vitro* digestion (bioaccessibility) was reported from cookies (22.0% ± 14.1%) compared to fruit juice (90.0% ± 12.7%) and chocolate bars (99.5% ± 0.7%) [71]. These results were related to the complexity of the sugar/starch/protein matrix in cookies, which may have hindered the extraction of isoflavones. However, these findings were not replicated in a human study (bioavailability), unveiling the difficulties in extrapolating results from *in vitro* experimentation to humans. Apparently, these differences could be explained because during *in vivo* digestion the gut microflora degrades isoflavones, in particular, daidzein. Additionally, interactions between released isoflavones and proteins are more likely to happen *in vivo* than *in vitro* (as is the case, in general, for all polyphenols) [73].

Various extents of release, partitioning, and stability of the isoflavones occur at different stages of digestion. Sanz and Luyten [74] using an *in vitro* method studied custard desserts made with starch or carboxymethylcellulose (CMC) and enriched with a soy germ extract as source of isoflavones. Incubation under simulated mouth conditions did not affect the amount and partitioning of isoflavones (aqueous/fat phase). A lower recovery and different partitioning were found after the stomach incubation, which was associated with the low pH, whereas after the intestine incubation, a higher recovery and an effect on partitioning were found. Regarding the matrix effect, custards containing starch released a significantly higher amount of isoflavones than those made with CMC, probably due to the higher enzymatic resistance of the latter. Finally, the presence of fat significantly increased the bioaccessibility of the aglycone forms, especially of genistein. The complexity in interpreting experimental results is also confirmed in other studies; for example, it has been observed that fractional absorption of isoflavones (as genistein) is influenced by the matrix and chemical composition of the food, and by gender [70, 75, 76]. Thus, isoflavones in supplements are likely to be absorbed at a faster rate compared with those ingested within a food matrix [77].

Starch

Starch, a complex glucose made carbohydrate, is the most important source of energy in the human diet and the main carbohydrate derived from foods around the world. At present, it is accepted that to achieve a healthy status, complex carbohydrates should provide around 60% of the total energy in the daily food consumption [78-80]. The main metabolic relevance of starch compared with simple carbohydrates such as sugars (glucose, fructose, etc.) is that it is slowly digested in the gastrointestinal tract, thus producing a more moderate glycemic response (GR) [81]. This slow digestion involves a gradual release of glucose and therefore, a slow transfer of this sugar from the small intestine to the blood stream. Glucose causes a metabolic stress when present in the blood at elevated levels and high postprandial blood glucose concentrations are associated with increased risk of type 2 diabetes and cardiovascular disease. Lower glucose and insulin levels are associated with an improved metabolic profile of high-density lipoprotein cholesterol, glycosylated proteins, oxidative status, hemostatic variables and endothelial function, while limited evidence suggests that a low-glycemic index diet may also protect against obesity, colon cancer and breast cancer. [82-86].

Raw starch has a semicrystalline structure that limits the penetration of enzymes into the granule and therefore, the rate and total quantity of sugar released are slower and less than in processed starch [87]. When the starch granule is heated in the presence of abundant water, whether inside cells or by external hydration as in doughs or pastes, its microstructure undergoes important changes, a phenomenon called *gelatinization*. This process is limited by water lack. During gelatinization granule structure changes from a crystalline to a disordered structure that is more easily accessible for the digestive enzymes [10, 88-92]. Gelatinization is the main structural transformation of starch granules in a food when it is heat processed or cooked in the presence of water. After gelatinization, if granules are stored for sufficient time (hours, days), amylose and the linear regions of amylopectin chains tend to interact by hydrogen bonding, losing water from the fine structure and undergoing an incomplete re-crystallization called *retrogradation*. Retrogradation can lower the digestibility of gelatinized starch because the resulting structure is less accessible to enzymes, and thus the GR is more moderate [87, 93-98]. Dextrinization or partial hydrolysis of starch is a third transformation that occurs mainly during extrusion processes where fragmentation is favored by low moisture and high-shear conditions. Both the mechanical and thermal energies transferred to starch molecules during extrusion affect the breakdown of covalent and hydrogen bonds, increasing the susceptibility of starch to enzyme action [99].

Additionally to the state of starch chains (drastically changed by processing and storage), digestibility of starch in foods is also affected by:

1) presence of substances that interfere with the action of the digestive enzymes (i.e. anti-enzymatic compounds),
2) food matrix (protein, fiber, etc), which controls the accessibility to the substrate and the mobility of enzymes in the food bolus throughout the digestion process, and
3) the intimate interactions of starch with other components present in the bolus which preclude the direct contact between starch and enzymes during digestion, as observed in the formation of complexes between amylose and free fatty acids [100].

3.4. Nutrients in Designed Matrices for Delivery

Man-made matrices can improve the stability of purified nutrients during storage, increase the effectiveness at the absorption site, and ensure optimal dosage. Thus, encapsulation or microencapsulation of bioactive substances, nutrients, and beneficial microorganisms (probiotics) is becoming a widely used technology in the pharmaceutical and food industries. Among microencapsulation techniques are spray-drying, spray-chilling, extrusion, coacervation, liposomes, cocrystallization, and freeze-drying [101]. Sanz and Luyten [74] commented that the selection of the food matrix into which the bioactive ingredient is incorporated was crucial to deliver an effective dose in the human body. To be bioavailable, the ingredient should be released from the food matrix, dissolved in the appropriate phase of digesta (usually aqueous phase), and subsequently absorbed in the human body.

Structuring matrices for nutrient delivery is a subject of enormous interest nowadays, and several matrix materials are under study. Chen et al. [102] describes the potential role of food proteins as materials in nutraceutical delivery systems for bioactive compounds (for example, vitamins, probiotics, bioactive peptides, and antioxidants) in the form of hydrogels and micro- or nano-particles. Embedding lycopene into whey protein matrices enhanced its bioavailability to that equal to tomato paste, the most valuable food source of bioavailable lycopene for humans [13]. Hydrocolloids are potential capsule materials and have been widely used as matrices for delivery. Yoo et al. [103] found that β-tocopherol encapsulated in sodium alginate microcapsules was largely protected when exposed to simulated gastric fluid and subsequently largely released in a simulated intestinal fluid. A study reports that over 80% of the original lycopene could be embedded in the walls of gelatine/sucrose microcapsules by spray drying, although no information was provided as far as the activity and release [104]. Protein hydrogels are attractive carriers for controlled release of bioactive molecules when weak interactions occur with the polymeric as is the case of flavor compounds in gelatin gels [105]. Remondetto et al. [106], using protein hydrogels, showed that different iron release profiles could be obtained depending on the microstructure of the gels in which the mineral was entrapped. This result is of relevance since extrusion encapsulation of micronized dispersible ferric pyrophosphate in rice meal has proven to result in a low bioavailability [31].

Probiotics are defined as "live microbial food supplements (mainly lactic acid bacteria belonging to the genera *Lactobacillus* and *Bifidobacterium*) that benefit the health of consumers beyond inherent general nutrition by maintaining or improving their intestinal microbial balance" [107]. In general, these bacteria exhibit a low ability to survive the harsh conditions in the gastrointestinal tract and need to be protected to preserve their activity, and several food matrices and encapsulation techniques have been successfully used for this purpose [108, 109]. Dairy products are obvious carriers of probiotics; thus, yogurt, fermented milks, and cheeses containing probiotics are well established in the market [110]. The tolerance of dairy *Propionibacteria* to immobilization in several food matrices was studied by Leverrier et al., [111], who showed that some matrices can significantly improve protection of bacterial cells from stress injury (*in vitro* tolerance to digestive stresses). Capela et al. [112] concluded that microencapsulation with alginate improved the viability of probiotics organisms in freeze-dried yogurt stored for 6 mo at 4 and 21 °C. Similarly, Krasaekoopt et al. [113] concluded that the survival of encapsulated probiotic bacteria in chitosan-coated alginate beads was higher than that of free cells by approximately 1 log cycle over a period of 4 wk at 4 °C. The problem is that processing conditions to protect microorganisms seem to be specific for each genus and even for each particular strain. Picot and Lacroix [114] reported that the viable counts of *Bifidobacterium breve* R070 cells entrapped in whey protein microcapsules were significantly higher than those of free cells after 28 d in yogurt stored at 4 °C (+2.6 log cycles), and after sequential exposure to simulated gastric and intestinal juices

(+2.7 log cycles). However, no protective effect of encapsulation was observed with the strain *Bifidobacterium longum* R023.

The use of vegetable matrices (for example, fruit pieces, spent grains after extraction) as carriers of nutrients is a novel concept in the design of functional foods that opens new product categories and commercial opportunities. Vacuum and/or atmospheric impregnation allows introduction of controlled quantities of a nutrient solution into the porous structure of fruits and vegetables [115]. Alzamora et al. [116] described the main aspects of the kinetics of matrix fortification via solution impregnation, the stability of some active compounds (probiotics and minerals), interactions between calcium and the cell structure, and the mechanical properties of impregnated fruit and vegetable tissues. Anino et al. [117] studied the potential of fresh apple pieces as a matrix for calcium incorporation by 2 different impregnation techniques, under vacuum and at atmospheric pressure. Impregnation treatments promoted a significant increase in calcium concentration, especially during a long-term atmospheric process, with the amount of Ca^{2+} incorporated in pieces enough to satisfy about 23% to 62% of the recommended daily intake. Preliminary results of sensory characteristics of the final product have shown that, in spite of the softening observed, textural characteristics of infused apple pieces appeared to be acceptable.

3.5. Food Matrix and Allergenicity

Because accumulating evidence that the activity of food allergens depends on the microstructure of foods, this topic will be briefly reviewed here. Allergenicity is an extreme case where a food component elicits a negative immunological reaction in the body. In the United Kingdom approximately 1% to 2% of adults and 5% to 7% of children are thought to suffer some kind of IgE-mediated food allergies [118]. In order to produce sensitization, allergens have to be released from the food matrix, survive digestion, and be absorbed through the gut epithelial barrier in an immunological active form [119]. The action of food processing on the food matrix may affect the stability and release of allergens, as well as destroy or induce "neo-epitopes" in food proteins [120, 121]. For example, it has been reported that texturization neutralizes the action of a major allergen present in soy protein [122].

Unlike their common role as nutrients, some proteins, in particular glycoproteins present in a number of foods, may be major food allergens. Certain proteins may not exert their allergenicity unless they are released from protein body organelles in which they are naturally present. Digestion, hydration, interactions with other proteins, and other matrix effects may contribute to the ability of a protein to reach the sites of immune action in the gastrointestinal mucosa and thus exert their potential allergenicity. Moreover, in the case of peanut extracts the food matrix itself activates immune cells, thus eliciting immune responses to peanut protein [119, 123]. It has been suggested that allergens from tree nuts and peanuts may become protected during digestion by the fat released from the cells. Formation of colloidal structures in the gastrointestinal tract and their effect on the action of allergens or the bioavailability of nutrients is a subject that requires further research.

CONCLUSION

Nutrient bioavailability is nowadays the main parameter in order to know the actual impact of food on health, and food microstructure (or food matrix) affects it. Some nutrients found in plants are protected in nature against degradation inside cells, whether attached to membranes, occluded inside cell organelles, bound to cell walls, or packaged as stable structures, but this natural protection lowers bioavailability. Thermal and physical processing, mastication, and to limited extent digestion break down the cell walls and native structures, making the release of nutrients from the food matrix easier and rendering them available for absorption in the intestine. However, even if released during processing and digestion, nutrients may possibly interact with other food components in the gastrointestinal tract by binding to macromolecules, forming chemical complexes and colloidal structures that reduce or improve their bioavailability. Alternatively, food microstructure can be manipulated to our advantage by protecting nutrient extracts and beneficial microorganisms during storage and through transit in the stomach inside man-made matrices. Figure 3 summarizes some possible mechanisms related to microstructure that influence the bioavailability of nutrients in the gastrointestinal tract.

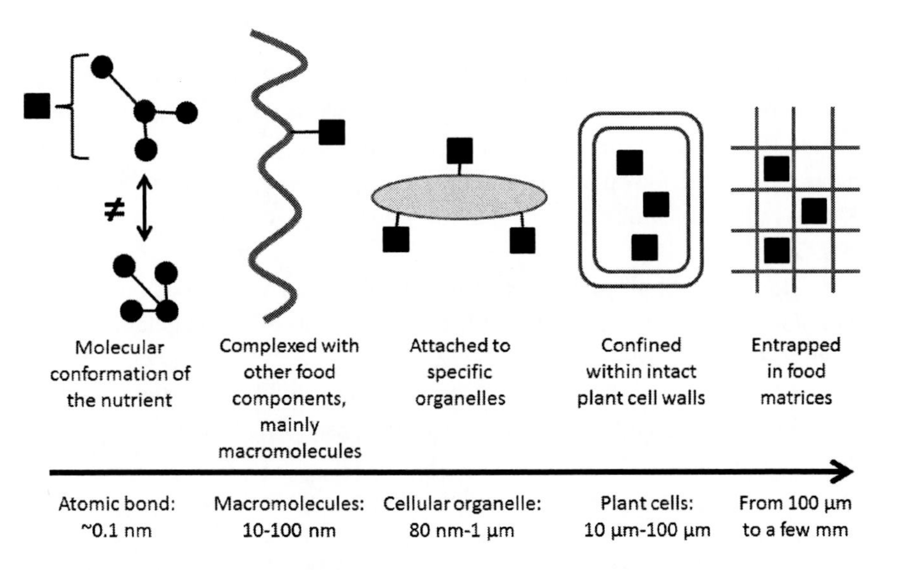

Figure 3. Mechanisms that affect the bioavailability of a nutrient (■) in a food matrix. There should be noted that several mechanisms can be acting together for a nutrient.

REFERENCES

[1] Schakel, S.F., I.M. Buzzard, and S.E. Gebhardt, Procedures for estimating nutrient values for food composition databases. *Journal of Food Composition and Analysis,* 1997. 10(2): p. 102-114.

[2] Shi, J. and M. Le Maguer, Lycopene in tomatoes: chemical and physical properties affected by food processing. *Crit Rev Food Sci Nutr*, 2000. 40(1): p. 1-42.

[3] Gregory, J.F., E.P. Quinlivan, and S.R. Davis, Integrating the issues of folate bioavailability, intake and metabolism in the era of fortification. *Trends in Food Science & Technology*, 2005. 16(6): p. 229-240.

[4] Hedrén, E., G. Mulokozi, and U. Svanberg, In vitro accessibility of carotenes from green leafy vegetables cooked with sunflower oil or red palm oil. *International journal of food sciences and nutrition*, 2002. 53(6): p. 445-453.

[5] Faulks, R.M. and S. Southon, Challenges to understanding and measuring carotenoid bioavailability. *Biochimica et Biophysica Acta (BBA)-Molecular Basis of Disease,* 2005. 1740(2): p. 95-100.

[6] Boyer, J. and R.H. Liu, Apple phytochemicals and their health benefits. *Nutr J,* 2004. 3(5): p. 12.

[7] Yeum, K.J. and R.M. Russell, Carotenoid bioavailability and bioconversion. *Annual Review of Nutrition*, 2002. 22(1): p. 483-504.

[8] van het Hof, K.H., et al., Carotenoid bioavailability in humans from tomatoes processed in different ways determined from the carotenoid response in the triglyceride-rich lipoprotein fraction of plasma after a single consumption and in plasma after four days of consumption. *The Journal of nutrition*, 2000a. 130(5): p. 1189-1196.

[9] van het Hof, K.H., et al., Dietary factors that affect the bioavailability of carotenoids. *The Journal of nutrition*, 2000b. 130(3): p. 503-506.

[10] Heacock, P.M., S.R. Hertzler, and B. Wolf, The glycemic, insulinemic, and breath hydrogen responses in humans to a food starch esterified by 1-octenyl succinic anhydride. *Nutrition research*, 2004. 24(8): p. 581-592.

[11] Manach, C., et al., Bioavailability and bioefficacy of polyphenols in humans. I. Review of 97 bioavailability studies. *The American journal of clinical nutrition*, 2005. 81(1): p. 230S-242S.

[12] Van het Hof, K.H., et al., Influence of feeding different vegetables on plasma levels of carotenoids, folate and vitamin C. Effect of disruption of the vegetable matrix. *British Journal of Nutrition*, 1999. 82: p. 203-212.

[13] Richelle, M., et al., A food-based formulation provides lycopene with the same bioavailability to humans as that from tomato paste. *The Journal of nutrition*, 2002. 132(3): p. 404-408.

[14] Verwei, M., et al., The effect of folate-binding proteins on bioavailability of folate from milk products. *Trends in Food Science & Technology*, 2005. 16(6-7): p. 307-310.

[15] Glahn, R.P., et al., Caco-2 cell ferritin formation predicts nonradiolabeled food iron availability in an in vitro digestion/Caco-2 cell culture model. *The Journal of nutrition*, 1998. 128(9): p. 1555-1561.

[16] Parada, J. and J. Aguilera, Food microstructure affects the bioavailability of several nutrients. *J Food Sci*, 2007. 72(2): p. R21-R32.

[17] Gil-Izquierdo, A., P. Zafrilla, and F.A. Tomás-Barberán, An in vitro method to simulate phenolic compound release from the food matrix in the gastrointestinal tract. *European Food Research and Technology*, 2002. 214(2): p. 155-159.

[18] Krul, C., et al., Antimutagenic activity of green tea and black tea extracts studied in a dynamic in vitro gastrointestinal model. *Mutat Res*, 2001. 474(1-2): p. 71-85.

[19] Hoebler, C., et al., Development of an in vitro system simulating bucco-gastric digestion to assess the physical and chemical changes of food. *International journal of food sciences and nutrition*, 2002. 53(5): p. 389-402.

[20] Nagah, A.M. and C.J. Seal, In vitro procedure to predict apparent antioxidant release from wholegrain foods measured using three different analytical methods. *Journal of the Science of Food and Agriculture*, 2005. 85(7): p. 1177-1185.
[21] Garrett, D.A., M.L. Failla, and R.J. Sarama, Development of an in vitro digestion method to assess carotenoid bioavailability from meals. *J Agric Food Chem*, 1999. 47(10): p. 4301-4309.
[22] Garrett, D.A., M.L. Failla, and R.J. Sarama, Estimation of carotenoid bioavailability from fresh stir-fried vegetables using an in vitro digestion/Caco-2 cell culture model. *The Journal of nutritional biochemistry,* 2000. 11(11): p. 574-580.
[23] TNO. 2012 [cited 2012 Accessed January 15]; Available from: http://www.tno.nl/content.cfm?context=thema&content=markt_product&laag1=891&laag2=195&laag3=320&item_id=1100&Taal=2.
[24] Aguilera, J.M. and D.W. Stanley, Microstructural principles of food processing and engineering1999: Springer.
[25] Cuvelier, M.E., V. Bondet, and C. Berset, Behavior of phenolic antioxidants in a partitioned medium: structure—Activity relationship. *Journal of the American Oil Chemists' Society*, 2000. 77(8): p. 819-824.
[26] Aguilera, J.M., Food product engineering: building the right structures. *Journal of the Science of Food and Agriculture*, 2006. 86(8): p. 1147-1155.
[27] Ellis, P.R., et al., Role of cell walls in the bioaccessibility of lipids in almond seeds. *The American journal of clinical nutrition*, 2004. 80(3): p. 604-613.
[28] Brown, E.D., et al., Vegetable concentrates interact with canthaxanthin to affect carotenoid bioavailability and superoxide dismutase activity but not immune response in rats. *Nutrition research*, 1997. 17(6): p. 989-998.
[29] Rondini, L., et al., Bound ferulic acid from bran is more bioavailable than the free compound in rat. *J Agric Food Chem*, 2004. 52(13): p. 4338-4343.
[30] Brouns, F. and C. Vermeer, Functional food ingredients for reducing the risks of osteoporosis. *Trends in Food Science & Technology*, 2000. 11(1): p. 22-33.
[31] Moretti, D., et al., Iron status and food matrix strongly affect the relative bioavailability of ferric pyrophosphate in humans. *The American journal of clinical nutrition,* 2006. 83(3): p. 632-638.
[32] Aguilera, J.M., Why food microstructure? *Journal of Food Engineering*, 2005. 67(1): p. 3-11.
[33] Kulp, K.S., et al., An in vitro model system to predict the bioaccessibility of heterocyclic amines from a cooked meat matrix. *Food and Chemical Toxicology*, 2003. 41(12): p. 1701-1710.
[34] Suzuki, H., et al., Effects of thorough mastication on postprandial plasma glucose concentrations in nonobese Japanese subjects. *Metabolism*, 2005. 54(12): p. 1593-1599.
[35] Deming, D.M. and J. Erdman, Mammalian carotenoid absorption and metabolism. *Pure and Applied Chemistry*, 1999. 71(12): p. 2213-2224.
[36] Zaripheh, S. and J.W. Erdman, Factors that influence the bioavailability of xanthophylls. *The Journal of Nutrition*, 2002. 132: p. 531S-534S.
[37] Pérez-Gálvez, A., et al., Incorporation of carotenoids from paprika oleoresin into human chylomicrons. *British Journal of Nutrition*, 2003. 89(6): p. 787-794.
[38] Edwards, A.J., et al., α- and β-Carotene from a Commercial Carrot Puree Are More Bioavailable to Humans than from Boiled-Mashed Carrots, as Determined Using an

Extrinsic Stable Isotope Reference Method. *The Journal of nutrition*, 2002. 132(2): p. 159-167.

[39] Zhou, J., E. Gugger, and J. Erdman Jr, The crystalline form of carotenes and the food matrix in carrot root decrease the relative bioavailability of beta-and alpha-carotene in the ferret model. *Journal of the American College of Nutrition*, 1996. 15(1): p. 84-91.

[40] Serrano, J., I. Goni, and F. Saura-Calixto, Determination of β-Carotene and Lutein Available from Green Leafy Vegetables by an in Vitro Digestion and Colonic Fermentation Method. *J Agric Food Chem*, 2005. 53(8): p. 2936-2940.

[41] Rock CL, et al., Bioavailability of beta-carotene is lower in raw than in processed carrots and spinach in women. *Journal of Nutrition*, 1998. 128: p. 913-916.

[42] Livny, O., et al., ß-carotene bioavailability from differently processed carrot meals in human ileostomy volunteers. *European journal of nutrition*, 2003. 42(6): p. 338-345.

[43] Omoni, A.O. and R.E. Aluko, The anti-carcinogenic and anti-atherogenic effects of lycopene: a review. *Trends in Food Science & Technology*, 2005. 16(8): p. 344-350.

[44] Re, R., et al., Isomerization of lycopene in the gastric milieu. *Biochem Biophys Res Commun,* 2001. 281(2): p. 576-581.

[45] Takimoto, H. and T. Tamura, Increasing trend of spina bifida and decreasing birth weight in relation to declining body-mass index of young women in Japan. *Medical hypotheses,* 2006. 67(5): p. 1023-1026.

[46] Larsson, S.C., E. Giovannucci, and A. Wolk, Folate intake, MTHFR polymorphisms, and risk of esophageal, gastric, and pancreatic cancer: ameta-analysis. *Gastroenterology*, 2006. 131(4): p. 1271-1283.

[47] Abou-Saleh, M.T. and A. Coppen, Folic acid and the treatment of depression. *Journal of psychosomatic research,* 2006. 61(3): p. 285-287.

[48] Rychlik, M., et al., Application of stable isotope dilution assays based on liquid chromatography–tandem mass spectrometry for the assessment of folate bioavailability. *Journal of Chromatography B*, 2003. 792(2): p. 167-176.

[49] Verwei, M., et al., Folic acid and 5-methyltetrahydrofolate in fortified milk are bioaccessible as determined in a dynamic in vitro gastrointestinal model. *The Journal of nutrition*, 2003. 133(7): p. 2377-2383.

[50] McNulty, H. and K. Pentieva, Folate bioavailability. *Proceedings of the Nutrition Society*, 2004. 63(04): p. 529-536.

[51] Balasundram, N., K. Sundram, and S. Samman, Phenolic compounds in plants and agri-industrial by-products: Antioxidant activity, occurrence, and potential uses. *Food Chemistry*, 2006. 99(1): p. 191-203.

[52] Scalbert, A. and G. Williamson, Dietary intake and bioavailability of polyphenols. *The Journal of nutrition*, 2000. 130(8): p. 2073S-2085S.

[53] Bermúdez-Soto, M.J., F.A. Tomás-Barberán, and M.T. García-Conesa, Stability of polyphenols in chokeberry (Aronia melanocarpa/) subjected to< i> in vitro</i> gastric and pancreatic digestion. *Food Chemistry*, 2007. 102(3): p. 865-874.

[54] Laurent, C., P. Besançon, and B. Caporiccio, Flavonoids from a grape seed extract interact with digestive secretions and intestinal cells as assessed in an in vitro digestion/Caco-2 cell culture model. *Food Chemistry*, 2007. 100(4): p. 1704-1712.

[55] Manach, C., et al., Polyphenols: food sources and bioavailability. *The American journal of clinical nutrition*, 2004. 79(5): p. 727-747.

[56] Milbury, P.E., et al., Bioavailablility of elderberry anthocyanins. *Mechanisms of Ageing and Development*, 2002. 123(8): p. 997-1006.

[57] Aherne, S.A. and N.M. O'Brien, Dietary flavonols: chemistry, food content, and metabolism. *Nutrition*, 2002. 18(1): p. 75-81.

[58] Stewart, A.J., et al., Occurrence of flavonols in tomatoes and tomato-based products. *J Agric Food Chem*, 2000. 48(7): p. 2663-2669.

[59] Simonetti, P., et al., Glycosylated flavonoids from tomato puree are bioavailable in humans. *Nutrition research*, 2005. 25(8): p. 717-726.

[60] King, R.E., J.A. Bomser, and D.B. Min, Bioactivity of resveratrol. *Comprehensive Reviews in Food Science and Food Safety*, 2006. 5(3): p. 65-70.

[61] Adams, D.O., Phenolics and ripening in grape berries. *American Journal of Enology and Viticulture*, 2006. 57(3): p. 249-256.

[62] Hazak, J.C., et al. The phenolic components of grape berries in relation to wine composition. 2004.

[63] Van de Wiel, A., P. Van Golde, and H.C. Hart, Blessings of the grape. *European journal of internal medicine*, 2001. 12(6): p. 484-489.

[64] Wu, X., G. Cao, and R.L. Prior, Absorption and metabolism of anthocyanins in elderly women after consumption of elderberry or blueberry. *The Journal of nutrition*, 2002. 132(7): p. 1865-1871.

[65] Felgines, C., et al., Strawberry anthocyanins are recovered in urine as glucuro-and sulfoconjugates in humans. *The Journal of nutrition*, 2003. 133(5): p. 1296-1301.

[66] Mazza, G., et al., Absorption of anthocyanins from blueberries and serum antioxidant status in human subjects. *J Agric Food Chem*, 2002. 50(26): p. 7731-7737.

[67] McDougall, G.J., et al., Assessing potential bioavailability of raspberry anthocyanins using an in vitro digestion system. *J Agric Food Chem*, 2005. 53(15): p. 5896-5904.

[68] Beattie J., Crozier A., and D. G.G., Potential Health Benefits of Berries. *Current Nutrition and Food Science,* 2005. 1: p. 71-86.

[69] Setchell, K.D.R. and A. Cassidy, Dietary isoflavones: biological effects and relevance to human health. *The Journal of nutrition*, 1999. 129(3): p. 758S-767S.

[70] Birt, D.F., S. Hendrich, and W. Wang, Dietary agents in cancer prevention: flavonoids and isoflavonoids. *Pharmacology & therapeutics*, 2001. 90(2): p. 157-177.

[71] de Pascual-Teresa, S., et al., Absorption of isoflavones in humans: effects of food matrix and processing. *The Journal of nutritional biochemistry*, 2006. 17(4): p. 257-264.

[72] Setchell, K.D.R., et al., Evidence for lack of absorption of soy isoflavone glycosides in humans, supporting the crucial role of intestinal metabolism for bioavailability. *The American journal of clinical nutrition*, 2002. 76(2): p. 447-453.

[73] Cassidy, A., et al., Factors affecting the bioavailability of soy isoflavones in humans after ingestion of physiologically relevant levels from different soy foods. *The Journal of nutrition*, 2006. 136(1): p. 45-51.

[74] Sanz, T. and H. Luyten, Release, partitioning and stability of isoflavones from enriched custards during mouth, stomach and intestine in vitro simulations. *Food Hydrocolloids*, 2006. 20(6): p. 892-900.

[75] Hendrich, S., Bioavailability of isoflavones. *Journal of Chromatography B,* 2002. 777(1): p. 203-210.

[76] Faughnan, M.S., et al., Urinary isoflavone kinetics: the effect of age, gender, food matrix and chemical composition. *British Journal of Nutrition*, 2004. 91(04): p. 567-574.
[77] Rowland I, et al., Bioavailability of phyto-oestrogens. *The British Journal of Nutrition*, 2003. 89: p. S45-S58.
[78] Björck, I., et al., Food properties affecting the digestion and absorption of carbohydrates. *The American journal of clinical nutrition*, 1994. 59(3): p. 699S-705S.
[79] Frost, G. and A. Dornhorst, The relevance of the glycaemic index to our understanding of dietary carbohydrates. *Diabetic medicine*, 2001. 17(5): p. 336-345.
[80] Copeland, L., et al., Form and functionality of starch. *Food Hydrocolloids,* 2009. 23(6): p. 1527-1534.
[81] Berti, C., et al., In vitro starch digestibility and in vivo glucose response of gluten–free foods and their gluten counterparts. *European journal of nutrition*, 2004. 43(4): p. 198-204.
[82] FAO/WHO, Carbohydrates in Human Nutrition. Report of a Joint FAO/WHO Expert Consultation. Rome, Italy: Food and Agriculture Organization of the United Nations. *FAO Food and Nutrition*, Paper, 1998. 66.
[83] Brand-Miller, J.C., Glycemic load and chronic disease. Nutrition reviews, 2003. 61: p. S49-S55.
[84] Wolever, T., Carbohydrate and the regulation of blood glucose and metabolism. *Nutrition reviews*, 2003. 61: p. S40-S48.
[85] Granfeldt, Y., X. Wu, and I. Björck, Determination of glycaemic index; some methodological aspects related to the analysis of carbohydrate load and characteristics of the previous evening meal. *European journal of clinical nutrition,* 2005. 60(1): p. 104-112.
[86] Lehmann, U. and F. Robin, Slowly digestible starch–its structure and health implications: a review. *Trends in Food Science & Technology*, 2007. 18(7): p. 346-355.
[87] Chung, H.J., H.S. Lim, and S.T. Lim, Effect of partial gelatinization and retrogradation on the enzymatic digestion of waxy rice starch. *Journal of Cereal Science*, 2006. 43(3): p. 353-359.
[88] Goñi, I., L. Valdivieso, and A. Garcia-Alonso, Nori seaweed consumption modifies glycemic response in healthy volunteers. *Nutrition research*, 2000. 20(10): p. 1367-1375.
[89] Osorio-Díaz, P., et al., Effect of processing and storage time on in vitro digestibility and resistant starch content of two bean (Phaseolus vulgaris L) varieties. *Journal of the Science of Food and Agriculture*, 2003. 83(12): p. 1283-1288.
[90] Tester, R., J. Karkalas, and X. Qi, Starch structure and digestibility enzyme-substrate relationship. *World's Poultry Science Journal*, 2004. 60(2): p. 186-195.
[91] Zhou, Y., R. Hoover, and Q. Liu, Relationship between α-amylase degradation and the structure and physicochemical properties of legume starches. *Carbohydrate Polymers*, 2004. 57(3): p. 299-317.
[92] Han, X.Z., et al., Development of a low glycemic maize starch: preparation and characterization. *Biomacromolecules*, 2006. 7(4): p. 1162-1168.
[93] Rosin, P.M., F.M. Lajolo, and E.W. Menezes, Measurement and characterization of dietary starches. *Journal of Food Composition and Analysis*, 2002. 15(4): p. 367-377.

[94] Karlsson, M.E. and A.-C. Eliasson, Gelatinization and retrogradation of potato (Solanum tuberosum) starch in situ as assessed by differential scanning calorimetry (DSC). *LWT - Food Science and Technology*, 2003. 36(8): p. 735-741.
[95] Fernandes, G., A. Velangi, and T. Wolever, Glycemic index of potatoes commonly consumed in North America. *Journal of the American Dietetic Association,* 2005. 105(4): p. 557-562.
[96] Leeman, A.M., L.M. Bårström, and I.M.E. Björck, In vitro availability of starch in heat-treated potatoes as related to genotype, weight and storage time. *Journal of the Science of Food and Agriculture*, 2005. 85(5): p. 751-756.
[97] Morita, T., et al., In vitro and in vivo digestibility of recrystallized amylose and its application for low glycemic foods. *J Food Sci*, 2005. 70(3): p. S179-S185.
[98] Burton, P. and H. Lightowler, The impact of freezing and toasting on the glycaemic response of white bread. *European journal of clinical nutrition*, 2007. 62(5): p. 594-599.
[99] Lai, L. and J. Kokini, Physicochemical changes and rheological properties of starch during extrusion (a review). *Biotechnology Progress*, 2008. 7(3): p. 251-266.
[100] Parada, J. and J.M. Aguilera, Microstructure, mechanical properties, and starch digestibility of a cooked dough made with potato starch and wheat gluten. *LWT-Food Science and Technology*, 2011. 44(8): p. 1739-1744.
[101] Gouin, S., Microencapsulation: industrial appraisal of existing technologies and trends. *Trends in Food Science & Technology*, 2004. 15(7): p. 330-347.
[102] Chen, L., G.E. Remondetto, and M. Subirade, Food protein-based materials as nutraceutical delivery systems. *Trends in Food Science & Technology*, 2006b. 17(5): p. 272-283.
[103] Yoo, S.-H., et al., Microencapsulation of α-tocopherol using sodium alginate and its controlled release properties. *Int J Biol Macromol*, 2006. 38(1): p. 25-30.
[104] Shu, B., et al., Study on microencapsulation of lycopene by spray-drying. *Journal of Food Engineering*, 2006. 76(4): p. 664-669.
[105] Boland, A.B., et al., Influence of gelatin, starch, pectin and artificial saliva on the release of 11 flavour compounds from model gel systems. *Food Chemistry*, 2004. 86(3): p. 401-411.
[106] Remondetto, G.E., E. Beyssac, and M. Subirade, Iron availability from whey protein hydrogels: an in vitro study. *J Agric Food Chem*, 2004. 52(26): p. 8137-8143.
[107] Guarner, F. and G. Schaafsma, Probiotics. *Int J Food Microbiol*, 1998. 39(3): p. 237.
[108] Krasaekoopt, W., B. Bhandari, and H. Deeth, Evaluation of encapsulation techniques of probiotics for yoghurt. *International Dairy Journal*, 2003. 13(1): p. 3-13.
[109] Chen, K.N., M.J. Chen, and C.W. Lin, Optimal combination of the encapsulating materials for probiotic microcapsules and its experimental verification (R1). *Journal of Food Engineering*, 2006a. 76(3): p. 313-320.
[110] Doleyres, Y. and C. Lacroix, Technologies with free and immobilised cells for probiotic bifidobacteria production and protection. *International Dairy Journal*, 2005. 15(10): p. 973-988.
[111] Leverrier, P., et al., In vitro tolerance to digestive stresses of propionibacteria: influence of food matrices. *Food Microbiol*, 2005. 22(1): p. 11-18.

[112] Capela, P., T. Hay, and N. Shah, Effect of cryoprotectants, prebiotics and microencapsulation on survival of probiotic organisms in yoghurt and freeze-dried yoghurt. *Food Research International*, 2006. 39(2): p. 203-211.

[113] Krasaekoopt, W., B. Bhandari, and H.C. Deeth, Survival of probiotics encapsulated in chitosan-coated alginate beads in yoghurt from UHT-and conventionally treated milk during storage. *LWT-Food Science and Technology*, 2006. 39(2): p. 177-183.

[114] Picot, A. and C. Lacroix, Encapsulation of bifidobacteria in whey protein-based microcapsules and survival in simulated gastrointestinal conditions and in yoghurt. *International Dairy Journal*, 2004. 14(6): p. 505-515.

[115] Fito, P., et al., Vacuum impregnation and osmotic dehydration in matrix engineering: Application in functional fresh food development. *Journal of Food Engineering,* 2001. 49(2): p. 175-183.

[116] Alzamora, S.M., et al., Novel functional foods from vegetable matrices impregnated with biologically active compounds. *Journal of Food Engineering*, 2005. 67(1): p. 205-214.

[117] Anino, S.V., D.M. Salvatori, and S.M. Alzamora, Changes in calcium level and mechanical properties of apple tissue due to impregnation with calcium salts. *Food Research International*, 2006. 39(2): p. 154-164.

[118] IFST. 2005 January 31, 2012]; Available from: http://www.ifst.org/science_technology_resources/for_food_professionals/information_statements/19505/Food_Allergy.

[119] van Wijk, F., et al., The Effect of the Food Matrix on In Vivo Immune Responses to Purified Peanut Allergens. *Toxicological Sciences*, 2005. 86(2): p. 333-341.

[120] Maleki, S.J., Food processing: effects on allergenicity. *Current opinion in allergy and clinical immunology,* 2004. 4(3): p. 241-245.

[121] Mills, E., et al., The effects of food processing on allergens. *Managing allergens in food*, 2007: p. 117-133.

[122] Franck, P., et al., The allergenicity of soybean-based products is modified by food technologies. *International archives of allergy and immunology*, 2002. 128(3): p. 212-219.

[123] Teuber, S.S., Hypothesis: the protein body effect and other aspects of food matrix effects. *Annals of the New York Academy of Sciences*, 2002. 964(1): p. 111-116.

In: Chemical Food Safety and Health
Editors: F. Pedreschi Plasencia and Z. Ciesarová

ISBN: 978-1-62948-339-9

Chapter 8

SHELF-LIFE CALCULATION AND TEMPERATURE-TIME INDICATORS: IMPORTANCE IN FOOD SAFETY

R. N. Zúñiga[1] and E. Troncoso[2]

[1] Department of Biotechnology, Universidad Tecnológica Metropolitana, Santiago Metropolitan Region, Chile

[2] Department of Chemistry, Universidad Tecnológica Metropolitana, Santiago Metropolitan Region, Chile

ABSTRACT

Foods are metastable systems from a thermodynamic point of view. Hence, the deteriorative processes that occur in foods after harvesting and during storage and distribution are unavoidable. Foods suffer a series of microbiological, biochemical and physical changes that are remarkably time and temperature dependent. These changes could impair the quality of food and even they can affect the safety of the final product. Assuming that throughout storage the temperature is maintained constant, a point in time will be reached when the product quality degrades to a level taken as a cutoff limit. That point in time corresponds to the product shelf-life. Consumers are better educated about healthy foods and are more careful in selecting products with unexpired dates of freshness. However, food risks associated with eating cannot be eliminated completely. Currently, food risk can only be reduced to a reasonable certainty that the consumption of a particular food will not be harmful to the great majority of individuals eating it. Due to temperature fluctuations in the distribution chain the quality and safety loss experienced by a food product may be larger than expected. Accordingly, if technological strategies are to be devised to retard such deterioration and to minimize the consequent loss of quality, it is crucial to understand the nature of constituent instabilities and the factors that control microbial growth. In this regard, the type of information than can be provided by time-temperature indicators can be linked to shelf-life of foods ensuring a safe purchase of foods by consumers. The new paradigm is to establish a consumer-oriented shelf-life dating system, reflecting the quality loss dynamics.

1. INTRODUCTION

Currently consumers are demanding safe, natural, healthy and convenient food products. The current informed consumer demands foods with high standards of nutritional, sensory, and health benefits at low cost. Also, foods are viewed as a source of pleasure and well-being [1, 2]. These demands have accelerated the development of minimally processed fruits and vegetables (MPFV), which are economically important commodities due to a combination of factors, such as "fresh-like" characteristics, convenience, healthiness and desirable sensory properties, that require only a minimum effort and time for their preparation [3-5]. The primary requirement for a food is that it should remain safe until consumption. However from the consumer point of view, foods must fulfill our expectations of quality at the moment of purchasing. Thus, one of the biggest challenges for food producers is to minimize unwanted changes in sensory quality and safety during storage. Foods are biological perishable materials where the deteriorative processes during storage and distribution are unavoidable [6, 7]. Due to perishability, the economic impact of managing food products becomes a serious challenge for food processors; about $30 billion dollars are lost due to perishable products in US grocery industry [8]. According to Labuza [9], the shelf-life paradigm is to bring food products from production to consumer at the highest quality level and ensure they are safe. On this regard, shelf-life is defined as the time during which the product will: (i) remain safe; (ii) be certain to retain desired microbiological, sensory, chemical, and physical characteristics; and (iii) comply with any label declaration of nutritional data [6]. However, although shelf-life is defined in units of time, "*shelf life is not a function of time; rather it is a function of the environmental conditions and the amount of quality change that can be allowed*" [9].

The definition of shelf-life leaves interpretation of the term "desired ...characteristics" highly ambiguous. Many others definitions of shelf-life can be found in literature [7, 10-12], but the concept of consumer's perception about food quality is always present. Food quality involves a sum of attributes or characteristics of a product that determine consumer's satisfaction and compliance to legal standards [13, 14]. Safety is an important and essential component of quality, being the first requisite of any food. Although sensorial acceptation by consumers is one of the most important parameters in defining the quality of foods, from the safety point of view, sensory techniques cannot be used as the sole source of food quality monitoring. Foods should be tested with analytical techniques in order to objectively ensure the microbiological and toxicological food safety [15]. In addition, spoilage-causing microorganism produce detrimental changes that could not detected by human senses; hence the absence of deleterious sensory changes cannot be relied upon as an indicator of microbial safety [16].

Another issue with the definition of shelf-life is the assumption of "constant" storage conditions, which it is supposed to be valid during the entire food distribution chain and also during consumer handling, assumption highly improbably. In general, the current chain distribution systems deviate from recommended temperature conditions and cannot adequately meet the requirements for the safety and quality maintenance of extended shelf-life refrigerated products [17-19]. This becomes a great problem because the common factor of MPFV is necessity of maintaining the temperature of the chill distribution chain to ensure the quality of this kind of MP foods [4]. In a recent survey, it was shown that one-third of the foods produced for human consumption is lost or wasted globally, which it amounts to about 1.3 billion tons per year. In medium- and high-income countries more than 40% of the food losses occurring at retail and consumer levels. At home level, insufficient purchase planning and expiring "best-before-dates" also cause large amounts of waste [20]. In addition, there almost no data on food storage at refrigerator conditions (*i.e.* most refrigerators and freezers have no thermometers) and home "warehouses" are non-controlled areas [9], making difficult the task of ensuring the food quality and safety at consumer level.

All foods are susceptible to quality and safety losses. Within the past decade, food safety has been an increasing concern for consumers, retailers, and all production and processing areas of the food industry. Food safety is also of crucial importance to a nation economy and health systems [21]. However, absolute safety is just not possible. The probability of not suffering some hazard from consuming a specific food is never zero. Potential undesirable residues in foods span a broad range, from natural (*e.g.* mycotoxins) and environmental contaminants (*e.g.* dioxins) to agro-chemicals (*e.g.* nitrates and pesticides), veterinary drugs, growth promoters, packaging components, and many others. Microbiological considerations are an even greater challenge to safety of foods because potentially harmful microorganisms have the ability either to grow rapidly from very low numbers in food or to proliferate in the human body once ingested. Although incidences of bacterial contamination of food are occasional cases, their consequences are vast, resulting in illnesses, deaths, and loss of public confidence in the food industry [22].

This chapter initially reviews the main mechanisms of food degradation affecting the shelf-life of foods with emphasis on microbial growth and safety issues, then the kinetics of quality change and the effect of temperature over microbial growth are discussed and some mathematical equations are presented, after that the use of temperature-time indicators (TTIs) technologies to help the consumer in their search for food safety and quality are reviewed and, finally an integrated concept of shelf-life of foods is discussed.

2. Quality Degradation in Foods Focused on the Effect of Microbial Growth on Food Safety

Food products being composed of biological raw materials inherently deteriorate over time. Degradation of foods is a complex process which may involve many mechanisms. The main categories of food deterioration that can occur are physical (*e.g.*, bruising of fresh fruits and vegetables, and chill injury), chemical (*e.g.*, development of off-flavor, discoloration, and vitamin degradation), biochemical (*e.g.*, enzymatic protein breakdown by proteases and enzymatic browning by polyphenol oxidase) and microbiological (*e.g.*, growth of microorganisms and production of metabolites or toxins) [4, 23, 24]. Multiple factors influence deterioration rates, and hence, the shelf-life of foods. These factors can be classified into intrinsic factors, including water activity (a_W), pH, use of preservatives, available oxygen, and natural microflora; or extrinsic factors, including temperature and relative humidity control during storage, composition of atmosphere in the packaging, consumer handling, etc. In conjunction, all these factors can operate in an interactive and often unpredictable way, therefore shelf-life prediction is a difficult problem for processors and researchers [6, 10, 23]. From the safety point of view, the risk produced by growth of pathogenic microorganisms and formation of toxic substances during storage of MP foods is much important than the physical or chemical spoilage. For this reason the discussion in this point is focused on the growth of microorganisms and loss of food safety.

Foodborne disease outbreaks are one of the main health problems all over the world. Outbreaks have an extensive impact on human health (*i.e.*, causing morbidity and mortality) and also are a significant burden on nation economies and public health [25]. Moreover, the increasing trend in infectious diseases produced by emerging pathogens has caused significant impact on global health in the last decades [26]. The Center for Disease Control and Prevention estimated that each year roughly 48 million people gets sick in USA, 128,000 are hospitalized and 3,000 die due to foodborne diseases. The main pathogens causing diseases and/or death were *Salmonella* spp, *Listeria monocytogenes*, *Campylobacter spp*., and *E. coli* O157:H7 [27]. In this context, a recent survey performed in urban Chilean areas between 2005 and 2010 showed that a total of 12,196 people were affected by foodborne diseases with an incidence rate of 32 cases per 100 inhabitants. The main etiologic agents found were *Salmonella* spp, *Shigella* spp and *Vibrio parahaemolyticus* [28]. The researchers concluded that the largest numbers of outbreaks happened in the households, which were due to bad handling and/or inappropriate storage of the foods, confirming that home storage is a critical point for consumer safety.

Growth of microorganisms during storage can strongly affect the food safety. On this regard, manufacturers must have the means to predict the end-point of shelf-life under a given set of storage conditions. Criteria based on the microbial limits of spoilage and pathogenic microorganisms for rejection of a food can be reasonably well set [6, 12]. Even though consumers find a product still acceptable it may be not acceptable anymore because of the presence of pathogens or toxins, unnoticeable to consumers [12]. The growth of food-poisoning organisms such as *Salmonella* species and *Listeria monocytogenes* will not necessarily be accompanied by changes in appearance, odor, flavor or texture that could be detected by the human senses, and consequently pose serious health concerns [6]. Foods may be considered to be microbiologically unsafe owing to the presence of microorganisms that may invade the body (*e.g.*, *Salmonella*, *Listeria monocytogenes*, *E. coli* O157:H7 and *Campylobacter*) or those that produce a toxin ingested with a food (*e.g.*, *Clostridium botulinum*, *Staphylococcus aureus* and *Bacillus cereus*) [16]. Growth of a specific microorganism during storage depends on several factors, the most important being:

1) the initial microbial loading at the start of storage;
2) the physicochemical properties of the food;
3) the processing methods used in the food production line; and
4) the external environment of the food, such as the surrounding gas composition and storage temperature [6].

Rates of deteriorative changes and microbial growth at normal food storage conditions often depend on a_W. Food deterioration due to microbial growth is not likely to occur at $a_W <$ 0.6 [29], but to maintain the characteristics of fresh-like products, MPFV kept a similar a_W of the fresh tissue.

Microbiological changes are of primary importance for short-life products. Roughly speaking, food products can be classified as either fresh or processed, recognizing that there are levels within and between these classifications. MPFV fall between these two classifications [30]. In general, microbial deterioration becomes the dominant process affecting safety and quality of fresh and MPFV, their shelf-life will be determined mainly by microbial and biochemical changes, whereas biochemical and physical deterioration become the dominant mechanisms in determining shelf-life of processed foods [12]. MPFV can also be contaminated with human pathogens, present from before, during or after harvest [5]. Safety of MPFV relies on a combination of preserving factors which, rather than inactivating microorganisms, inhibit their growth [14]. MP and ready-to-eat products are one of the major growing segments in food retail establishments. There has been an increased demand for ready-to-eat and MPFV mainly because of the health benefits associated with their consumption, but the risk associated with consumption of these products has also increased. In addition, MPFV are still under study because of the difficulties in preserving their fresh-like quality during prolonged periods [31, 32].

Growth of microorganisms sets the limit on storage of fresh or MPFV. However, if biochemical processes (*e.g.*, enzymatic browning and rancidity development) occurring on a time scale shorter than microbial growth can determine the cut-off [30]. Processing operations used for preparing MPFV or ready-to-eat products (*e.g.*, peeling, cutting or shredding) create practical problems regarding shelf-life, safety and packaging. Physicochemical properties and cut surfaces condition the microbiological invasion of MPFV, causing both microbiological and physiological mechanisms to be possible limitations for the shelf-life [5, 31, 32]. After minimal processing, a relatively stable agricultural product with a shelf-life of several weeks or months will become one that has only a very short shelf-life, generally no more than 7 to 10 days, but it should be preferably longer, up to 21 days, depending on the market [4, 24]. In general, total counts of microbiological populations in MPFV after processing range from 3 to 6 log CFU/g. When changes in sensory quality factors of MPFV result in rejection of the product, microbiological counts are in most cases high (> 7–8 log CFU/g) [5]. For this kind of products the goal is maximizing taste and fresh-like characteristics while minimizing the risk from foodborne pathogens.

3. Kinetics of Quality Loss and Microbial Growth

No universal mathematical theory exists that can be used to model all quality changes in foods. Because food is a system of high complexity, involving numerous physical and chemical variables, it is impossible or impractical to quantitatively determine all these variables. One objective for food scientists is to identify a marker for food degradation (*i.e.*, a chemical compound or a physical measurement) which is easily detectable in the food, increases in quantity as deteriorations progress and is invariably a sign of deterioration [33].

A chemical kinetics approach has been widely used in food research to quantify quality loss as function of time. Here is assumed that the loss of quality factor follow the same pattern as a chemical reaction of n-th order. Thus, regardless of the order of the reaction, the quality loss of foods can be expressed as follows (Eq. 1):

$$f(\mathrm{A}) = \mathrm{kt} \tag{1}$$

where $f(A)$ is the quality function, k is the apparent reaction rate constant and t is time. The sign of the quality function can be positive or negative depending on the evolution of the quality loss process to be evaluated.

It is advisable to include in the kinetic model the effect of the environmental factors, being temperature the factor most often considered and studied. This is justifiable because temperature not only strongly affects post-processing reaction rates but is also imposed directly from the environment (storage conditions), the other factors being at least to some extent controlled by the food packaging [19, 34]. The Arrhenius model (Eq. 2), developed theoretically for chemical reactions, has been experimentally shown to hold empirically for a number of complex food quality loss reactions [19, 34, 35].

$$k=k_0 \exp\left(\frac{-E_A}{RT}\right) \tag{2}$$

where k_0 is the Arrhenius's equation constant, E_A is the activation energy of the quality loss reaction, R is the universal gas constant, and T is the absolute temperature. In Eq. 2 k_0 is the value of the reaction rate at 0K, which is of no practical interest. Alternatively, the use of a reference temperature (T_{ref}) is recommended, corresponding to a representative value in the temperature range of storage (Eq. 3):

$$k=k_{ref} \exp\left[\frac{-E_A}{R}\left(\frac{1}{T}-\frac{1}{T_{ref}}\right)\right] \tag{3}$$

where k_{ref} is the apparent reaction rate constant at T_{ref}.

The reference temperature used is characteristic of the storage temperature range of the food, for instance T_{ref} = 273K for chilled foods and 295K for ambient-temperature stored foods [19, 34]. In this way, the shelf-life of food products (t_{SL}) can be evaluated knowing the lowest (or highest) level accepted for the quality factor A (A_{SL}) using Eq. 4.

$$f(A) = kt = k_{ref} \exp\left[\frac{-E_A}{R}\left(\frac{1}{T}-\frac{1}{T_{ref}}\right)\right]t \tag{4}$$

Although this methodology is widely accepted and employed in food science, different phenomena could induce deviation from linearity in Eq. 2, hence leading to erroneous calculation of shelf-life [29]. Food quality modeling is typically conducted at constant temperature conditions, but it can be extended to variable temperature conditions in order to simulate the real conditions found in the distribution chain (Eq. 5).

$$f(A)_t = k_{ref} \int_0^t \exp\left[\frac{-E_A}{R}\left(\frac{1}{T(t)}-\frac{1}{T_{ref}}\right)\right]dt \tag{5}$$

where T(t) represents a function of the variation of temperature with time.

Here, the concept of effective temperature (T_{eff}) is introduced as the constant temperature that results in the same quality change as a defined variable temperature distribution, T(t), and Eq. 4 becomes [17, 34]-Eq. 6-.

$$f(A) = kt = k_{ref} \exp\left[\frac{-E_A}{R}\left(\frac{1}{T_{eff}} - \frac{1}{T_{ref}}\right)\right]t \tag{6}$$

The process of microbial growth is more complex than the spoilage due to chemical or biochemical reactions. Many isothermal microbial growth curves have a sigmoid shape (*i.e.*, typical growth curves exhibiting lag, logarithmic, and stationary phases) whose mathematical modeling requires in many cases at least three constants (Table 1). Growth models can be used to design safe product formulations and to set appropriate storage conditions [36]. Increasing the temperature generally accelerates the rate of chemical reactions and microbial growth that may result in food deterioration, although there is an upper limit up to which the rate decreases again [6, 12]. Temperature is a major factor determining the rate at which pathogenic bacteria will grow in a food. Temperature potentiates the effect of other factors and, in many situations, is the factor most likely to fluctuate [37]. The Arrhenius's model has also used to describe the effect of temperature on microbial growth (Eq. 7); however this type of equation is purely empirical for biological systems,

$$\mu_{max} = \mu_{ref} \exp\left[\frac{-E_A}{R}\left(\frac{1}{T} - \frac{1}{T_{ref}}\right)\right] \tag{7}$$

where μ_{max} is the specific growth rate, and μ_{ref} is the growth rate at T_{ref}.

Accelerated storage tests have been a widely used method to assess the shelf-life of foods. The main objective of these tests is to reduce the time needed to calculate the shelf-life of long-life foods by raising the storage temperature [38]. Accelerated storage can also be helpful in predicting the shelf-life of perishable commodities, such as refrigerated MPFV. When an Arrhenius-type model is used for accelerated shelf-life testing it is assumed that the deterioration process has a valid kinetic model, which does not change at higher temperature, k values are independent of the thermal history of the food and exists a single value of E_A [12, 38]. A clear explanation about scientific basis and methodologies to perform accelerated storage tests can be found in the book chapter of Mizrahi [38]. By another side, the Peleg's group has proposed a methodology in which no kinetics is assumed and the thermal history is considered to affecting food deterioration [39, 40]. The authors stated that the assumptions involved in accelerated shelf-life tests may not hold for some spoilage processes, like microbial growth. It is known that the microorganisms themselves can change the conditions in the food (*e.g.*, by increasing the pH) due to their metabolic activities [33], hence invalidating the assumptions employed in the chemical kinetic model used. Besides, it is highly improbable that complex biochemical processes having several pathways (like microbial growth) must be coordinate to produce a single E_A [40].

Table 1. Commonly used primary models to describe microbial growth curves

Model	Parameters (cell concentration is expressed as CFU/g)
Baranyi $y(t)=y_0+\mu_{max}A_n(t)+\ln\left\{1+\frac{\exp[\mu_{max}A_n(t)-1]}{\exp(y_{max}-y_0)}\right\}$	$y(t)$ = ln of cell concentration at time t, y_0 = ln of the initial cell concentration, y_{max} = ln of the maximum cell concentration, μ_{max} = specific growth rate, A_n = adjustment function for lag phase
Modified Gompertz $y(t)=y_0+(y_{max}-y_0)\exp\{-\exp[-B(t-M)]\}$ Modified logistic $y(t)=y_0+\frac{(y_{max}-y_0)}{1+\exp(-B(t-M))}$	$y(t)$ = $\log_{10}$ of cell concentration at time t, y_0 = initial cell concentration, y_{max} = the upper asymptotic $\log_{10}$ cell concentration as t increases indefinitely, B = relative maximum growth rate, M = time at which maximum growth rate occurs Specific growth rates (μ_{max}) are: $\mu_{max}=\frac{y_{max}-y_{min}}{\exp(1)}\times B$ and $\mu_{max}=\frac{y_{max}-y_{min}}{4}\times B$ for Gompertz and Logistic model, respectively

A major issue with MPFV is that they are not sterile and so reduced temperatures are required to achieve reasonable commercial shelf-life from the microbiological safety perspective. In the interest of predicting bacterial growth in MP foods, growth studies gain more and more significance. Within the frame of risks, hazards, and consumer trends, predictive microbiology (PM) emerges as a powerful tool to quickly explore the microbiological impact of varying conditions within food formulation, processing, and/or distribution and retail conditions [14]. PM utilizes mathematical models (built with data from laboratory testing) and computer software to graphically describe microbial behavior (*i.e.*, growth, death, and toxin production) in a food product [41]. PM is a description of the microorganisms's responses to a particular environmental condition (*e.g.*, temperature, a_W, and pH) and it is based upon the premise that these responses are reproducible, and that it is possible taking into account past observations, to predict the specific responses under particular environments [21, 41]. In PM, temperature, pH, and a_W are considered as the critical environmental variables determining bacterial growth in food; factors as food structure, composition of the atmosphere, or possible preservatives, are considered only modifying the basic models but not changing their main structure [42]. In their book chapter, Legan and co-workers [36] lucidly explain the scientific and experimental basis for the development of microbial growth models. These models are quick and economical ways to assess food safety objectively. Therefore, PM has been accepted by industry and regulatory authorities as an alternative, perhaps preferable, approach to predict the shelf-life and safety of foods [37].

Scientific literature on PM is expanding rapidly, with models varying greatly in theory and complexity. They evolve from simple probabilistic models to linear and logistic regression based on models and sigmoidal functions for fitting microbial growth [14, 33]. Empirical models are only expected to describe accurately a set of observations, without taking into account the intrinsic mechanism by which these data are generated. A mechanistic model describes rather the process, either directly observable or unobservable, that generates those data. In PM, most models used to date are empirical in nature. Microbial system biology is also gaining interest and it is being incorporated into PM. In this regard, ''black boxes'' are being exchanged for "grey" or even "white box" models, in which modeling is more and more a mechanistic basis (with thermophysical or biological assumptions) and thus the description of well-characterized microbial responses to environmental factors also has a physiological meaning [21, 37, 42].

PM presents advantages during development of food products. From the safety point of view, it is critical to be able to calculate how fast microorganisms will grow in foods. In former years this has been achieved by costly and time-consuming shelf-life testing and challenge testing with the organism of interest [33]. Use of a PM incorporated in user-friendly software, which it permits the operator to make changes to the environmental factors controlling microbial growth, allows the prediction of the shelf-life. Currently software or database packages are available in the web, such as the USDA Pathogen Modeling Program (http://portal.arserrc.gov/PMP.aspx), ComBase (http://www.combase.cc/index.php/en/), among others. In this regard, it is important to consider what we want to predict, the growth rate of pathogens, the absence of toxin, the lag-time to microorganism detection [12]. Having that knowledge is the basis for the prediction of shelf-life in relation to microbial activity.

4. Time- Temperature Indicators as a Dynamic and Simple Method to Evaluate Shelf-Life

TTIs are small measuring devices or tags attached to the food package that show in an easy, accurate and precise way a measurable irreversible change, which is time-temperature dependent, and gives an indication on the quality storage conditions of a food. The irreversible change mimics the change produced in a relevant characteristic, or target attribute, related to food undergoing the same variable temperature exposure [21, 34]. TTIs can be classified in mechanical, chemical, electrochemical, enzymatic or microbiological systems, according to the working principle. The irreversibly change, from the time of their activation, is usually expressed as a visible response in the form of a mechanical deformation, color development or color movement. The visible response reflects the full or partial temperature history that the TTI has been exposed too. The rate of change increases at higher temperatures in a manner similar to the most physicochemical reactions [17, 21, 34, 43]. In this regard, a prerequisite for application of TTI is the systematic kinetic modeling of the temperature dependence of shelf-life products and the same equations applied for the quality loss of the food are used for the response of the TTI [17, 34]. Equation 3 is used to relate the effect of temperature on the TTI response and the E_A of the response is obtained. Then, by using Eq. 6 the value of T_{eff} for the TTI is calculated. If the TTI and the food product quality deterioration reactions have similar temperature dependence, translated into activation energies differing by less than 25 kJ/mol, the same T_{eff} can be used for the food [34]. In designing an indicator, it may be important that the activation energy of the device is similar to that of the food deteriorations as well as rate of deterioration [18].

The relevant characteristic of the food to be monitored can be any safety or quality attribute of interest, such as microbial load, loss of a specific vitamin, texture, or color [21, 43]. Of major interest are important hidden quality attributes like microbiologic safety. TTIs can be used to monitor the temperature exposure along time to which a perishable product is subjected (*e.g.*, during distribution of a chilled food), from the point of manufacture to the display shelf at the supermarket and as end point indicators readable by the consumer [17, 21, 34]. Principal advantages and disadvantages in the use of TTIs are listed in Table 2.

Table 2. Main advantages and disadvantages of TTIs

Advantages
• Ability to quantify the integrated time-temperature impact on a target attribute of individual products without the need for information on the actual temperature history of the product. • Facilitate scheduling of distribution, thus products approaching the end of their shelf-life are moved first at the warehouse and retail level. • Capacity to indicate problem areas in the distribution system so that they could be resolved and it could reduce food waste and ensure that a consistent quality food product reaches the consumer. • Practical advantage in use over certain other types of monitoring equipment of giving a simple and individual indication of temperature abuse, which makes them an attractive addition to assuring safety and quality to the consumer.
Disadvantages
• Using only a TTI to monitor food safety loss would result in error if temperature is not the only rate determining factor, as other factors that change with time can be critical. • A single enzymatic reaction could not be representative of the quality spectrum and temperature profile across the package. • Application to the outside of a food pack means that surface temperatures are being used to change the indicators. • Difference in temperature sensitivity between TTI response and spoilage reaction can result in an accumulative error of the response to the real quality loss.

Several patents have been developed on processes which could be used as a basis for TTIs (Figure 1). These include changes with temperature based on melting-point temperature, enzyme reaction, polymerization, electrochemical corrosion, and liquid crystals. Here, we updated the list of TTI patents tabulated by Taoukis [34], listing relevant TTI patents from the year 2000 to the present (Table 3). However, only few types of TTIs are current commercial products for food applications, for instance we can mention: Fresh-Check® from TEMPTIME, based on polymerization reaction (www.freshcheck.com); (eO)™ from

CRYOLOG, based on bacterial lactic acid production (www.cryolog.com); and CheckPoint® I and III from Vitsab, based on enzymatic and diffuse reaction leading to pH change (www.vitsab.com).

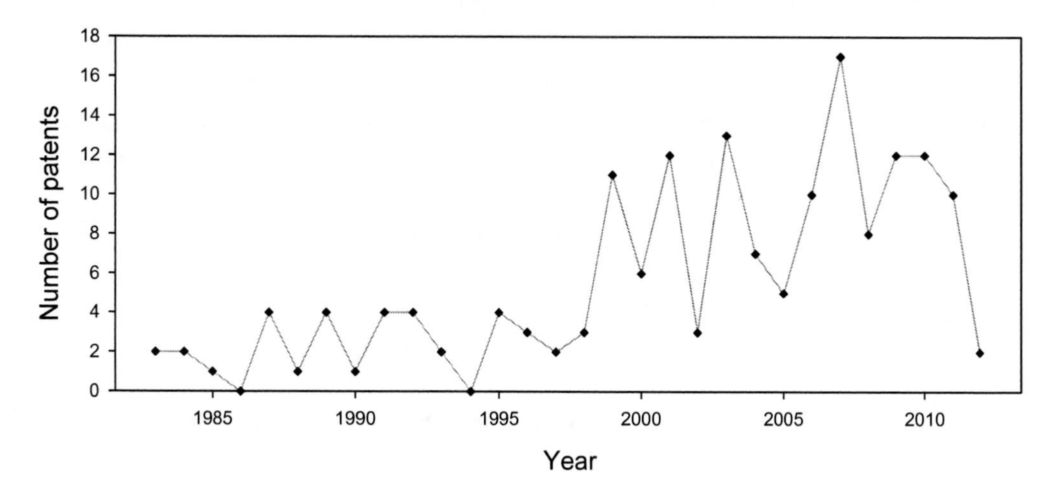

Figure 1. Time evolution of patents related with TTIs. The search was done using the Matheo Patent™ software version 9.61 (Matheo Software, Marseille, France) in the database of patents solicited in USA and Europe, using the following search: "temperature" and "indicator" or "integrator". Most of the patents found belong to the following International Patent Classification: G01K3/04 Detection of temperature changes to compensate the measurement of other variables or compensation of lectures over instruments, taking into account temperature variations.

Table 3. Selected list of TTI patents published during the last ten years. The search was done using the Matheo Patent™ software version 9.61 (Matheo Software, Marseille, France) in the database of patents solicited in USA and Europe, using the following search: "temperature" and "indicator" or "integrator"

Date	Inventor	Patent name	Patent number
2003	Tester, R; Al-Ghazzewi, F	Time temperature indicators linked to sensory detection	WO03006941A1
2003	Spevacek, JA	Time-temperature integrating indicator	WO03025530A1
2004	Zweig, SE	Electronic time-temperature indicator and logger	WO2004097357A2
2005	Levy, Y; Haarer, D	Time-temperature indicator based on valence isomerizations	WO2005075978A2
2005	Varlet-Grancher, X	Time temperature indicator (TTI) system	WO2005078402A1
2006	Reichert, H; Simmendinger, P; Bolle T	Enzyme-based time temperature indicator	WO2006015961A2

Table 3. (Continued)

Date	Inventor	Patent name	Patent number
2006	Azizian, F; Leonard, MW; Herlihy, SL	Novel time/temperature indicators	WO2006091466A1
2006	Azizian, F; Leonard, MW; Herlihy, SL	Time/temperature indicators, their preparation and use	WO2006091465A1
2006	Azizian, F; Leonard, MW; Herlihy, SL	Improved time/temperature indicators	WO2006091464A1
2007	Craig, V; Senden, TJ; Kugge, C	Time-temperature indicators	WO2007012132A1
2007	Barmore, C	Carbon monoxide modified atmosphere packaging having a time temperature indicator	US2007059402A1
2007	Azizian, F; Leonard, MW	Improved time/temperature indicators	WO2007035365A1
2007	Weder, C; Kinami, M; Crenshaw, B	Time-temperature indicators	US2007158624A1
2007	Patel, G	Time-temperature, UV exposure and temperature indicator	WO2007117273A2
2007	Ren, FC	Enzyme type time-temperature indication card production method	CN101055255A
2008	Feuerstack, M; Jannasch, U	Time temperature indicator for identifying goods	EP1882919A2
2008	Haarer, D; Gueta-Neyroud, T; Salman, H	Time temperature indicator	WO2008083926A1
2009	Haarer, D; Gueta-Neyroud, T; Salman, H	Time temperature indicator	WO2009156285A1
2009	Xinglian X, Guanchong Z; Nan, Z; Peng N	Enzyme type time-temperature indication card	CN201255668Y
2010	Reichert, H; Huegin, M; Dueggeli, M; Feiler, L	Time temperature indicator comprising indolenin based spiropyrans	WO2010079114A1
2010	Salman, H; Tenetov, H	Time-temperature indicator based on thioalkyl and thioaryl substituted spiroaromatics	WO2010092030A1
2010	Ying, C; Lixin, L; Zhiye, L	Time-temperature indicator based on lipase reaction	CN201512536U
2010	Zhilu, A; Jianxin, L; Meijuan, L; Zhili, P; Xiaorui, S; Na, W; Xinhua, X	Diffusible time-temperature indicator, indicator card and preparation method of the indicator card	CN101718597A

Date	Inventor	Patent name	Patent number
2010	Wenjie, Y; Xingmin, L; Yuan, A; Danyang, C; Zheng, W; Ruifeng, R	Method for manufacturing microbial time-temperature indicator card	CN101900685A
2011	Lixin, L; Ying, C; Weizhou, Z	Preparation method and application of time temperature indicator based on lipase reaction diffusion	CN102175677A
2012	Huffman, B; Smith, DE; Lentz, CM	Temperature-activatable time-temperature indicator	WO2012050824A1

Utilizing TTIs to predict the extent of quality change in a product based on temperature history provides the link for implementing a quality-based criterion for inventory management [15]. Kouki et al. [8] performed a survey in which the objective was to answer the question of whether the TTI technology can effectively reduce the total operating cost. The researchers formulated an inventory model for perishable foods and derived the operating cost of the model with or without a TTI technology applied to the inventory system. It was showed that for a food product with an average shelf-life of 7 days, TTI can reduce operating costs in a range of 7 to 37%, depending on the variability of the shelf-life. The authors concluded that TTIs can considerably improve the inventory management, but the reduction in total operating cost depending on TTI price.

5. Shelf-Life as an Integrated Approach

Shelf-life assessment of foods has always represented a challenge for food scientists. During the last decades, the prediction of food shelf-life has been a topic of continuous and extensive research, with many books and book chapters dedicated to the subject (for instance, many of the references cited in this chapter). A lot of progress has been made toward a scientific approach to the study of the different deteriorative mechanisms occurring in food systems [44]. The extension of shelf-life with minimum processing requires not only intense optimization and control of formulation, processing, packaging, storage and handling, but also often innovative techniques to ensure safety and reduce food deterioration [23, 34]. Alternative food processing and preservation technologies attract special interest in the food industry because of the growing consumer demand for foods not only safe, but also for products that retain the characteristics of fresh or MP foods [21].

In order to convert kinetic data into shelf-life data, knowing related to the acceptability limit is absolutely necessary. Thus, shelf-life assessment requires the exact definition of the criterion for assessing the end of product life [44]. In this regard, the question of what evaluate and the tolerance limit is graphically shown in Figure 2. In defining shelf-life we accept a lowest value of the quality factor (A) as A_{SL}, if A declines to or below A_{SL}, the quality is assumed as unacceptable. The time to reach a pre-determined level of microbial count will be considered to be the end-point. The time at which this happens is defined as the shelf-life [35]. Shelf-life is strongly influenced by changes occurring in the food after it has been processed and is distributed, stored at retailers and at the consumer's home, until the moment of consumption [12]. No single factor has a more pronounced impact on the quality of stored perishables than does temperature history [15]. The cold chain should be maintained both in production and in storage to minimize microbial development and ensure optimal shelf-life extension [5]. Certain stages of the chill distribution chain are being recognized as important critical control points for MPFV.

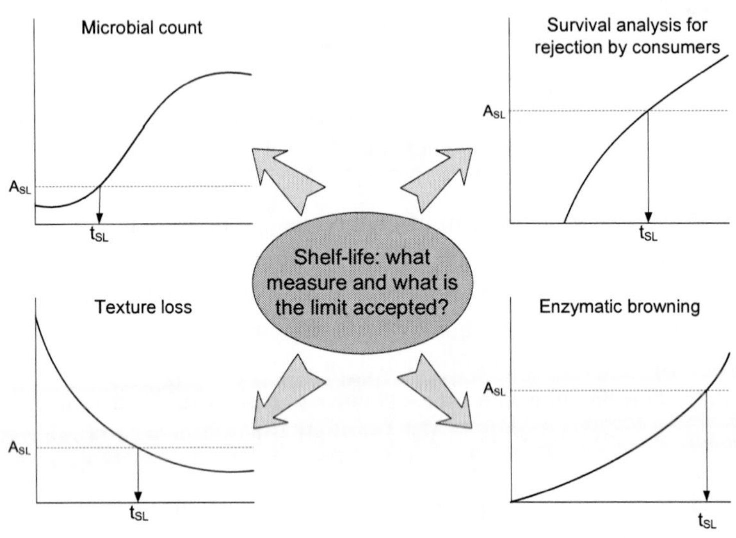

Adapted from Van Boekel [12].

Figure 2. Possible measurements to evaluate the shelf-life of food products.

The rationale for arriving at a particular shelf-life will undoubtedly encompass safety, quality and commercial decisions. It is unlikely that all of these requirements will be in agreement and the safety of the product must always assume the highest priority [10]. The food industry is an active market that requires rapid development of new product formats and ingredient combinations with short launch times. Traditionally, the safety and quality of new products would have been evaluated solely by the use of laboratory studies which are time consuming and expensive. As discussed in a previous point, user-friendly software based on PM techniques are now available and are gaining increasing use in the development of new products. In addition to commercial pressures for extensive and rapid product development, there is a consumer pressure for fresh tasting products with less salt and preservatives which require minimum preparation. These requirements have the potential to increase the growth of food spoilage organisms and pathogens and thus decrease the likely shelf-life attainable under chilled storage conditions. Such product changes mean that new combinations of ingredients and preservative factors need to be used to maximize shelf-life [10].

Independent of the methodology employed to calculate the shelf-life of foods, the product dating or open dating system used on a package only indicates how long a food should be in storage or how soon it should be used (*e.g.*, Best if Used by Date, Sell by Date, Better if Used by Date, or Best Before). Clearly this terminology can be confusing for the consumer and do not represent the decay in quality experimented by the food, because the reference temperature is not provided and the temperature history is not known [30]. Traditional methods for shelf-life dating and small-scale distribution chain tests cannot reproduce in a laboratory the real conditions of storage, distribution, and consumption on food quality [7].

The distribution of food products occurs over a wide geographic area and can involve multiple modes of transportation and diverse warehousing in urban as well as in rural areas. The complex nature of the distribution system and the wide range of daily and seasonal temperatures impose significant stresses on the products that need to be monitored [30]. In this regard, it is important that shelf-life reflects the dynamics of quality and safety loss and not simply the number of days when foods should be removed from the market [7]. When a TTI technology is not used, the expiry date printed on a product packaging is based on the margin of precaution that supply chain actors take [8]. TTIs can be an alternative to the dating system, providing an easy and dynamic way to evaluate the loss of quality in foods and a form to increase the consumer safety.

CONCLUSION

In recent years, food safety and provision of fresh-like foods, requiring minimal preparation, have arisen as consumer's driven demands for the food industry. Research on minimally processed foods is still needed to obtain microbiologically safe products, keeping their nutritional value and sensory quality. The shelf-life accomplished for these products have to be extended in order to allow a more prolonged distribution and marketing time. Focus on this issue, the use of TTIs is becoming more important to ensure food stability and safety. By using this technology, food stores could provide a wide variety of minimally processed food products that preserve their quality and safety attributes. In this scenario, more research is needed to give value to TTI technology which is a useful tool to be recognized for raising confidence in retail handling and safety when food is taken home and stored in refrigerators.

REFERENCES

[1] Palzer, S., Food structures for nutrition, health and wellness. *Trends in Food Science & Technology*, 2009. 20(5): p. 194-200.

[2] Zúñiga, R.N. and E. Troncoso, Improving Nutrition Through the Design of Food Matrices, in Scientific, Health and Social Aspects of the Food Industry, V. B, Editor 2012, *InTech-Open Access* Publisher Croatia. p. 295-320.

[3] Gorris, L. and B. Tauscher, Quality and safety aspects of novel minimal processing technologies, in Quality Optimization and Process Assessment, O. FAR and O. JC, Editors. 1999, CRC Press, Boca Raton: USA. p. 325-340.

[4] BM., M., Shelf-life prediction of minimally processed chilled foods, in Engineering and Food for the 21st Century, J. Welti-Chanes, G.V. Barbosa-Cánovas, and J.M. Aguilera, Editors. 2002, CRC Press, Boca Raton: USA. p. 607-614.

[5] Ragaert, P., F. Devlieghere, and J. Debevere, Role of microbiological and physiological spoilage mechanisms during storage of minimally processed vegetables. *Postharvest Biology and Technology*, 2007. 44(3): p. 185-194.

[6] Kilcast, D. and P. Subramaniam, Introduction, in The stability and shelf-life of food, D. Kilcast and P. Subramaniam, Editors. 2000, Woodhead Publishing Limited Cambridge, England. p. 1-22.
[7] Martins, R.C., et al., Computational shelf-life dating: complex systems approaches to food quality and safety. *Food and Bioprocess Technology*, 2008. 1(3): p. 207-222.
[8] Kouki, C., et al., Assessing the impact of perishability and the use of time temperature technologies on inventory management. International Journal of Production Economics, 2010. In press.
[9] Labuza, T.P. 2007; Available from: http://www.ardilla.umn.edu/Ted_Labuza/.
[10] Betts, G. and L. Everis, Shelf-life determination and challenge testing. *Chilled Foods: A Comprehensive Guide*, 2000: p. 259-285.
[11] Eskin, M. and D.S. Robinson, Preface, in Food shelf life stability: chemical, biochemical, and microbiological changes, M. Eskin and D.S. Robinson, Editors. 2001, CRC Press, Boca Raton: USA. p. 3-35.
[12] van Boekel, M.A.J.S., Kinetic modeling of reactions in foods, 2008, USA: CRC Press, Boca Raton.
[13] Cardello, A.V., Perception of food quality. Food Storage Stability. CRC Press, Boca Raton, FL, 1998: p. 1-38.
[14] Alzamora, S. and A. López-Malo, Microbial behavior modeling as a tool in the design and control of minimally processed foods, 2002, CRC Press, Boca Raton, FL. p. 631-650.
[15] Wells, J. and R. Singh, Quality management during storage and distribution, in Food Storage Stability, T. IA and S. RP, Editors. 1998, CRC Press, Boca Raton: USA. p. 369-386.
[16] Walker, S. and G. Betts, Chilled foods microbiology, in Chilled Foods: A Comprehensive Guide, S. M and D. C, Editors. 2000, Woodhead Publishing Limited: Cambridge, England. p. 153-186.
[17] Fu, B. and T.P. Labuza, Considerations for the application of time-temperature integrators in food distribution. *Journal of Food Distribution Research*, 1992. 23(1): p. 9-18.
[18] ML, W., Temperature monitoring and measurement, in Chilled foods: a comprehensive guide, M. Stringer and C. Dennis, Editors. 2000, Woodhead Publishing Limited: Cambridge, England. p. 99-134.
[19] Taoukis, P., M. Giannakourou, and R. Steele, Temperature and food stability: analysis and control, in Understanding and measuring the shelf-life of food, S. R, Editor 2004, Woodhead Publishing Limited: Cambridge, England. p. 42-68.
[20] FAO. Global food losses and food waste. 2011; Available from: http://www.fao.org/docrep/014/mb060e/mb060e00.pdf.
[21] López-Gómez, A., et al., Food safety engineering: An emergent perspective. *Food Engineering Reviews*, 2009. 1(1): p. 84-104.
[22] Wilcock, A., et al., Consumer attitudes, knowledge and behaviour: a review of food safety issues. *Trends in Food Science & Technology*, 2004. 15(2): p. 56-66.
[23] Singh, R. and B. Anderson, The major types of food spoilage: an overview, in Understanding and measuring the shelf-life of food, S. R, Editor 2004, Woodhead Publishing Limited: Cambridge, England. p. 3-23.

[24] Goómez-Galindo, F., et al., The potential of isothermal calorimetry in monitoring and predicting quality changes during processing and storage of minimally processed fruits and vegetables. *Trends in Food Science & Technology*, 2005. 16(8): p. 325-331.
[25] WHO, WHO Initiative to estimate the global burden of foodborne diseases, 2008.
[26] Jones, K.E., et al., Global trends in emerging infectious diseases. *Nature*, 2008. 451(7181): p. 990-993.
[27] Center for Disease Control and Prevention, C. Estimates of foodborne illness in the United States. 2011; Available from: http://www.cdc.gov/foodborneburden/PDFs/FACTSHEET_A_FINDINGS_updated4-13.pdf.
[28] Alerte, V., et al., Foodborne disease outbreaks around the urban Chilean areas from 2005 to 2010]. Revista chilena de infectología: *órgano oficial de la Sociedad Chilena de Infectología,* 2012. 29(1): p. 26.
[29] Roos, Y.H., Water activity and plasticization, in Food Shelf Life Stability: Chemical, Biochemical and Microbiological Changes, E. NAM and R. DS, Editors. 2001, CRC Press, Boca Raton: FL, USA. p. 3-35.
[30] Wright, B.B. and I.A. Taub, Stored product quality: open dating and temperature monitoring, in Food Storage Stability, T. IA and S. RP, Editors. 1998, CRC Press, Boca Raton: USA. p. 353-368.
[31] Soliva-Fortuny, R.C. and O. Martín-Belloso, New advances in extending the shelf-life of fresh-cut fruits: a review. *Trends in Food Science & Technology*, 2003. 14(9): p. 341-353.
[32] Martin-Diana, A., et al., Calcium for extending the shelf life of fresh whole and minimally processed fruits and vegetables: a review. *Trends in Food Science & Technology*, 2007. 18(4): p. 210-218.
[33] J, S., Modeling food spoilage, in Food preservation techniques, P. Zeuthen and L. Bøgh-Sørensen, Editors. 2003, CRC Press. p. 277-291.
[34] PS, T., Modeling the use of time-temperature indicators in distribution and stock rotation, in Food Processing Modeling, Tijskens LMM, Hertog MLATM, and N. BM, Editors. 2001, Woodhead Publishing Limited: Cambridge, England. p. 402-401.
[35] Ross, E.W., Mathematical modeling of quality loss, in Food Storage Stability, S. RP, Editor 1997, CRC Press, Boca Raton: USA. p. 331-352.
[36] Legan D, et al., Modeling the growth, survival and death of bacterial pathogens in foods, in Foodborne pathogens: hazards, risk analysis, and control, C.W. Blackburn and P.J. McClure, Editors. 2009, CRC Press, Boca Raton: USA. p. 53-96.
[37] McMeekin, T., et al., The future of predictive microbiology: strategic research, innovative applications and great expectations. *Int J Food Microbiol*, 2008. 128(1): p. 2.
[38] Mizrahi, S., Accelerated shelf-life tests, in Understanding and measuring the shelf-life of food, S. R, Editor 2004, Woodhead Publishing Limited: Cambridge, England. p. 317-337.
[39] Corradini, M.G. and M. Peleg, Shelf-life estimation from accelerated storage data. *Trends in Food Science & Technology*, 2007. 18(1): p. 37-47.
[40] Corradini, M., M. Normand, and M. Peleg, Nonlinear Kinetics: Principles and Potential Food Applications. *Food Engineering: Integrated Approaches*, 2008: p. 47-71.
[41] Devlieghere, F., et al., Predictive microbiology. Predictive *Modeling and RiskAssessment*, 2009: p. 29-53.

[42] Baranyi J and P. C, Modeling microbiological safety, in Food Processing Modeling, Tijskens LMM, Hertog MLATM, and N. BM, Editors. 2001, Woodhead Publishing Limited: Cambridge, England. p. 383-401.

[43] van Loey A, et al., Enzymic time temperature integrators for the quantification of thermal processes in terms of food safety, in Processing Foods: Quality Optimization and Process Assessment, O. FAR and O. JC, Editors. 1999, CRC Press, Boca Raton: USA. p. 13-40.

[44] Nicoli, M., S. Calligaris, and L. Manzocco, Shelf-Life Testing of Coffee and Related Products: Uncertainties, Pitfalls, and Perspectives. *Food Engineering Reviews*, 2009. 1(2): p. 159-168.

In: Chemical Food Safety and Health
Editors: F. Pedreschi Plasencia and Z. Ciesarová

ISBN: 978-1-62948-339-9

Chapter 9

Glassy State: A Way to Extend Shelf-Life of Food

J. I. Enrione** and P. Díaz-Calderón
School of Nutrition and Dietetics, Faculty of Medicine,
Universidad de los Andes, Santiago, Chile

Abstract

The increasing demand for safe and structurally stable fresh or minimally processed foods, encourages the need for an understanding of the mechanism driving the spoilage of these systems. It is well known that several chemical reactions and microorganism growth occur in foods during storage. Although the dependence of the kinetics of such processes on water activity has been applied by industry for decades, the limitations of such approach food systems have been argued, recommending it quality control tool applicable only for the same products at the same temperature. Indeed, foods are known to be non-equilibrium systems, therefore significant changes in their structure can occur with time depending on the glass transition temperatures (Tg) of the matrix. This chapter discusses the limitations of water activity as only parameter to control food shelf-life and the relevance of Tg as indicator of molecular mobility and therefore of time dependent phenomena such as diffusivity, non-enzymatic browning and oxidation. Also the effect of plasticisers on biopolymer structure at nano scale is explored, presenting novel concepts such of molecular packing as a mechanistic approach for the understanding of the well known antiplastization effect in glassy biomaterials. Finally structure relaxation processes of these materials in the glassy state are also presented using the encapsulation of bioactives as an applied example of the relevance of such phenomenon.

1. Introduction

Food stability is paramount for food producers and manufacturers following today's consumer awareness in food safety and shelf life. The increasing demand for safe and

* Corresponding author: Dr. Javier Enrione, School of Nutrition and Dietetics, Faculty of Medicine and School of Service Management, Universidad de los Andes, San Carlos de Apoquindo 2200, Las Condes, Santiago, Chile. Phone: +56-02-2618 1610; Ee-mail: jenrione@uandes.com.

structurally stable fresh or minimally processed foods during storage, encourage the need for an understanding of the mechanism driving the spoilage of foods systems. It is well known that several chemical reactions and microorganism growth occur in foods during storage. Some reactions include lipid oxidation and lypolisis, Maillard reaction and enzymatic browning [1]. Bacteria, yeast and mold will grow during storage depending on the water activity (Aw) or ambient relative humidity (RH) at which foods are equilibrated. Labuza [2] proposed the well-known stability map that relates the chemical reactions and microorganism growth kinetics as a function of water activity. Despite these diagrams have proved to be extremely useful for the food industry, some critics have suggested that since the reaction rates (kinetics) shown in the map do not represent a relationship with partial vapour pressure in true equilibrium the stability map is useful, at best, as a quality control tool applicable only for the same products at the same temperature [3]. Indeed, foods are known to be non equilibrium systems, therefore significant changes in their structure can occur with time, which is dependant on the molecular mobility of the matrix. Water plays a key role in determining mobility by its plasticising effect of the amorphous fraction present in food components. The mobility increases dramatically as the water content increased to a level, which results in the glass transition temperatures (Tg) being at or below the storage temperature [4]. This mobility facilitates phenomena such as increase in softening, crystallization [5], stickiness and caking commonly detected for powders [6].

The following sections describes the importance of the glass transition temperature on the stability of food matrices and how this concept is related to food safety through the application of the concept to molecular mobility. Also new ideas brought from soft matter physics relevant to glassy systems will be discussed by several examples in food applications.

2. Water Activity

Water plays an important role with respect to the properties of food systems. It influences the physical or textural characteristics of food products as well as its chemical stability [7]. Moisture loss or gain from one region to another would continue in order to reach thermodynamic equilibrium. The term water activity (*Aw*) is used to indicate an intrinsic parameter of a food and equilibrium relative humidity, a property of the surrounding atmosphere in equilibrium with the food system under consideration (Van den Berg and Bruin, 1981). The thermodynamic concept of activity of a component can be explained in terms of its fugacity *(f)* and the fugacity of the component in a standard state, [8, 9]. The ratio for a component is called activity (relative activity) a_i of the component i (Eq. 1):

$$A_i = \left(\frac{f_i}{f_i^{\theta}}\right) \tag{1}$$

Fugacity is considered as a measure of the tendency of a component to escape. At equilibrium between different phases, the fugacity of each component is the same throughout the heterogeneous system. In this case, the activity is the same throughout the system when the reference fugacities are defined equally for each phase [10]. Gal [11] showed that in experimental terms there is small difference between *water activity* and the concept equilibrium relative humidity. Therefore Aw can be express in the following relation (Eq. 2):

$$Aw = \left(\frac{p_W}{p_W^{\theta}}\right) \qquad (2)$$

where p_w is the equilibrium water vapour pressure over the system and p_w^{θ} the vapour pressure of pure water at the same temperature and pressure. Van den Berg and Bruin [10] mentioned the following considerations regarding the definition of water activity: i) Aw refers only to the true equilibrium state (real food systems do not always fulfil this requirement), ii) Aw is defined at a specific temperature and total pressure and iii) the reference state must be well specified. The relationship between the total moisture content and the water activity, over a range of values, at constant temperature, yields the sorption isotherm when expressed graphically. It can be obtained by absorption or desorption. In both cases, "equilibrium" is achieved when there is no water migration from/to the sample during storage (no changes in material mass is detected). Brunauer et al. [12] classified the adsorption isotherms into five general types, from which type I, II and III are the more to relevant for food systems. Type I is related to the Langmuir sorption behaviour, eg. non-swelling porous solids [13], whilst Type II is a combination of Type I and III. Moisture sorption isotherms of most foods are generally sigmoidal in shape and they have been classified as Type II [14-19]. The interpretation of the sorption isotherm for food systems may be divided in three regions (Figure 1), although the distinction between the three areas can not be expressed in terms of precise ranges of water contents, rather is an indication of the differences in the overall nature of the interaction between water and the solids in the three stages [20]. Region I represents strong interactions with water with an enthalpy of vaporisation considerably higher than of pure water [10, 20]. Usually water molecules in this region are unfreezable and are not available for chemical reaction. Most dried products are empirically observed to display their greatest stability at moisture contents comparable to the monolayer [20]. In region II, the energy associated the water-polymer interactions is lower than in the region I. The enthalpy of vaporisation is little greater than the enthalpy of vaporisation of pure water. These water molecules sorbed near or on the top of the first molecules or penetrate into the newly created spaces of the swollen structure [10]. The water is available as a solvent for low-molecular weight solutes and for some biochemical reactions [18]. The initially hard and brittle material undergoes a glass transition, by the plasticising effect of water, becoming weak, plastic, or rubbery depending of the polymer. Compared to the region I, water molecules show a sharp increase in molecular mobility and therefore in diffusion [4], taking longer to reach "equilibrium", as the rate of polymer swelling can become the limiting factor. In region III, water is present in macro-capillaries or as a part of the fluid phase in high moisture materials. Swelling is exactly in proportion to the volume of water sorbed [20].This moisture exhibits nearly all properties of bulk water and thus is capable of acting as a solvent. Microbial growth becomes the major deteriorative reaction in this region [18]. Rahman [13] discussed the stability of foods in terms of reaction kinetics and sensory attributes as a function of water activity (Aw) presenting the stability map based on Labuza's work presented in the 70's. The above diagram has been useful in relating the rates of reaction for different food stability parameters to the water activity. Nevertheless, it must be considered that the term "activity" is based on thermodynamic equilibrium, and most real foods do not reach this state between their various components nor with their environment. Some critics [3] have suggested that since the reaction rates (kinetics) shown in the map do not represent a relationship with partial vapour pressure in true equilibrium the stability map is useful, at best, as a quality control tool applicable only for the same products at the same temperature. It has been suggested that the glass to rubber transition provided useful information related to food stability, as it account for water dynamic and molecular mobility of the matrix constituents under various environmental conditions.

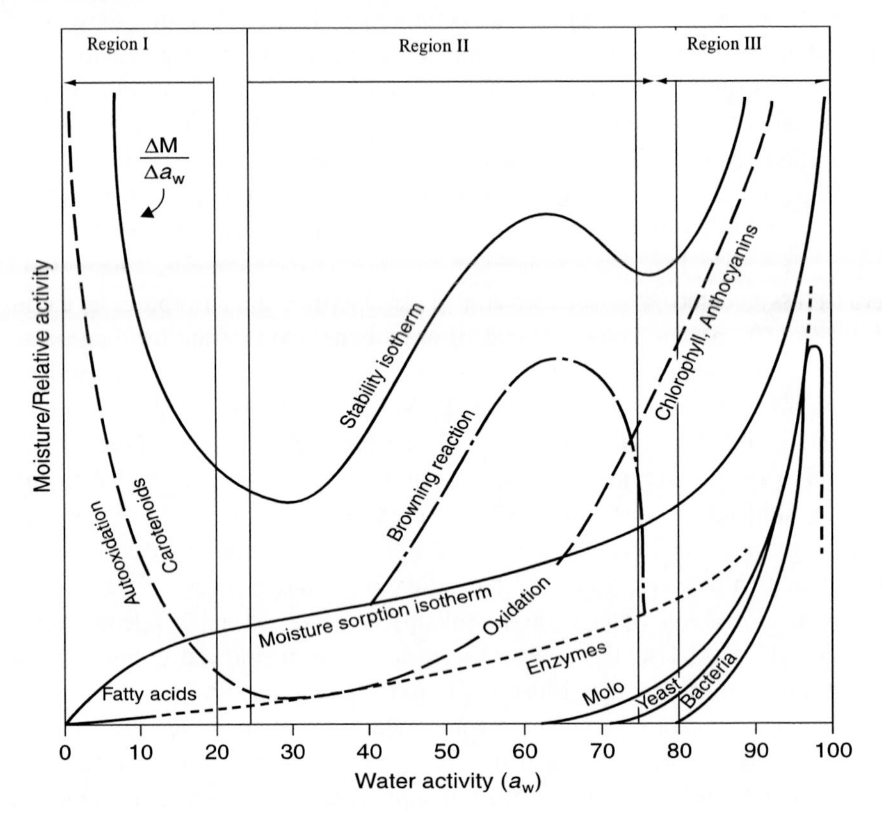

Figure 1. Food stability as a function of water activity modified from Rahman [13].

3. Glass Transition Temperature

As stated in the previous section, water activity shows some limitations as predictor for the stability of foods. Foods are complex systems where their main constituents, carbohydrates and proteins, are not in a thermodynamic equilibrium, being time, temperature and water content dependants. In addition numerous physical phenomena that affect foods such as crystallization, caking, stickiness, diffusivity, etc. cannot be explained entirely by water activity.

The glass transition temperature or Tg, which occurs over a temperature range, has been defined as a single temperature at which, on rapid cooling, an amorphous material becomes extremely viscous (~10^{-12} Pa) [21]. Mechanically the material behaves as solid but maintains its amorphous structure as a liquid, therefore containing an excess in free energy. At temperatures below Tg, the molecular mobility is restricted to vibrations and short range rotational motions [22].

Thermodynamically, the glass transition temperature can be described as a second order transition, as it is characterised by a discontinuity in the heat capacity (Cp) or thermal expansion coefficient (α_T), the first derivates of the thermodynamic quantities *volume (V)* and *enthalpy (H)* as a function of temperature (Figure 2).

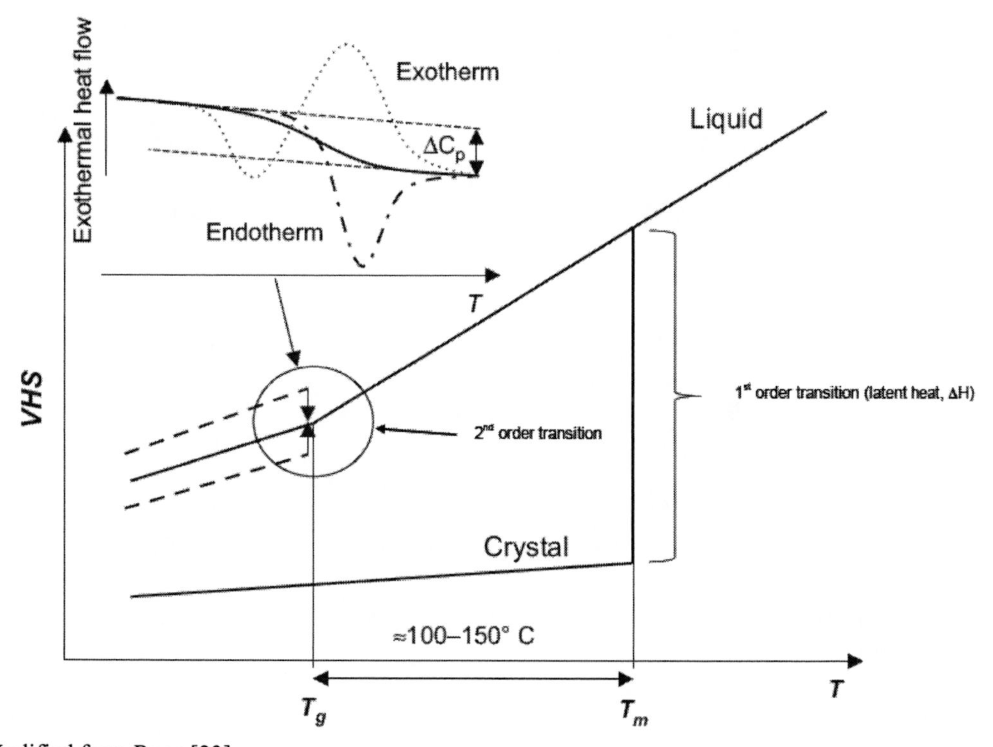

Modified from Roos [23].

Figure 2. Changes of thermodynamic functions volume (V), enthalpy (H) and entropy (S) as function of temperature. Glass transition is observed as a change in slope of the VHS curve and a change in heat capacity of the material (ΔCp). As the glass transition is a time dependant phenomenon, relaxation in thermal properties can occur (insert).

This is very important, as it is related to its non-equilibrium and time dependent physical state. Indeed, the phenomenological description of the glass transition in polymers considers the use of the concepts of free volume and the relaxation phenomenon. The free volume has been defined as the extra volume required for large scale and long range coordinated movement of the main chain of the polymer. Below the Tg, various configurations of free volumes exist depending on thermal history of the polymer, where the least free volume represent the most relaxed structure [24]. Figure 3 shows the various motions of a polymer chain following the crankshaft model [24], where free volume is required by a series of jointed segments for motions to occur. This model, although very simplistic, helps to describe the different relaxation scales as the polymer material is subjected to variations in temperature. The increase in movement, by side chains and small groups, results in greater compliance of the molecule, which has been describe as γ and β transitions [25]. If the temperature is increased, the Tg is reached where large scale coordinated motions of the polymer chain occur. This transition has also been defined as α transition or Tα [25]. The variations in free volume with respect to the Tg has been successfully described by the WLT empirical relation [26] (Eq. 3).

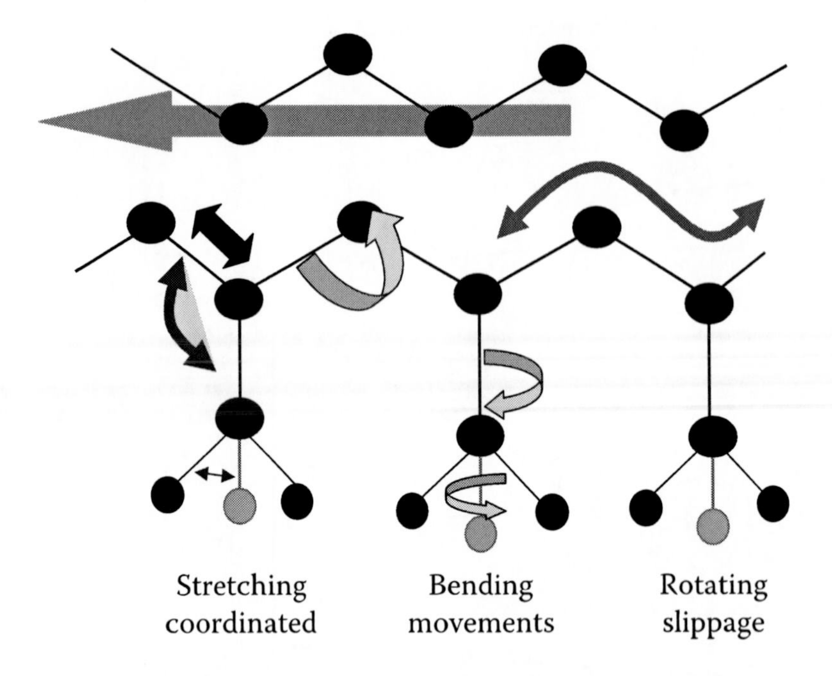

Figure 3. A schematic example of free volume and the crankshaft model showing motions scales of a polymer chains [24].

$$\log a_T = -C_1(T - T_S)/(C_2 + T - T_s) \tag{3}$$

where a_T is the ratio of any mechanical and electrical relaxation times at temperature T to their values at the reference temperature T_s and C_1 and C_2 are constants (-17.4 and 51.6 respectively for biomaterials). Kasapis [27] applied the free volume concept to mathematically represent the change in viscosity with temperature of dehydrated foods. By using the time-temperature superimposition (TTS) principle, it was possible to assess the mechanical glass transition temperature of complex model systems such as gelatin and dried fruits. Shift factors (a_T) were calculated based on the superimposing of modulus traces generated from frequency sweeps at different temperatures. The application of the WLF and Andrade equations [27] confirmed the description of the phase transition as the minimum value of the first derivate of the modulus with temperature. In a later study, Kasapis and Sablani [27] calculated the mechanical glass transition based of free volume and energy associated to molecular motions as deviation of the WFM predicted values to an Arrhenius like behaviour of the variations of the shift factors (log scale) with temperature on rapid cooling (Figure 4).

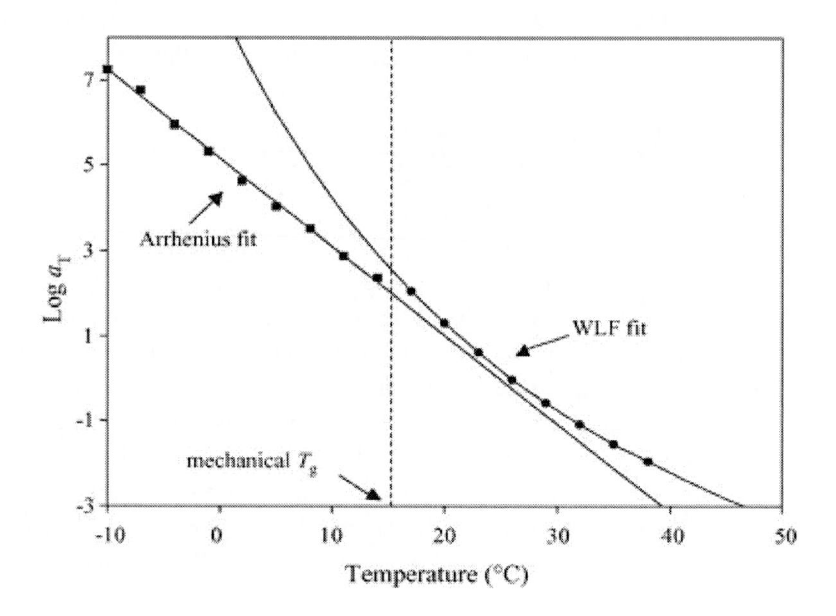

Figure 4. Determination of Tg based on the reduction factor, a_T, for a 80%gelatin suspensión plotted against temperature from the data of a master curve using the TTS principle [27].

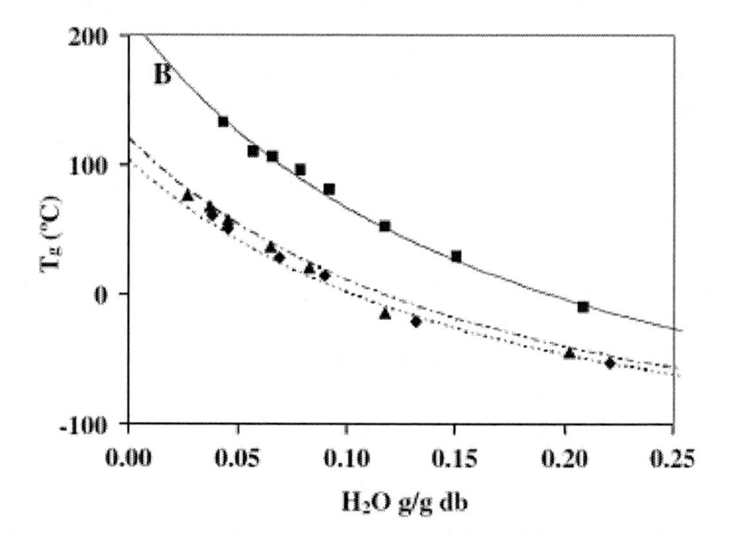

Figure 5. Dependence of the Tg of maltodextrins with different DE on the water content. Filled squares: DE6; filled triangles: DE29; filled diamonds: DE32. The lines represent the best fit of the Couchman-Karasz model [28].

For the prediction of Tg for mixtures, several equations have been proposed based on free volume theory [29], which accounts for the true density of the polymer and plasticizer and their changes in thermal expansivity (Δα) at Tg [30]. Another approach follows thermodynamic considerations assuming Tg as a second order transition with a continuity in entropy and volume when this transition is reached [31]. The derived equation relates the heat capacity changes of pure polymer components at their Tg to the Tg of the mixture [32](Eq. 4).

$$Tg = \frac{w_d \Delta Cp_d Tg_d + w_p \Delta Cp_p Tg_p}{w_d \Delta Cp_d + w_p \Delta Cp_p} \quad (4)$$

where Tg is the glass transition temperature of the mixture, ΔCp_p is the change in specific heat capacity of the polymer, ΔCp_d a is the change in specific heat capacity of the diluent, Tg_p is the Tg of pure polymer and Tg_d is the Tg of the pure diluent. w_p and w_d are the weight fractions of the polymer and diluent, respectively. This equation has been successfully applied to represent the Tg of waxy maize starch-water-glycerol extrudates [32], starch, dextrans and pullulan [33], maltodextrins [28, 33, 34] (Figure 5) and bovine gelatine films [35].

As described previously, the reduction in Tg by the addition of plasticizers can be explained by the free volume theory, which indicates that low molecular weight compounds increase the free volume of a polymeric system increasing its overall molecular mobility and therefore improving its mechanical properties. However recent studies have showed that presence of low molecular weight can modify the matrix structure through densification (stated by a decrease in specific volume probed by gas pycnometry) at temperatures below Tg. This has been clearly observed when the mass fraction of low molecular weight compounds increase in polymeric matrices in the glassy state [36-38]. Such studies have been performed firstly in carbohydrate and recently in protein based systems (e.g. gelatin). When volumetric changes are evaluated at nanoscale, literature reports a lineal correlation between hole volume (a measurement of free volume between polymeric chains) and temperature (matrix thermal expansion) both below and above the glass transition temperature. Indeed a change in the slope of specific volume isoline is associated to the glass transition temperature with good agreement with DSC data [36, 39].

The hole volume decreases when the mass fraction of low molecular weight compounds increases, indicating a correlation between volumetric changes at macro (specific volume) and nano scale (free volume) (Figure 6). The role of water at nanoscale and its effect in volumetric changes in glassy materials has been related to plasticization and antiplasticization phenomenon. At very low water content a decrease in hole volume with increasing water content reflects the antiplasticization, while in approach to Tg an increase in hole volume with increasing water content correspond to plasticization phenomenon.

The effect of molecular weight distribution in changes in specific volume (macroscale) and hole volume (nanoscale) has been related with the novel concept of molecular packing, which represents the volumetric changes at macro and nanoscale with increasing molecular weight in the glassy state [38]. The increase in matrix density and decrease in hole size as a consequence of molecular packing appears to have a profound effect on numerous physical properties of polymeric matrices, such as diffusion of oxygen, the stabilization of sensitive biological materials by glassy state encapsulation and hydrogen bonding, and the sorption of water [36, 37].

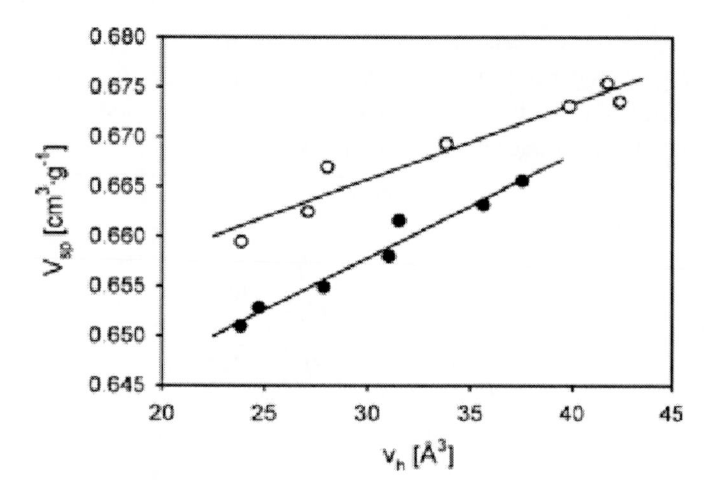

Figure 6. Correlation between the hole volume and the specific volume at two water content (Qw): open circles Qw=0 and filled circles Qw= 0.05 (T=25°C). The solids line are the regressions of the experimental data and were higher than 0.93 in both cases [38].

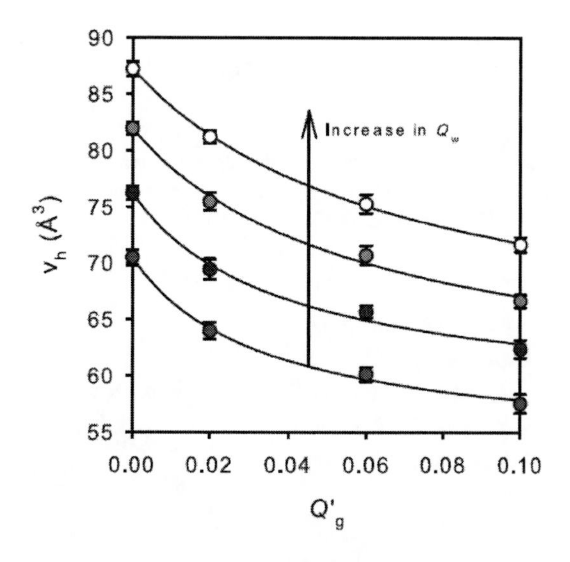

Figure 7. Average molecular hole volume as a function of increasing glycerol content for glassy gelatin matrices with well-defined water contents (Qw): Qw=0.02 (pink series), Qw=0.04 (purple series), Qw=0.06 (cyan series) and Qw=0.08 (white series) measured at 25°C [39].

Recently the effect of glycerol as an enhancer of molecular packing in gelatin films in the glassy state has been stated (Figure 7) [39], however the effect of water in hole volume size in this biopolymer has shown to be quiet complex. A pronounced increase in the average hole volume was observed, reaching a maximum value at water content near 10% (dry basis), after which a decrease in this parameter upon further sorption of water was detected (Figure 8) [39]. The initial increase in the average hole volume of the gelatin matrices upon sorption of water indicates that water acts as a plasticizer (confirmed by a decrease in Tg).The decrease in average hole volume above certain moisture content suggests a different structural conformation of the polymer which may be attributed to the formation of small pockets/clusters of water between the polypeptide chains [39, 40]. These recent findings provide new insights regarding the well-known antiplasticization phenomenon widely reported in the literature and possible mechanisms for its modulation with potential implications in food and pharmaceutical industries.

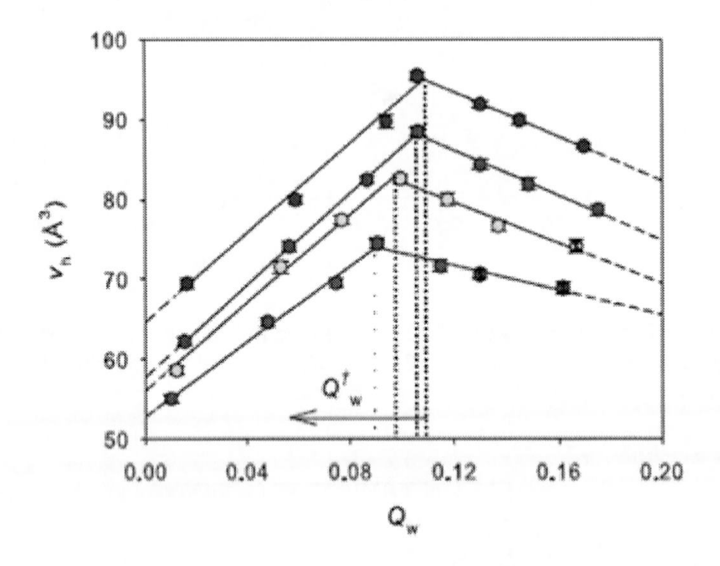

Figure 8. Average molecular hole size as a function of increasing water content for gelatin matrices with well-defined glycerol contents (Qg) measured at 25°C. Green series Qg=0.00; blue series Qg=0.02; yellow series Qg=0.06 and red series Qg=0.10. [39].

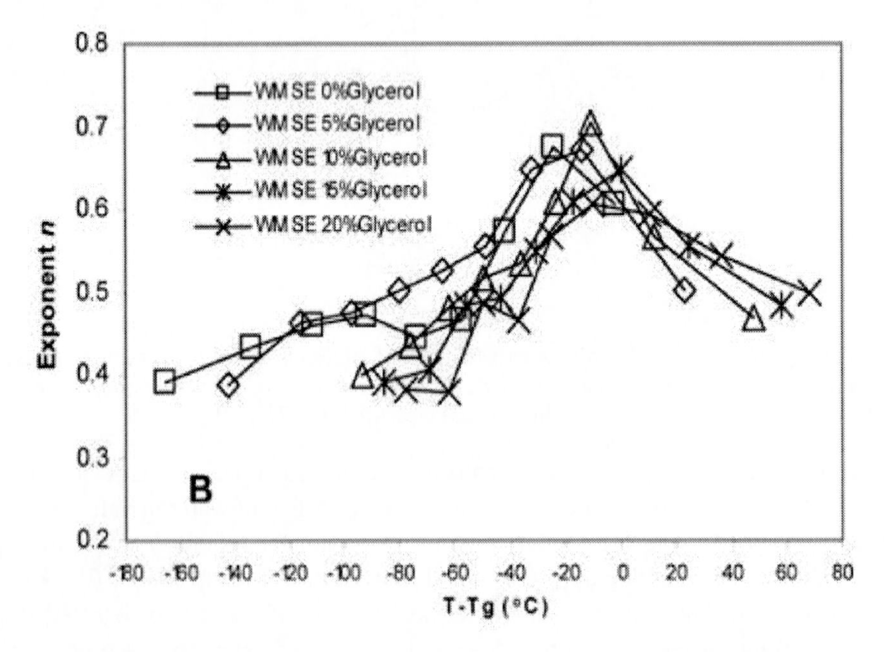

Figure 9. Diffusional exponent *n* as a function of glass transition temperature (*T*g) T = 20°C calculated on experimental data obtained by DVS from 0 to 90 RH [32].

4. Relevance of the Glassy State on Food Stability

4.1. Diffusion

The increase in viscosity and mobility at Tg of a food matrix has a significant effect on the diffusivity and therefore on the rate of moisture sorption-desorption modulating the water activity and the release of high value bioactive compounds during storage. Interestingly the reduction in diffusivity as the temperature decreases is not abrupt as expected but changes in the slope at Tg have been reported [5, 32]. The rationale of these changes has been related to changes in diffusion mechanisms, which are dependant on the structural relaxation kinetics of the matrix. Enrione et al [32] detected, by dynamic vapour sorption (DVS), variations in water diffusion mechanisms, named coupling of Fickian and Case II, in extruded waxy maize starch in presence of different contents of glycerol by calculating the diffusional exponent (n) of a semi-empirical equation developed to describe water transport in glassy polymers (Figure 9) [41]. Entrapped flavours and volatiles in glassy systems are also very important in food stability, therefore Tg becomes determinant to modulated rate at which this high value compounds are released.

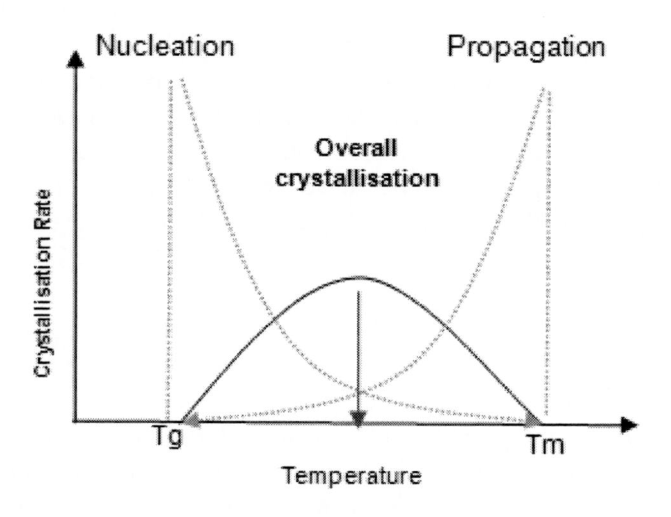

Figure 10. Diagram showing the polymer crystallization kinetics [42].

4.2. Crystallization

Crystallization and melting are a first order phase transitions that occur in liquid and solid physical states. For the crystallization to occur toward a thermodynamic equilibrium state, enough molecular mobility is required. Literature suggests that the Tg can have a significant effect on retrogradation kinetics [43]. At temperatures near Tg, the rate of nucleation is high but the rate propagation is low due to a dramatic increase in viscosity (Figure 10). At higher temperatures the increase in molecular mobility leads to an increase in crystal growth. For temperatures near melting (Tm), the rate of propagation is increased but the rate of nucleation is low. Over Tm, crystal nucleation and propagation would cease. Therefore, the maximum rate of crystallization occurs at intermediate levels of supercooling [44, 45]. Several theories exist to describe the effect of the temperature on the kinetics of polymer crystallization. The Lauritzen-Hoffman [46] theory based on the growth of chain-folded polymer crystals by deposition of the polymer chains on an existing crystal subtract is viewed as a secondary nucleation [47]. The crystallization rate as a function of time is given by the following equation (Eq. 5):

$$G(T) = G_o \exp\left[-\frac{U^*}{R(T - T_\infty)}\right]\exp\left[-\frac{K_g}{T\Delta Tf}\right] \tag{5}$$

where T is the crystallization temperature, U^* is the activation energy, R is the gas constant, ΔT is the undercooling ΔT= Tm-T, Tm being the melting temperature, f is a factor accounting for the change in the heat of fusion with temperature and K_g is a constant (Eq. 6).

$$f = \frac{2T}{Tm + T} \quad T_\infty = T_g - \delta T \tag{6}$$

T_∞ is a hypothetical temperature at which viscous flow is supposed to cease and it is related to Tg. For most synthetic polymer, δT=30K and $U^* \approx 6$ $kJmol^{-1}$.

Farhat et al [48] presented predicted data related to the effect of temperature and moisture contents on isothermal retrogradation kinetics of extruded waxy maize starch assessed by proton relaxation nuclear magnetic resonance (NMR). They successfully used a combination of the Lauritzen-Hoffman approach and predicted values of Tg and Tm calculated by the Couchman-Karasz [31] and Flory equations [49] respectively (Figure 11).

4.3. Texture

Moisture content has a clear effect on textural properties of hydrophilic polymers. Champion et al [50] established a lost of crispness of products such as chips, crackers, cornflakes or extruded products when the moisture content or temperature increased. This change was explained by the glass transition allowing a brittle-ductile type transition, although not always the brittle to ductile behavior coincided with the glass transition temperature. Nicholls et al [51] showed the brittle to ductile transition in glassy samples of gelatinized starch probed by DSC analysis. They concluded that the brittle-ductile transition depended on a number of extrinsic factors such as strain rate, temperature, stress state, specimen geometry and flaws inside the material [52]. Payne and Labuza [53] studied the brittle-ductile transition in chocolate wafer cookies showing the increase in brittleness and softness when the temperature and moisture content increase, measuring the phenomena using three different mechanical testing. On the other hand textural and structural changes may occur when a polymeric matrix is stored above its glass transition temperature, allowed by the higher level of molecular mobility. Enrione et al [54] have recently reported structural changes in a starch based commercial product. A reduction of amorphous fraction, as a function of storage time was assessed by differential calorimetry, which was correlated with an increase of elastic modulus.

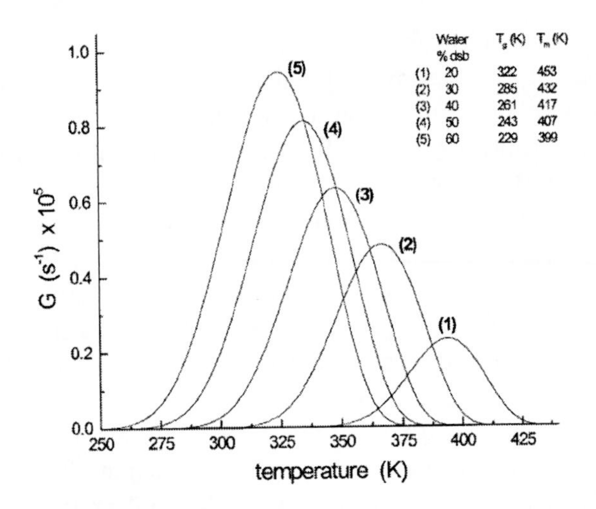

Figure 11. Lauritzen–Hoffman prediction of the effect of simultaneously varying Tg and Tm the dependence of the rate of retrogradation on temperature. The lines were computed using $U^* = 6.3$ kJ mol-1, $K_g = 1.2$ E10^5 K^2 and $G_0 = 1$ s^{-1} [48].

4.4. Oxidation

The oxidation process of lipids (via free-radicals) and phenolic compounds (via polyphenoloxydase enzyme) have important effects on the organoleptic, nutritional and toxicological quality of foods. A very effective way to prevent the oxidation process is by encapsulation by glassy matrices. Encapsulation systems based on amorphous carbohydrates in the glassy state have been very effective in minimizing the rate of oxidation of oxygen-sensitive compounds by environmental oxygen [55]. The process involves the diffusion of guest molecule through the glassy carbohydrate matrix which is a very slow process. For instance Partanen et al [56] used maltodextrins to encapsulate kernel oil showing that stability of encapsulated oil was dependent of the storage condition, highlighting the importance of the physical state of material. Researchers reported an increase in oil stability when the matrix was in the glassy state. Similar results were obtained by Soottitantawat et al [57], whom showed an increasing in oxidation rate when encapsulated D-limonene was stored at higher water activity, however at around Tg the rates decreased sharply to increase again at a further increase in Aw. Authors concluded that release rate was controlled by the interaction between the encapsulated flavor and the surrounding matrixes. However not always encapsulant materials follow this rule. Beristain et al [58] reported higher oxidative stability of encapsulated orange peel oil when samples were in the rubbery state and higher oxidation rate in glassy microcapsules. Their results seem to indicate the storing microcapsules in the zone of minimum integral entropy (rubbery state) provide the best stability against oxidation.

4.5. Non-Enzymatic Browning

The well reported reaction between non-reducing sugars and proteins (oligopeptides and free-amino acids) can be affected by the physical state of food matrix. In the glassy state the high viscosity of system hinders the encounter between reactants, reducing the reaction kinetic. Indeed Karmas et al [59] showed that the rate of reaction was lower at T<Tg. Bell [60] studied the kinetic of pigment formation in Maillard reaction using a PVP matrix as model system, showing significant changes browning rate (sevenfold increase) after the glass to rubber state transition. Bell et al [61] also studied the glycine loss and Maillard browning as a function of Tg showing that reaction rates were low when T-Tg difference was close to zero and it increased when T-Tg values were positive.

However the occurrence of non-enzymatic browning in food matrices in the glassy state has been clearly demonstrated. Schebor et al [62] reported the browning develop in polymeric matrix (gelatinized starch, maltodextrins and polyvinylpyrrolidone) and skim-milk powder samples, stored well below its glass transition temperature. These results suggest that Tg cannot be considered as an absolute threshold of stability. Most recently, Hill et al [63] studied the effect of physical aging on the chemical reaction, showing the depletion of glucose, lysine and development of coloured products during the relaxation but the effect was not very large, suggesting that densification of the matrix upon relaxation slowed the rate of reaction. Rotational mobility, the aging of the glassy materials and the diffusion through pores or defects of the glasses may explain the occurrence of chemical reactions in the glassy state [62].

4.6. Microbial Stability

Studies on microbial stability and glass transition have been related to the thermal resistance of sporulating microorganisms. Sapru and Labuza [64] reported that at a given temperature, the inactivation rate of bacteria decreased with the increasing Tg of spores. Inactivation rates of lyophilized microorganism, studied by Hill et al [63], showed an increase in inactivation rate when cells were stored in their rubbery state, although not as rapid as expected by the temperature dependence of the viscosity above Tg. Selma et al [65] studied the mortality of starters cultures as a function of T-Tg, reporting that the survival was impaired at 15-20 °C below Tg, suggesting that molecular mobility above a critical temperature plays a role in the microbial mortality. The microbial growth in the glassy state foods may be due to micro and macro heterogeneities within the matrix, inducing areas with higher mobility, and non-homogeneous distribution of water and phase separation [50].

5. Application of the Glassy State in a Food System: Encapsulation

New trends in food product developments aim for new formulations that improve general well being and health of consumers. Examples include improvements in cognitive and physical performance and to enhance the immune defense of the human body by selected micronutrients and bioactive substances extracted from plants, fungi, micro algae or marine biomass [66]. The classical approach follows the incorporation of bioactive compounds (i.e. antioxidants, vitamins, prebiotics, bioactive peptides, omega-3 fatty acids, etc) in foods in order to enhance their functionality. Such compounds can be added directly during food formulation or encapsulated in a solid matrix or structured emulsions [55]. Encapsulation technologies (e.g. micro and nanoencapsulation) have the potential to meet food industry challenges concerning the effective delivery of health functional ingredients and controlled release of flavor compounds [67]. Solubility and chemical stability of bioactive strongly depends on the structural and chemical composition of the respective matrix and chosen encapsulation system [66], being the encapsulation of such bioactive compounds in amorphous matrices in the glassy state a common practice [68]. The advantages are related to stability of flavors and natural food-coloring dispersion, controlled release and better dispersability of water-insoluble food compounds and additives [69, 70]. However the use of encapsulation technology requires a broad expertise associated to material science such as a deep understanding of the physical properties of encapsulate materials at macro and nano scale. Gressler et al [71] and Hernández-Ledesma et al [72] have stated the purposes and potential benefits of encapsulation in food by nanostructured materials; i) enhance solubility (e.g. coloring agents), ii) controlled release (e.g. prevention of bad taste of an ingredient which is beneficial, iii) improve bioavailability (eg. amount of a nutritional ingredient which is actually absorbed by the body), iv) protect micronutrients and bioactive compounds during processing, storage and retail. Moreover the release of active molecules from the food matrix during digestion and their following absorption into the blood stream are a function of the microstructure of the food and the encapsulation system carrying the active molecules [55].

One of the central issues in the design of an optimal encapsulating material is the molecular mobility in the matrix (determining its barrier properties), which would control the release of the bioactive or the inward migration of surrounding molecules (e.g. oxygen or water) during production and storage [68, 69]. The glass transition temperature (Tg) of the amorphous matrix therefore has been used as the central physical parameter for the optimization of processing and storage stability [38].

As it has been stated previously in this chapter, a key factor affecting the molecular mobility is the plasticization effect of water and the presence of other low molecular weight compounds, which can reduce Tg. However, the presence of plasticizers in polymeric matrices in the glassy state ($T<Tg$) can generate unexpected variation in the structure of the encapsulant material.

Indeed, the molecular packing by addition of low molecular weight can modify the sorption properties of glassy biomaterials (Figure 12). An increase in plasticizer content produces a decrease in the equilibrium moisture content, which was firstly explained by a reduction in sorption polar sites [73, 74], however recent findings indicated a densification of the matrices generating fewer sites available to accommodate water molecules, consequently less water can be absorbed a defined water activity [68, 75]. This highlights the relevance of the molecular packing concept for the sorption of water and hence its modulation at given water activity [76]. Thus, in the glassy state, it is possible to reduce the amount of water absorbed by increasing the content of low molecular weight compounds and simultaneously they will reduce the water activity at which the polymeric matrix will pass into the rubbery state [76]. The aforementioned behavior is consistent with the decrease in the value of BET monolayer (m_0) and Freundlich parameter (K_{Fr}), which are in agreement with the densification phenomenon [36, 39, 68, 75]. An important implication of molecular packing and densification is related to the permeability of biopolymers to gas and moisture at temperatures below Tg. Anandaraman and Reineccius [77] showed a reduction in oxygen uptake rate by maltodextrins capsules used to protect citrus oil (Figure 13) when the dextrose equivalent (DE) values increased. This behavior is in agreement with result on carbohydrate molecular packing in the glassy state reported in the literature. However neither water content nor density was measured in this study, so better controlled studies are necessaries [76].

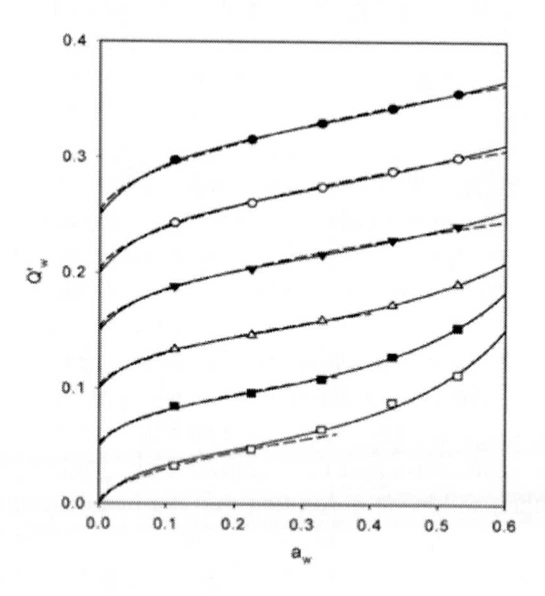

Figure 12. Moisture sorption isotherms at 25°C for maltodextrin matrices (DE12) as a function of glycerol content. The solid and dashed lines represent GAB and Freundlich equations respectively. Filled circles Qg=0; open circles Qg=0.02; filled triangles Qg=0.06; open triangles Qg=0.10; filled squares Qg=0.15; open squares Qg=0.20 [68].

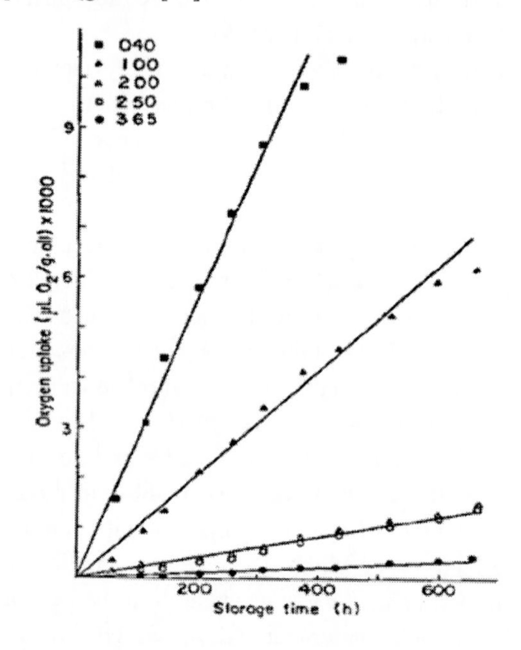

From [77].

Figure 13. Oxidation of citrus oil encapsulated in maltodextrins in varying molecular weight distribution at 45°C. Filled squares DE 4; filled triangles DE 10; open triangles DE 20; open squares DE 25; filled squares DE 37.

6. Stability Food Systems in the Glassy State

A glass corresponds to a supercooled, amorphous solid which is in a nonequilibrium or metastable state and exhibit time-dependent changes as they approach to thermodynamic equilibrium [21, 22]. When a glass is stored below its Tg, it will spontaneously approach the lower energy state and a microstructural evolution will take place, with some loss in enthalpy and volume [25, 78]. This phenomenon has been described as structural relaxation, enthalpy relaxation or physical aging. From observation in the field of materials science, it is known that more compact molecular organization and strengthening of interactions result in changes in many physical properties such as increasing rigidity and brittleness, a decrease in dimensions and transport properties [25].

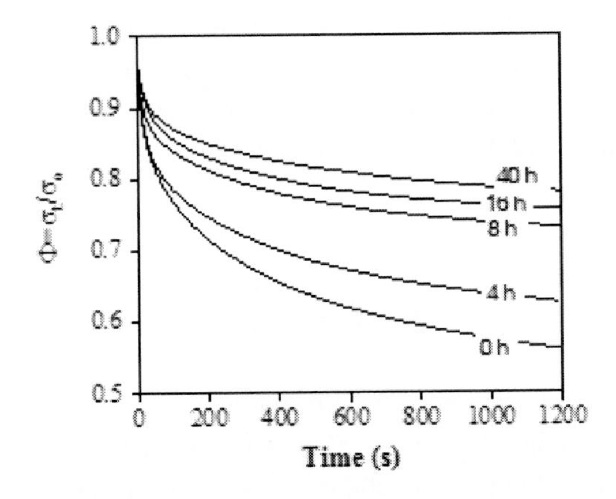

Ageing time (h)	τ_0 (s)	$SD_{\tau 0}$	B	SD_{β}	SE
0	6.1E+03	3.1E+02	0.32	0.03	6.4E-02
4	1.7E+04	1.9E+03	0.28	0.01	4.1E-02
8	1.3E+05	5.3E+03	0.24	0.03	6.4E-02
16	3.8E+05	1.9E+04	0.22	0.03	5.6E-03
40	9.0E+05	2.1E+04	0.21	0.01	3.0E-03

Figure 14. Top: stress relaxation, φ (normalized) for salmon gelatin films in glassy state aged at 29°C (Tg−Ta=5°C) for 0, 4, 8, 16, and 40 h. Bottom: Parameters β and τ_0 for the same storage times, SE standard error from KWW equation fitting, SD standard deviation [80].

Due to heterogeneities of materials at micro and nano scale, the structural relaxation cannot be described by a single relaxation function [78]. As the structural change is dependent of time and type of glass, the relaxation process is described as a non-exponential process which can be well-represented by the empirical Kohlrausch-Williams-Watts (KWW) expression [79] -Eq. 7-:

$$\phi = exp\left[-(t/\tau_0^{\beta})\right] \tag{7}$$

where Φ is the property of concern which is a function of time (t). τ is the mean relaxation time and β is a constant characterizing the width of the relaxation time distribution ($0 \leq \beta \leq 1$). β=1 correspond to a single relaxation time with exponential behavior. The lower the value of β, the greater the distribution of molecular motion deviated from a single exponential behavior. In other words, if β is significantly different from 1, it indicates a distribution of relaxation time rather than a single relaxation time [78].

Indeed, literature has shown a decrease in β as a function of ageing time in stability experiments of carbohydrate and protein bases systems [80, 81] (Figure 14). Although many studies have reported the occurrence of physical ageing in carbohydrate [82-87] and more recently in proteins [54, 80, 88, 89], not much work is available looking at its technological effects in food materials, some examples include the modification of sorption properties [90], the increase in stiffness [81] and the change in the permeability [91, 92]. In pharmaceutical sciences has been also highlighted the effect of enthalpy relaxation in drug release and drug delivery systems [93]. It is clear that more research is required in this field specially, in particular between molecular packing on volumetric changes during relaxation and the modulation of its kinetic by addition of low molecular weight compounds in order to obtain safer and healthier foods.

CONCLUSION

Food polymeric matrices are complex and heterogeneous structures. Structural changes are induced by differences in moisture content and molecular mobility, which have been successfully modeled by mathematical relations drawn from the synthetic polymer science. The concepts of water activity and glass transition are different but both are linked by the plasticization effect of water and need to be considered in order to describe or predict food stability. The metastable condition of glassy materials generates the well known structural relaxation in food matrices leading to a reduction in molecular mobility with important technological effects. Several mathematical relations have been proposed to describe and predict the mobility of these systems in based on the free volume concept and thermodynamic considerations. Interestingly, new insights related to molecular packing by plasticizers provide valuable information for the design of protective biomaterials for bioactives such as probiotics, vitamins, bioactive peptides, antioxidants, etc. The potential for modulation of the nanostructure of these materials and its effect on transport properties open interesting perspectives to develop safer and healthier foods or extend the shelf life of labile food components.

REFERENCES

[1] Rahman, M.S., Food preservation: an overview, in Handbook of food preservation, S. Rahman, Editor 2007a, CRC Press.

[2] Labuza, T., S. Tannenbaum, and M. Karel, Water content and stability of low-moisture and intermediate-moisture foods. *Food Technol*, 1970. 24(5): p. 35-42.

[3] Franks, F., Hydration phenomena: un update and implications in Water Relationship in Foods, H. Levine and L. Slade, Editors. 1991, Plenum Press.

[4] Karel, M. and I. Saguy, Effect of water on diffusion in food systems, in Water Relationship in Foods, , H. Levine and L. Slade, Editors. 1991, Plenum Press.

[5] Rahman, M.S., Glass Transition and State Diagram of Foods in Handbook of food preservation, M.S. Rahman, Editor 2007b, CRC.

[6] Wallack, D.A. and C.J. King, Sticking and agglomeration of hygroscopic, amorphous carbohydrate and food powders. *Biotechnology Progress*, 2008. 4(1): p. 31-35.

[7] Labuza, T., Interpreting the complexity of the kinetics of the Maillard reaction, in Maillard reaction in Chemistry, Foods and Health, T. Labuza, et al., Editors. 1994, *The Royal Society of Chemistry*: London, UK. p. 176-181.

[8] Lewis, G., Das Gesetz physiko-chemischer Vorgange. *Zeitschrift fur Physikalische Chemie* 1901. 38: p. 205-226.

[9] Lewis, G., Umriss eines neuen tsystems der chemischen thermodynamic. *Zeitschrift fur Physikalische Chemie,* 1907. 61: p. 129-165.

[10] Van der Berg, C. and S. Bruin, Water activity and its estimation in food systems: Theoretical aspects, in Water Activity: Influences on Food Quality, L. Rockland and G. Stewart, Editors. 1981, Academic Press.

[11] Gal, S., Expression of concentration of water vapor in water vapor sorption measurements. *Helvetica Chimica Acta* 1972. 55: p. 1752.

[12] Brunauer, S., et al., On a theory of the van der Waals adsorption of gases. *J Am Chem Soc,* 1940. 62(7): p. 1723-1732.

[13] Rahman, M.S. and T.P. Labuza, Water activity and food preservation, in Handbook of food preservation M.S. Rahman, Editor 2007c, CRC.

[14] Iglesias, H.A. and J. Chirife, Handbook of food isotherms: water sorption parameters for food and food components1982: Academic Press.

[15] Peleg, M., Assessment of a semi-empirical four parameter general model for sigmoid moisture sorption isotherm. *Journal of Food Process Engineering*, 1993. 16(1): p. 21-37.

[16] Bader, H.G. and D. Göritz, Investigations on high amylose corn starch films. Part 2: Water vapor sorption. *Starch-Stärke*, 1994. 46(7): p. 249-252.

[17] Coupland, J.N., et al., Modeling the effect of glycerol on the moisture sorption behavior of whey protein edible films. *Journal of Food Engineering*, 2000. 43(1): p. 25-30.

[18] Al-Muhtaseb, A., W. McMinn, and T. Magee, Moisture sorption isotherm characteristics of food products: a review. *Food and Bioproducts Processing*, 2002. 80(2): p. 118-128.

[19] Al-Muhtaseb, A., W. McMinn, and T. Magee, Water sorption isotherms of starch powders: Part 1: Mathematical description of experimental data. *Journal of Food Engineering*, 2004. 61(3): p. 297-307.

[20] Van den Berg, C., Food-water relations: Progress and integration, comments and thoughts, in Water Relationships in Foods, L. Slade and H. Levine, Editors. 1991, Plenum Press. p. 21-28.

[21] Roos, Y.H., Phase transitions in foods1996: Academic Press.

[22] Slade, L. and H. Levine, Glass transitions and water-food structure interactions. *Advances in food and nutrition research*, 1995. 38: p. 103-269.

[23] Roos, Y., et al., Mapping the different states of food components using state diagrams. *Modern Biopolymer Science*, 2009: p. 261-276.
[24] Menard, K.P., Dynamic mechanical analysis: a practical introduction2008: CRC.
[25] Le Meste, M., et al., Glass transition and food technology: A critical appraisal. *J Food Sci*, 2002. 67(7): p. 2444-2458.
[26] Williams, M.L., R.F. Landel, and J.D. Ferry, The temperature dependence of relaxation mechanisms in amorphous polymers and other glass-forming liquids. *J. Am. Chem. Soc*, 1955. 77(14): p. 3701-3707.
[27] Kasapis, S. and S.S. Sablani, A fundamental approach for the estimation of the mechanical glass transition temperature in gelatin. *Int J Biol Macromol*, 2004. 36(1): p. 71-78.
[28] Renzetti, S., et al., Water migration mechanisms in amorphous powder material and related agglomeration propensity. *Journal of Food Engineering*, 2011. 110(2): p. 160-168.
[29] Gordon, M. and J. Taylor, Ideal copolymers and the second order traditions of synthetic rubbers I. Non-crystalline copolymers. *Journal of Applied Chemistry*, 1952. 2: p. 593-600.
[30] Steendam, R., et al., Plasticisation of amylodextrin by moisture: Consequences for drug release from tablets. *Int J Pharm*, 2000. 204(1): p. 23-33.
[31] Couchman, P. and F. Karasz, A classical thermodynamic discussion of the effect of composition on glass-transition temperatures. *Macromolecules*, 1977. 11(1): p. 117-119.
[32] Enrione, J.I., S.E. Hill, and J.R. Mitchell, Sorption and Diffusional Studies of Extruded Waxy Maize Starch-Glycerol Systems. *Starch-Stärke*, 2007a. 59(1): p. 1-9.
[33] van der Sman, R. and M. Meinders, Prediction of the state diagram of starch water mixtures using the Flory–Huggins free volume theory. *Soft Matter,* 2011. 7(2): p. 429-442.
[34] van Sleeuwen, R.M.T., S. Zhang, and V. Normand, Spatial Glass Transition Temperature Variations in Polymer Glass: Application to a Maltodextrin–Water System. *Biomacromolecules*, 2012. 13(3): p. 787-797.
[35] Díaz, P., et al., Effect of glycerol on water sorption of bovine gelatin films in the glassy state. *Procedia Food Science*, 2011. 1: p. 267-274.
[36] Kilburn, D., et al., Carbohydrate polymers in amorphous states: An integrated thermodynamic and nanostructural investigation. *Biomacromolecules*, 2005. 6(2): p. 864-879.
[37] Townrow, S., et al., Molecular packing in amorphous carbohydrate matrixes. *The Journal of Physical Chemistry B*, 2007. 111(44): p. 12643-12648.
[38] Townrow, S., et al., Specific volume− hole volume correlations in amorphous carbohydrates: Effect of temperature, molecular weight, and water content. *The Journal of Physical Chemistry B,* 2010. 114(4): p. 1568-1578.
[39] Roussenova, M., et al., A nanostructural investigation of glassy gelatin oligomers: molecular organization and interactions with low molecular weight diluents. *New Journal of Physics*, 2012. 14(3): p. 035016.
[40] Trotzig, C., S. Abrahmsén-Alami, and F.H.J. Maurer, Transport properties of water in hydroxypropyl methylcellulose. *European Polymer Journal*, 2009. 45(10): p. 2812-2820.

[41] Peppas, N. and J. Sinclair, Anomalous transport of penetrants in glassy polymers. *Colloid & Polymer Science*, 1983. 261(5): p. 404-408.
[42] Enrione, J., Mechanical stability of intermediate moisture starch-glycerol systems, 2005, University of Nottingham.
[43] Farhat, I.A., J.M.V. Blanshard, and J.R. Mitchell, The retrogradation of waxy maize starch extrudates: Effects of storage temperature and water content. *Biopolymers*, 2000. 53(5): p. 411-422.
[44] Slade, L. and H. Levine, Non-Equilibium Melting of Native Granular Starch: Part I: Temperature Location of the Glass Transition Associated with Gelatinisation of A type Cereal Starches. *Carbohydrate Research*, 1988. 8: p. 183.
[45] Roos, Y.H., Phase Transitions in Foods1995, San Diego, USA.: Academic Press.
[46] Lauritzen, J.I. and J.D. Hoffman, Extension theory of growth of chain-folded polymer crystals to large undercoolings. *Journal of Applied Physics*, 1973. 44(10): p. 4340.
[47] Mousia, Z., Structural and Mechanical Propereties of Biopolymer and Biopolymer-Sugar Blends, in Food Sciences2000, University of Nottingham: Sutton Bonington.
[48] Farhat, I., J. Blanshard, and J. Mitchell, The retrogradation of waxy maize starch extrudates: Effects of storage temperature and water content. *Biopolymers*, 2000. 53(5): p. 411-422.
[49] Flory, P.J., Principles of polymer chemistry1953: Cornell University Press.
[50] Champion, D., M. Le Meste, and D. Simatos, Towards an improved understanding of glass transition and relaxations in foods: molecular mobility in the glass transition range. *Trends in Food Science & Technology*, 2000. 11(2): p. 41-55.
[51] Nicholls, R., et al., Glass transitions and the fracture behaviour of gluten and starches within the glassy state. *Journal of Cereal Science*, 1995. 21(1): p. 25-36.
[52] Watanabe, H., et al., Fracture stress of fish meat and the glass transition. *Journal of Food Engineering*, 1996. 29(3): p. 317-327.
[53] Payne, C. and T. Labuza, The brittle-ductile transition of an amorphous food system. *Drying technology*, 2005. 23(4): p. 871-886.
[54] Enrione, J.I., et al., Mechanical and Structural Stability of an Extruded Starch-protein-polyol Food System. *Journal of Food Research*, 2012. 1(2): p. p224.
[55] Ubbink, J. and J. Krüger, Physical approaches for the delivery of active ingredients in foods. *Trends in Food Science & Technology*, 2006. 17(5): p. 244-254.
[56] Partanen, R., et al., Encapsulation of sea buckthorn kernel oil in modified starches. *Journal of the American Oil Chemists' Society*, 2002. 79(3): p. 219-223.
[57] Soottitantawat, A., et al., Effect of water activity on the release characteristics and oxidative stability of D-limonene encapsulated by spray drying. *J Agric Food Chem*, 2004. 52(5): p. 1269-1276.
[58] Beristain, C., E. Azuara, and E. Vernon-Carter, Effect of Water Activity on the Stability to Oxidation of Spray-Dried Encapsulated Orange Peel Oil Using Mesquite Gum (Prosopis Juliflora) as Wall Material. *J Food Sci*, 2006. 67(1): p. 206-211.
[59] Karmas, R., M. Pilar Buera, and M. Karel, Effect of glass transition on rates of nonenzymic browning in food systems. *J Agric Food Chem*, 1992. 40(5): p. 873-879.
[60] Bell, L.N., Kinetics of non-enzymatic browning in amorphous solid systems: Distinguishing the effects of water activity and the glass transition. *Food Research International*, 1995. 28(6): p. 591-597.

[61] Bell, L.N., et al., Glycine loss and Maillard browning as related to the glass transition in a model food system. *J Food Sci*, 1998. 63(4): p. 625-628.

[62] Schebor, C., et al., Color formation due to non-enzymatic browning in amorphous, glassy, anhydrous, model systems. *Food Chemistry*, 1999. 65(4): p. 427-432.

[63] Hill, S.A., et al., The effect of thermal history on the maillard reaction in a glassy matrix. *J Agric Food Chem*, 2005. 53(26): p. 10213-10218.

[64] Sapru, V. and T. Labuza, Glassy State in Bacterial Spores Predicted by Polymer Glass-Transition *Theory*. *J Food Sci*, 2006. 58(2): p. 445-448.

[65] Selma, M.V., et al., Optimisation of production and storage stability of the starter bacteria Streptococcus thermophilus and Lactobacillus plantarum. *Journal of the Science of Food and Agriculture*, 2007. 87(5): p. 765-772.

[66] Palzer, S., Food structures for nutrition, health and wellness. *Trends in Food Science & Technology*, 2009. 20(5): p. 194-200.

[67] Sekhon, B.S., Food nanotechnology–an overview. Nanotechnology, *science and applications*, 2010. 3: p. 1-15.

[68] Roussenova, M., et al., Plasticization, Antiplasticization, and Molecular Packing in Amorphous Carbohydrate-Glycerol Matrices. *Biomacromolecules*, 2010. 11(12): p. 3237-3247.

[69] Peters, R., et al., Identification and characterization of organic nanoparticles in food. *TrAC Trends in Analytical Chemistry*, 2011. 30(1): p. 100-112.

[70] Chaudhry, Q., et al., Applications and implications of nanotechnologies for the food sector. Food additives and contaminants, 2008. 25(3): p. 241-258.

[71] Gressler, S., et al., Nanoparticles and nanostructured materials in the food industry. *NanoTrust Dossier* 2010: p. 1-6.

[72] Hernández-Ledesma, B., M. del Mar Contreras, and I. Recio, Antihypertensive peptides: Production, bioavailability and incorporation into foods. *Adv Colloid Interface Sci*, 2011. 165(1): p. 23-35.

[73] Myllärinen, P., et al., Effect of glycerol on behaviour of amylose and amylopectin films. *Carbohydrate Polymers*, 2002. 50(4): p. 355-361.

[74] Enrione, J.I., S.E. Hill, and J.R. Mitchell, Sorption behavior of mixtures of glycerol and starch. *J Agric Food Chem*, 2007b. 55(8): p. 2956-2963.

[75] Ubbink, J., M.I. Giardiello, and H.J. Limbach, Sorption of water by bidisperse mixtures of carbohydrates in glassy and rubbery states. *Biomacromolecules*, 2007. 8(9): p. 2862-2873.

[76] Ubbink, J., Structural Advances in the Understanding of Carbohydrate Glasses, in Modern Biopolymer Science: Bridging the Divide between Fundamental Treatise and Industrial Application, Kasapis S, Norton IT, and U. J, Editors. 2009, Academic Press. p. 277-293.

[77] Anandaraman, S. and G. Reineccius, Stability of encapsulated orange peel oil. *Food Technology*, 1986. 40(11): p. 88-93.

[78] Liu, Y., B. Bhandari, and W. Zhou, Glass transition and enthalpy relaxation of amorphous food saccharides: a review. *J Agric Food Chem*, 2006. 54(16): p. 5701-5717.

[79] Williams, G. and D.C. Watts, Non-symmetrical dielectric relaxation behaviour arising from a simple empirical decay function. *Trans. Faraday Soc.*, 1970. 66: p. 80-85.

[80] Enrione, J.I., et al., Structural Relaxation of Salmon Gelatin Films in the Glassy State. *Food and Bioprocess Technology*, 2011: p. 1-8.

[81] Lourdin, D., et al., Structural relaxation and physical ageing of starchy materials. *Carbohydr Res*, 2002. 337(9): p. 827-833.

[82] Chung, H.J. and S.T. Lim, Physical aging of glassy normal and waxy rice starches: effect of aging temperature on glass transition and enthalpy relaxation. *Carbohydrate Polymers*, 2003. 53(2): p. 205-211.

[83] Chung, H.J., B. Yoo, and S.T. Lim, Effects of physical aging on thermal and mechanical properties of glassy normal corn starch. *Starch-Stärke*, 2005. 57(8): p. 354-362.

[84] Noel, T.R., et al., Physical aging of starch, maltodextrin, and maltose. *J Agric Food Chem*, 2005. 53(22): p. 8580-8585.

[85] Liu, Y., B. Bhandari, and W. Zhou, Study of glass transition and enthalpy relaxation of mixtures of amorphous sucrose and amorphous tapioca starch syrup solid by differential scanning calorimetry (DSC). *Journal of Food Engineering*, 2007. 81(3): p. 599-610.

[86] Surana, R., et al., Measurement of enthalpic relaxation by differential scanning calorimetry—effect of experimental conditions. *Thermochimica acta*, 2005. 433(1): p. 173-182.

[87] Truong, V., et al., Physical aging of amorphous fructose. *J Food Sci*, 2002. 67(8): p. 3011-3018.

[88] Badii, F., W. MacNaughtan, and I. Farhat, Enthalpy relaxation of gelatin in the glassy state. *Int J Biol Macromol*, 2005. 36(4): p. 263-269.

[89] Badii, F., et al., Enthalpy and mechanical relaxation of glassy gelatin films. *Food Hydrocolloids*, 2006. 20(6): p. 879-884.

[90] Surana, R., A. Pyne, and R. Suryanarayanan, Effect of aging on the physical properties of amorphous trehalose. *Pharm Res,* 2004. 21(5): p. 867-874.

[91] Hu, C.C., et al., Effect of physical aging on the gas transport properties of poly (methyl methacrylate) membranes. *Journal of Membrane Science*, 2007. 303(1): p. 29-36.

[92] Jin Kim, Y., et al., Kinetic process of enthalpy relaxation of glassy starch and effect of physical aging upon its water vapor permeability property. *Carbohydrate Polymers*, 2003. 53(3): p. 289-296.

[93] Allison, S.D., Effect of structural relaxation on the preparation and drug release behavior of poly (lactic-co-glycolic) acid microparticle drug delivery systems. *J Pharm Sci*, 2008. 97(6): p. 2022-2035.

In: Chemical Food Safety and Health
Editors: F. Pedreschi Plasencia and Z. Ciesarová
ISBN: 978-1-62948-339-9

Chapter 10

CHITOSAN FILMS WITH ANTIOXIDANT AND ANTIMICROBIAL PROPERTIES AS ACTIVE PACKAGING

J. F. Rubilar[1*], R. M. S. Cruz[2, 3], I. Khmelinskii[3, 4] and M. C. Vieira[2, 3]

[1]Departamento de Ingeniería Química y Bioprocesos, Pontificia Universidad Católica de Chile, Santiago, Chile
[2]Departamento de Engenharia Alimentar, Instituto Superior de Engenharia, Universidade do Algarve, Campus da Penha, Faro, Portugal
[3]CIQA- Centro de Investigação em Química do Algarve, Universidade do Algarve, Campus de Gambelas, Faro, Portugal
[4]Departamento de Química e Farmácia, Faculdade de Ciências e Tecnologia, Universidade do Algarve, Campus de Gambelas, Faro, Portugal

ABSTRACT

Edible films are thin layers of edible materials that can be applied onto food products, playing an important role in their distribution, marketing and preservation along of the food chain by acting as a barrier between the food and the surrounding environment. Their functions include protecting the product from mechanical damage, physical, chemical and microbiological deterioration. Edible films with antimicrobial and antioxidant properties constitute one of the most important kinds of active packaging, being developed to reduce, inhibit or stop the growth of microorganisms on food surface.

Thus, the objective of this chapter is to present and discuss selected aspects of hydrocolloid edible films and coatings. In particular, active compounds and film-forming materials are presented and their physical (*e.g.* thickness, water solubility, moisture content, optical, water vapor permeability, *FTIR* and *X-ray* structural data), mechanical

* Corresponding author: Dr. Javiera F. Rubilar Parra, Departamento de Ingeniería Química y Bioprocesos, Pontificia Universidad Católica de Chile, Av. Vicuña Mackenna 4860, Santiago, Chile. Phone: +56-2-23544264; E-mail: jrubilar@ing.puc.cl.

(*e.g.* tensile strength, elongation-at-break), antimicrobial and also antioxidant properties discussed.

1. Introduction

The biggest driving force for innovation in food packaging has been the increasing consumer demand for safe, high quality, minimally processed, and extended shelf-life foods. As a result of this demand, the area of food packaging had to make a major change in the direction of development and innovation [1-3]. Thus, it had to shift from the traditional concept of packaging aimed at protecting the product with minimum package/product interaction, to a new concept that focuses on the idea that some active interactions between the package and the product may have positive effects [1, 4, 5]. Active packaging (AP) is therefore one of the most innovative food packaging concepts, introduced as a response to the consumer preferences [1, 4-7].

Edible films with antimicrobial and antioxidant properties have reformulated the concept of active packaging, being developed to reduce, inhibit or stop the growth of microorganisms on food surface [3]. Indeed, in most fresh or processed products microbial contamination occurs at the surface of food, therefore, an effective system to control the growth of microorganisms is required [8, 9]. Traditionally, antimicrobial and antioxidant agents are added to foods directly, their activity, however, may be reduced or inhibited by different components of food products, decreasing their efficiency; on the other hand, the consumers dislike food with chemical additives. In such cases, implementation of films or coatings may be more efficient than bulk natural antimicrobial additives used in the foodstuffs, since they can migrate selectively and gradually from the active packaging material to the food surface, producing the desired effects [10].

2. Active Packaging

AP is a system that changes the package structure and condition to improve the preservation of food properties, improve safety, enhance sensory quality and further extend shelf-life [6]. On the other hand, intelligent packaging solutions may include an external or internal indicator, providing information on the product history or food quality [7]. Such intelligent packaging systems can sense and record changes in the external or internal environment of the product and inform the consumer on the effect of these changes upon safety and quality of the food product [6, 11, 12].

AP can be classified into scavenging (absorbers) and release systems (emitters). Scavenging systems can remove oxygen, excessive moisture, ethylene, carbon dioxide and other specific undesirable compounds. Release systems emit into packaged food compounds such as carbon dioxide, water, antioxidants (AOX) and antimicrobials (AM) [6, 12].

2.1. Antimicrobial Food Packaging

AM food packaging is a packaging system that can reduce, inhibit and/or stop the growth of microorganisms in food. AM packaging can minimize food spoilage caused by microorganisms contaminating the food surface [13, 14]. By releasing preservatives from the package (rather than mixing preservatives into the bulk of the food), a smaller amount of AM compound is needed to prevent the growth of microorganisms on food surfaces [1, 4, 15].

For the consumer, it seems safer when active agents are indirectly integrated in the food package and released into the food product thereafter. Moreover, consumers tend to accept products to which naturally occurring substances have been added rather than those containing synthetic agents [4]. This idea was first developed in the early 1980's when Ghosh et al. [16] developed a cheese wrapping paper containing sorbates as antifungal agents, using carboxy methyl cellulose (CMC) as a binder. In the last decade, AM packaging has become more interesting as shown by the increasing number of publications on this topic [5]. Several types of packaging materials, in which various polymeric matrices are mixed with different AM agents, have been described. This technology has resulted in advancements in food packaging and has opened up new options for AM packaging systems. Such packaging systems not only protect food from post-contamination but also inhibit growth of pre-contaminating microorganisms [1, 3, 4, 15, 17, 18].

2.1.1. Potential Antimicrobial Agents Used in Packaging Systems

There are several types of AM agents used in packaging systems. Several publications have reviewed previous studies and advances in AM food packaging using a wide range of AM agents. Brody et al. [19] reviewed 33 AM packaging systems that were studied during 1973-1999. A further review by Ahvenainen [20] assessed 61 research studies published between 1973 and 2002, and Han [4] extended the review to 70 studies between 1973 and 2003. These studies include synthetic chemicals, naturally occurring substances and biotechnology products. Han [10] has summarized some antimicrobial agents that may potentially be used in packaging materials (Table 1).

2.2. Active Agents in AM packaging

This section reviews the AM activity of common active agents used in AM packaging systems, in particular, plant-volatiles and plant extracts.

2.2.1. Plant-Volatiles

Despite modern improvements in hygiene and food production techniques, food safety is an increasingly important public health issue [21]. It has been estimated that as many as 30% of people in industrialized countries suffer from a food-borne disease each year and in 2000 at least two million people died from diarrhea worldwide [21]. Therefore, there is still a need for new methods for reducing or eliminating food-borne pathogens, possibly in combination with existing methods (the hurdle principle) [22]. At the same time, the Western society appears to be experiencing a trend for 'green' consumption [23, 24], desiring fewer synthetic food

Table 1. Antimicrobial agents for AP systems

Classification	Antimicrobial agents
Acid anhydrides	Benzoic anhydride, sorbic anhydride
Alcohol	Ethanol
Amine	Hexamethylenetetramine (HMT)
Ammonium compound	Silicon quaternary ammonium salt
Antibiotics	Natamycin, neomycin sulfate, reuterin
Antimicrobial Peptides	Attacin, cecropin, defensin, magainin, q4-residue synthetic peptide (6K8L)
Antioxidants	Butylated hydroxyanisole (BHA), butylated hydroxytoluene (BHT), tertiary butylhydroquinone (TBHQ), iron salts
Bacteriocins	Bavaricin, brevicin, carnocin, lacticin, mesenterocin, nisin, pediocin, sakacin, subtilin
Chelating agents	Citrate, conalbumin, ethylenediamine tetraacetic acid (EDTA), lactoferrin, polyphosphate, protoporphyrin IX, zinc protoporphyrin IX.
Enzymes	Chitinase, etanol oxidase, β-Glucanase, glucose oxidase, lactoperoxidase, lysozyme, myeloperoxidase
Oligosaccharides	Chitooligosaccharide
Organic acids	Acetic acid, ρ-aminobenzoic acid, benzoic acid, citric acid, lactic acid, malic acid, propionic acid, sorbic acid, succinic acid, tartaric acid
Organic acid salts	Potassium sorbates, sodium benzoate, sodium citrate, sodium propionate
Parabens	Ethyl paraben, methyl paraben, propyl paraben
Phenols	Catechin, ρ-cresol, epicatechin, epichatechin gallate, gallic acid hydroquinones
Plant-volatiles	Allyl isothiocyanate (AIT), carvacrol, cionele, cinnamaldehyde, citral, ρ-cymene, estragole (methylchavicol), eugenol, geraniol, hinokitiol (β-thujaplicin), linalool, pinene, terpineol, thymol
Plant/spice extracts	Grape seed extract, grapefruit extract, hop beta acid, Brassica erucic acid oli, rosemary oil, oregano oil, basil oil
Polysaccharides	Chitosan, konjac glucomannan
Probiotics	Lactic acid bacteria
Sanitising gas	Ozone, chloride dioxide, carbon monoxide, carbon dioxide
Sanitisers	Cetyl pyridinium chloride, acidified NaCl, triclosan
Fatty acids	Lauric acid, palmitoleic acid
Fatty acid esters	Glycerol mono-laurate, monolaurin (Lairicidin®)
Fungicides	Benomyl, imazalil, sulfur dioxide
Inorganic acids	Phosphoric acid
Metals	Copper, silver, zirconium

Source: Han [10] with modifications.

additives and products with a smaller impact on the environment. Furthermore, the World Health Organization (WHO) has recently called for a world-wide reduction in the consumption of salt in order to reduce the incidence of cardio-vascular disease [25]. If the level of salt in processed foods is reduced, it is possible that other additives will be needed to maintain the safety of foods. Therefore, there is scope for new methods of making food safe, with a natural or "green" image. One such possibility is the use of essential oils (EOs) as antibacterial additives [26].

The EOs (also called volatile or ethereal oils) are aromatic oily liquids obtained from plant material (flowers, buds, seeds, leaves, twigs, bark, herbs, wood, fruit, and roots). They can be obtained by expression, fermentation, enfleurage or extraction, although the method of steam distillation is the one most commonly used for commercial production of EOs [27]. The term "essential oil" is thought to derive from the name coined in the 16th century by the Swiss reformer of medicine, Paracelsus von Hohenheim; he named the effective component of a drug *Quinta essentia* [28]. An estimated, about 3000 EOs are known, of which about 300 are commercially important, destined chiefly for the flavors and fragrances market [27]. It has long been recognized that some EOs have AM properties [1, 29] and these have been reviewed in the past [30, 31], as have the AM properties of spices [30], but the relatively recent enhancement of interest in "green" consumerism has led to a renewal of scientific interest in these substances [10, 31]. Besides antibacterial properties [32], EOs or their components have been shown to exhibit antiviral [33], antimycotic [34], antitoxigenic [35], antiparasitic [36], and insecticidal [37] properties. These characteristics are possibly related to the function of these compounds in plants [38]. Many compounds of the EOs are generally recognized as safe (GRAS), status defined by FDA (US Food and Drug Administration) including carvacrol [1, 17, 39] and thymol [1]. The effects of plant-volatiles on different model systems are shown in Table 2.

2.2.2. Plant Extracts

The extension of shelf-life has been an increasing trend in the food industry. For this reason, plant extracts have been used as an alternative to chemical or synthetic AM and AOX against foodborne pathogens and as inhibitors of lipid oxidation [51]. Major groups of chemicals present in plant extracts include polyphenols, quinines, flavanols/flavanoids, alkaloids, and lectins [52]. Phenolic extracts prepared from sage, rosemary, thyme, hops, coriander, green tea, grape seed, cloves, and basil are known to have antimicrobial effects against foodborne pathogens [51].

Grapefruit seed extract (GFSE) was found effective against E. coli, S. aureus, and Bacillus subtilis [53]. Natural agents have been studied with the intention of replacing conventional preservatives as a response to consumers objecting to having synthetic substances in their food [53-55].

Natural plant extracts in conjunction with other hurdles like low storage temperature, low pH, anaerobic conditions, organic acids, bacteriocins, and irradiation showed synergistic AM action in various food systems [56-58].

Lipid oxidation is one of the major deteriorative chemical changes that decreases the shelf-life of food products and could decrease their overall acceptability [59]. Oxidation of labile double bonds in polyunsaturated fatty acids (PUFA) produces secondary oxidative compounds such as hexanal, pentanal, heptanal, and octanal, which are responsible for quality deterioration and warmed over flavors (WOF), also presenting health risks [60].

Table 2. Effects of plant-volatiles on different model systems

Model system	AM agents (concentrations)	Microbial dynamics	Quality attributes	References
Fruit yogurt	Vanillin (2000 ppm)	Yeast, bacteria (delays growth)	Shelf-life (↑)	[40]
Tomato juice	Clove oil (0.1%) Mint extract (1.0%)	Total plate count (3.9 LR) Total plate count (8.34 LR)	Shelf-life (↑), vitamin C (~)	[41]
Ready-to-eat fruit salad	Citral (25-125 ppm) Citron (300-900 ppm)	Yeasts and lactic acid bacteria (LAB) (delays growth)	Shelf-life (↑)	[42]
	Citron (600 ppm)	*Salmonella enteritidis* E4 (2.0 LR) *Escherichia coli* 555 (<4.5 LR) *Listeria monocytogenes Scott A* (4 LR)	Sensory characteristics (~)	
Raspberries	Methyl jasmonate Allyl isothiocyanate EO of *Melaleuca alternifolia* (tea tree oil)		AC (↑) AC (↓) AC (↑)	[43]
Lettuce	Thyme oil (1 ml/l)	*E. coli* (6.32 LR)	Quality (↑)	[44]
Baby carrot	Thyme oil (1 ml/l)	*E. coli* (5.57 LR)	Quality (↑)	[44]
Minimally processed carrots	Oregano oil (250 ppm)	Background spoilage microflora total viable count (>1.0 LR) Lactic acid bacteria (LAB) (>1.0 LR) *Pseudomonas* (<1.0 LR)	Sensory characteristics (~)	[45]
Minimally processed vegetables	Thyme oil (1%)	*Aeromonas spp* (2.0 LR) *Psyschrotrophic plate count* (4.19 LR) Plate count agar (5.44 LR)	Sensory properties(↓), Shelf-life(↑)	[46]
Chicken meat	EOs of mustard oil	Brochothrix thermosphacta (~) *Lactobacillus alimentarius* (~)	Proximate composition (~), shelf-life (↑)	[47]

Model system	AM agents (concentrations)	Microbial dynamics	Quality attributes	References
Beef hot dog	Clove oil (5 ml/l)	*L. monocytogenes* (1.15-1.71 LR)		[48]
	Thyme oil (1 ml/l)	*L. monocytogenes* (0.67-1.05 LR)		
Minced beef	*Capsicum annum* extract	*Salmonella typhimurium* (Minimum lethal concentration, MLC 15 g/Kg) *Pseudomonas aeruginosa* (MLC 30 g/Kg)		[49]
Chicken frankfurter	Clove oil (1.0%)	*L. monocytogenes* (4.5 LR)		[50]

LR: microbial log reduction. ↓ and ↑ indicate increase and decrease, respectively, ~ shows no significant difference with respect to control. AC = anthocyanin content.

The reaction-chain mechanism involved in lipid oxidation in foods can be described by three steps.

Step 1. Initiation

The free radicals ($R^{\bullet}$) are formed by loss of hydrogen radical ($H^{\bullet}$) from an unsaturated fatty acid (RH).

$$RH \xrightarrow{\text{Initiator}} R^{\bullet} + H^{\bullet}$$

Step 2. Propagation

The free radicals react with oxygen (O_2) in presence of light, heat or trace metals to form peroxyl radicals ($ROO^{\bullet}$). Next, peroxyl radicals react with more unsaturated fatty acids to form lipid hydroperoxides (ROOH) and more free radicals ($R^{\bullet}$), which in turn react with oxygen feeding the reaction chain. This propagation cycle will continue until step 3 takes place.

$$R^{\bullet} + O_2 \rightarrow ROO^{\bullet}$$
$$ROO^{\bullet} + \rightarrow RH\ ROOH + R^{\bullet}$$

Step 3. Termination

The chain oxidation process terminates when two free radicals react to produce a non-radical species (ROOR or RR).

$$ROO^{\bullet} + ROO^{\bullet} \rightarrow ROOR + O_2$$
$$ROO^{\bullet} + R^{\bullet} \rightarrow ROOR$$
$$R^{\bullet} + R^{\bullet} \rightarrow RR$$

The AOX activity refers to the act of delaying or inhibiting the oxidation of lipids or other molecules by inhibiting partially or totally the initiation or propagation step of the oxidative chain reactions or forming stable radicals ($A^{\bullet}$) that are either unreactive or form non-radical products [61].

$$ROO^{\bullet} + AR \rightarrow ROOR + A^{\bullet}$$

For example, polyphenolic compounds (mainly flavonoids) present in green tea extract and grape seed extract have demonstrated potential antioxidant properties due to their redox potential; this enables them to act in various ways, such as hydrogen donors, reducing agents, reactive oxygen quenchers, and chelating metal ions in numerous food applications [51, 62]. The active hydroxyl groups present in the molecular structure of polyphenols ((-)-epicatechin, (-)-epigallocatechin, (-)-epicatechin-3-gallate, (-)-epigallocatechin-3-gallate) are the active components of green tea extract that can interact with the free radicals to inhibit lipid oxidation [63]. Furthermore, tea polyphenols can exhibit scavenging activity against free radicals [64], superoxide radicals, peroxynitrite, and can chelate copper and iron, preventing metal-catalyzed free radical formation [65].

Flavonoids present in plant extracts terminate the radical chain reactions that occur during the oxidation of triglycerides in food systems (fats, oils, and emulsions) and thus can act as free radical scavengers [66].

3. AM Food Packaging Systems

Considering the void volume existing in a packaging system between the package and the food product as the headspace, most food packaging systems represent either a package/food system or a package/headspace/food system [20]. A package/food system is a package in contact with a solid product, or a low viscosity/liquid food without head space. Examples of food packages that can be included in this system are wrapped cheese, deli products and aseptic meat packages. Diffusion between the packaging material and the food and partitioning at the interface are the main migration phenomena involved in such a system [67]. An AM compound incorporated into the packaging material can migrate into the food through diffusion, affected by partitioning, as shown in Figure 1.1.

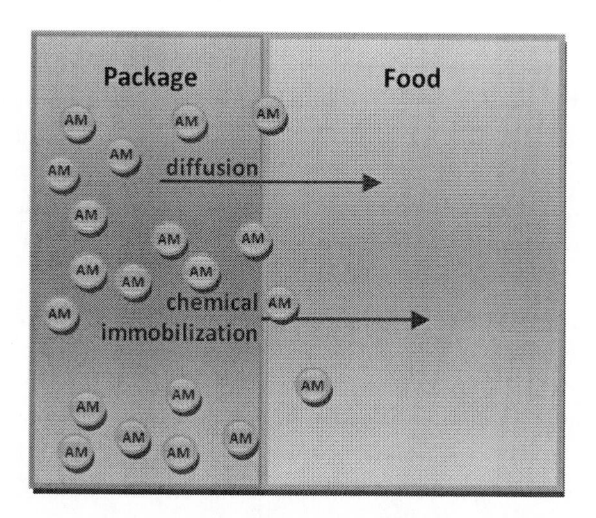

Figure 1.1. Diffusion of AM compound in a package/food system [68].

Examples of package/headspace/food systems include flexible packaging, bottles, cans, cups and cartons. Evaporation or equilibrated distribution of a substance among the head space, packaging materials and food are to be considered as parts of the main migration mechanism to estimate the interfacial distribution of an AM substance [67].

Compared to a non-volatile substance, which can only migrate through the contact area between the package and the food, a volatile substance can migrate through the headspace and air gap between the package and the food, as shown in Figure 1.2.

Other than diffusion and equilibrated sorption, some AM packaging systems use covalently immobilized antibiotics or fungicides. In this case, surface microbial growth is suppressed by immobilization of a non-food grade AM substance without diffusional mass transfer [67].

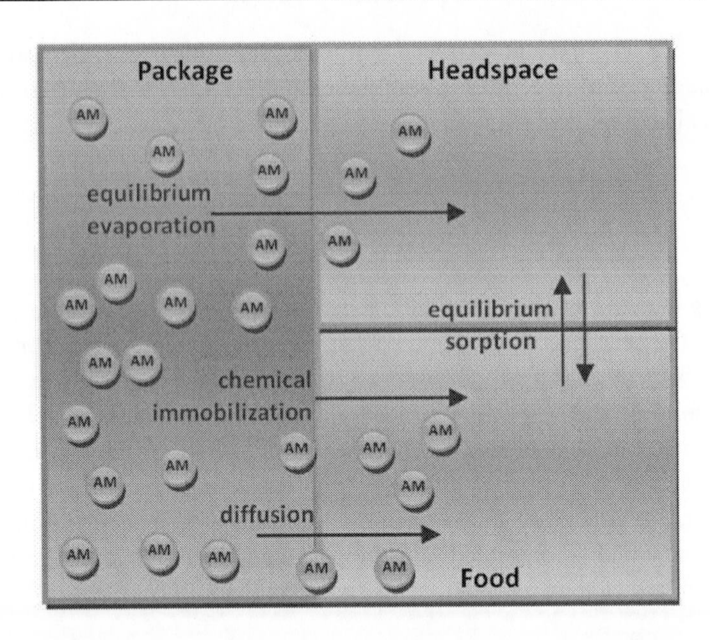

Figure 1.2. Diffusion of AM compound in a package/headspace/food system [13].

Sánchez et al. [69] produced and tested a multi-layer AM film made of polypropylene (PP), ethylene vinyl alcohol (EVOH), and polyethylene (PE), containing cinnamon extract. The PP/EVOH/PE film was observed to remotely inhibit the AM activity of fungi. In this case, vapors of an AM agent released from the multi-layer film produced a protective AM atmosphere, while direct contact was unnecessary.

3.1. Controlled Release

Design of an antimicrobial packaging system requires a balanced consideration of controlled release technology and microbial growth kinetics. When the mass transfer rate of an AM compound is faster than the growth rate of the target microorganism, the loaded AM compound will be diluted to less than the effective critical concentration (i.e. minimal inhibitory concentration, MIC) before the expected storage period is complete, and the packaging system will lose its AM activity because the packaged food has almost infinite volume compared to the volume of the packaging material and the amount of AM compound [4]. Consequently, the microorganism will start to grow following depletion of the AM compound. On the contrary, when the migration rate is too slow to maintain the concentration above the MIC, the microorganism can grow instantly, before the AM compound is released [26, 70]. Therefore, the release rate of the AM compound from the packaging material to the food must be controlled specifically to match the mass transfer rate with the growth kinetics of the target microorganism. Controversially, in the case of AM edible coating systems the mass transfer of antimicrobial agents is not desirable, since the migration of the incorporated AM compound from the coating layer into the food product dilutes the concentration in the coating layer. Once again, compared to the volume of the coating layer, the coated food has an almost infinite volume (Figure 1.3). Therefore, the migration will deplete the AM compound in the coating layer, decrease the concentration below the MIC, and thus reduce the AM activity of the coating system. The migration of incorporated AM agents contributes to AM effectiveness in the case of packaging systems; on the contrary, zero migration is beneficial in a coating system [67].

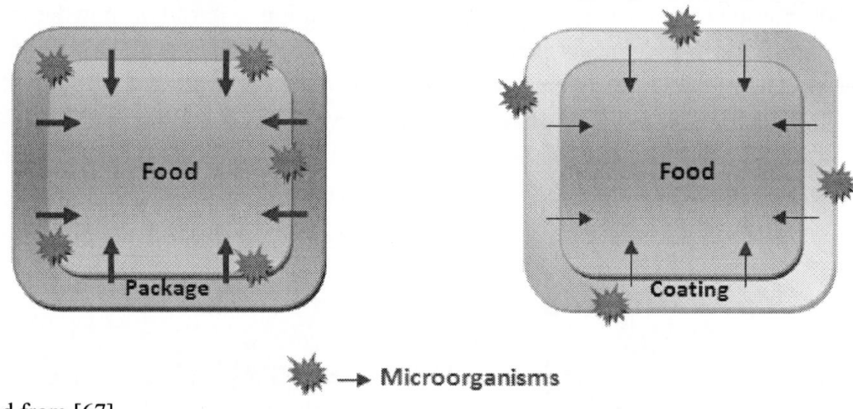

Modified from [67].

Figure 1.3. Antimicrobial packaging and edible coating systems.

The solubility of the AM agents in foods is a critical factor of AM release. If the AM compound is highly soluble in food, the migration profile will follow an unconstrained free diffusion, while the very low solubility creates a dissolution-dependent monolithic system. For example, when highly soluble potassium sorbate was incorporated in packaging materials (e.g. plastic films or papers) and the AM packaging materials were used for semi-solid or high-moisture foods, such as paste, yogurt, fruit jelly, soft cheese and sliced ham, potassium sorbate dissolved in food immediately after packaging. Initially, potassium sorbate concentration increased very rapidly on the food surface and next the surface concentration decreased slowly as potassium sorbate diffused into the food. Fast diffusion of the AM agents into food decreases their surface concentrations quite rapidly. Thus, the maintenance of required surface concentrations is highly dependent on the release rate from the packaging materials (diffusivity of packaging materials) and the migration rate in the foods (diffusivity of foods) [4].

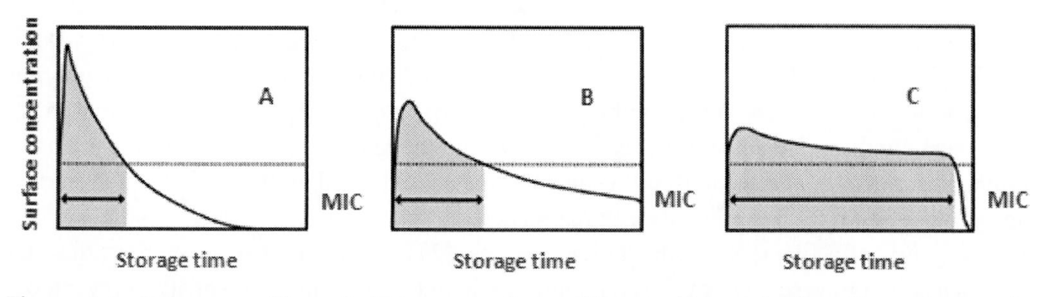

Figure 1.4. Release profiles of AM agents from different AM packaging films. System A- unconstrained free diffusion from packaging materials; system B — slow diffusion of very low solubility agents from monolithic packaging materials system C —slow dissolution from AM powder/tablets or gaseous agent release from concentrated antimicrobial sachets/tablets with constant volatility in a closed packaging system,modified from Han [4].

Release profiles of AM agents from three different AM packaging films are shown in Figure 1.4. System A is characterized by unconstrained free diffusion from packaging materials, or a fast dissolution of AM tablets; system B — slow diffusion of very low solubility agents from monolithic packaging materials; system C — membrane (reservoir) system with constant flux of permeation, slow dissolution from AM powder/tablets or gaseous agent release from concentrated antimicrobial sachets/tablets with constant volatility in a closed packaging system. System C is the best, once the concentration of the AM is kept above the MIC (dashed line). Dashed lines and arrows indicate the MIC of a target microorganism, and the period of shelf life maintaining the surface concentration over the MIC, respectively [4, 67].

4. Production of AM Films

There are five methods used to produce AM packaging films: (i) use of polymers that are inherently AM, (ii) addition of sachets/pads containing volatile AM agents into packages, (iii) incorporation of volatile and non-volatile AM agents directly into polymers, (iv) coating/spray AM onto polymer surfaces, (v) Immobilization of AM to polymers by ionic or covalent linkages [3].

4.1. Usage of AM Polymers

Some polymers are inherently AM and have been used in films and coatings. Cationic polymers such as chitosan and poly-L-lysine promote cell adhesion [71] since charged amines interact with negative charges on the cell membrane, causing leakage of intracellular constituents. Calcium alginate films reduced the growth of the natural flora and coliform inocula on beef, possibly due to the presence of calcium chloride [72]. Bactericidal acrylic polymers made by co-polymerizing acrylic protonated amine co-monomer have been proposed as packaging materials for increased shelf-life of fruit and vegetables [73]. Polymers containing biguanide substituents also yield AM activity [74].

Physical modification of polymers has been investigated as means to render surfaces AM. For example, the AM potential of polyamide films treated with UV irradiation has been reported with the AM activity presumably resulting from an increase in amine concentration on the film surface [75]. However, positively charged amine groups present on polymer surfaces may enhance cell adhesion but not necessarily death [76]. It is possible that in the tests mentioned, simple adsorption occurred, masking the lack of AM activity of the aminated polymer surface. A subsequent study on UV-treated nylon films showed that the surface amino groups were bactericidal, although bacterial cells were adsorbed to the surface, reducing the effectiveness of the amine groups [77]. In many cases, such studies are conducted in buffered systems. Still, addition of nutrients could potentially prevent cell membrane damage and enable bacterial recovery and/or inhibit the adhesion of the cells to the surface due to the interaction of salts and other cations with the surfaces [3].

4.1.1. Chitosan

During crustacean processing, shell wastes accounting for up to 60% of the original material are produced as a waste byproduct. One of the problems of the seafood industries is disposal of this solid waste. In 1970s, the Environmental Protection Agency (EPA) directed industries to stop dumping shell wastes of crab, lobster, and shrimp into the sea/land. These shells are rich in $CaCO_3$, protein, and polysaccharide, "chitin". The name "chitin" is derived from Greek word "chiton", meaning a coat of mail or envelope. Chitin is the second most abundant natural biopolymer after cellulose, being the major structural component of the exoskeleton of invertebrates, insects, yeast and fungal cells [78]. Invertebrates are the major source of chitin. Since biodegradation of chitin in crustacean shells is very slow, accumulation of large amount of waste from the processing of crustaceans has become a major concern in the seafood industry in coastal areas [79]. Globally, over 100 million tons of chitin is produced [80]. Hence, production of value-added products from such wastes and their application in different fields is of utmost interest. By two simple steps, demineralization (treatment with hot diluted hydrochloric acid, HCl) and deproteinization (treatment with hot diluted sodium hydroxide, NaOH), the amino polysaccharide chitin can be quantitatively recovered from crustacean wastes [81]. Chitin is known to form microfibrillar arrangement in living organisms. The fibrils having a diameter of 2.5-2.8 nm are usually embedded in the protein matrix; crustacean cuticles possess chitin microfibrils with diameters as large as 25 nm [82].

Chitosan is an N-deacetylated derivative of chitin (by treatment with hot alkali), with its structure composed of 2-amino-2-deoxy-β-D-glucose (GlcN) in a β(1,4) linkage, and with occasional N-acetyl glucosamine (GlcNAc) residues. The structure of chitin and chitosan resembles cellulose except at position C-2, being replaced by acetamido and/or amino groups, respectively (Figure 1.5) [83].

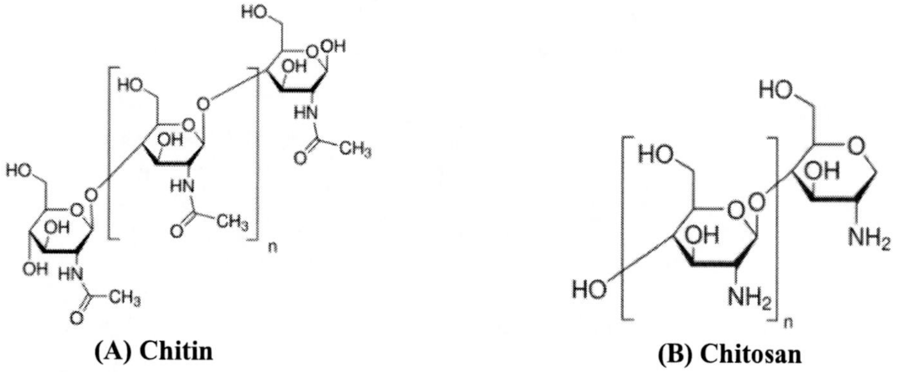

(A) Chitin **(B) Chitosan**

Figure 1.5. Chemical structures of chitin and chitosan.

The production of chitin and chitosan is currently based on crab and shrimp shells discarded by seafood canning industries. Since chitin is strongly associated with other constituents, harsh acidic/alkaline treatments are required to remove them from chitinous material. Figure 1.6 outlines the important steps in the extraction of chitin and chitosan. Initially proteins are removed by treating with hot NaOH solution. Minerals such as calcium carbonate and calcium phosphate are extracted with hot HCl. Discoloration (bleaching) is done with hydrogen peroxide or sodium hypochlorite solution followed by washing and drying. To obtain chitosan, chitin is again treated with strong NaOH at elevated temperature to deesterify the N-acetyl groups, thoroughly washed and dried [81].

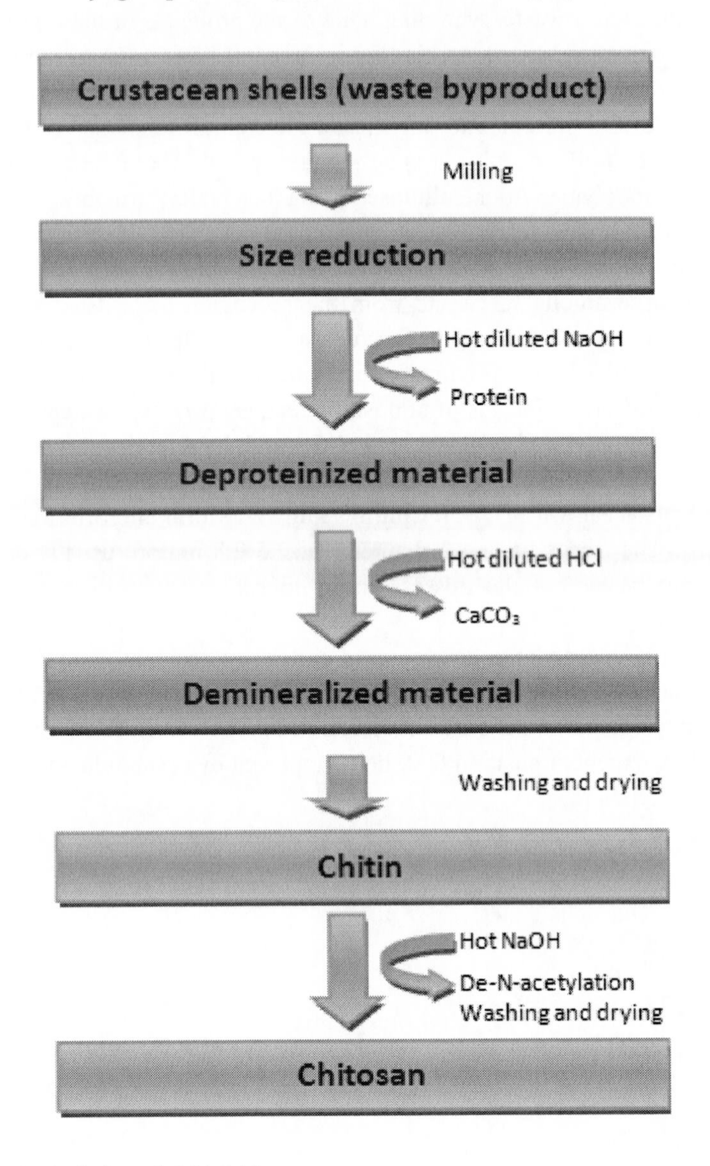

Figure 1.6. Steps for isolation of chitin/chitosan.

Having a positive charge on the C-2 of the glucosamine monomer below pH 6, chitosan is more soluble and has a better AM activity than chitin [84]. The exact mechanism of the AM action of chitin, chitosan and their derivatives is still imperfectly known, but different mechanisms have been proposed [85-87]. One of the reasons for the AM character of chitosan is its positively charged amino group which interacts with negatively charged microbial cell membranes, leading to the leakage of intracellular constituents of the microorganism [88]. Chitosan acts mainly on the outer surface of bacteria; at lower concentrations (0.2 mg/ml), the polycationic chitosan does probably bind to the negatively charged bacterial surface to cause agglutination, while at higher concentrations the larger number of positive charges may have imparted a net charge to the bacterial surface to keep bacteria in suspension [89, 90].

Studies based on UV absorption indicated that chitosan causes considerable losses of proteinic material to the *Pythium oaroecandrum* at pH 5.8 [91, 92]. Chitosan also acts as a chelating agent that selectively binds trace metals and thereby inhibits production of toxins and microbial growth [93]. It also activates several defense processes in the host tissue [94], acts as a water binding agent, and inhibits various enzymes. Binding of chitosan with DNA and inhibition of messenger ribonucleic acid (mRNA) synthesis occurs through chitosan penetration toward the nuclei of the microorganisms and interference with the synthesis of mRNA and proteins [90]. It has been proposed that when chitosan is liberated from the cell wall of fungal pathogens by plant host hydrolytic enzymes, it then penetrates to the nuclei of fungi and interferes with RNA and protein synthesis [95].

A microscopic examination of *Saccharomyces unisporus* after treatment with chitosan-salt, with a polymerisation degree of 25, showed agglutination of a refractive substance on the entire cell wall [96]. When chitosanase was added to the culture media containing chitosan-salt, no refractive substances were observed. In this study, there was an interaction between chitosan and the cell wall.

The mechanism of the AM activity of chitosan was different for gram-positive and gram-negative bacteria [97]. This study differentiated the effect of chitosan on *S. aureus* (gram-positive) and *E. coli* (gram-negative). For gram-positive *S. aureus*, the AM activity increased on increasing the molecular weight of chitosan. On the other hand, for gram-negative *E. coli*, the AM activity increased on decreasing molecular weight. The authors suggested two different mechanisms for the AM activity: (1) for *S. aureus*, chitosan on the cell wall forms a polymeric membrane, that inhibits nutrients from entering the cell and, (2) for *E. coli*, chitosan of lower molecular weight entered the cell through pervasion.

Chitosan inhibited the growth of *Aspergillus flavus* and aflatoxin production in liquid culture, pre-harvest maize, and groundnut, and it also enhanced phytoalexin production in germinating peanut [93]. It has also been found to inhibit growth and toxin production by *Alternaria alternata* fungal species *lycopersici* in culture [98, 99].

A solution at 0.10 mg/ml markedly inhibited the growth of *Xanthomonas* pathogenic bacteria (isolated from *Euphorbia pulcherrima*) of different geographical origins [100]. The bacterial activity of chitosan solution against *Xanthomonas axonopodis* pv. *Poinsettiicola* (strain R22580) increased with the increase of this compound concentration up to 0.10 mg/ml.

The antibacterial activity of chitosan was investigated by assessing the mortality rates of *E. coli* and *S. aureus* based on the extent of damaged or missing cell walls and the degree of leakage of enzymes and nucleotides from different cellular locations [101]. The inactivation of *E. coli* by chitosan occurred via a two-step sequential mechanism: an initial separation of the cell wall from its cell membrane, followed by destruction of the cell membrane. Chitosan has been used as a coating, appearing to protect fresh vegetables and fruit from fungal degradation. Although the AM effect is attributed to its antifungal properties, it may also be that it acts as a barrier between the nutrients contained in the produce and microorganisms [72]. In addition, chitosan-based AM films have been produced to carry organic acids and spices [10].

The AM properties of different chitosan films with the incorporation of different AM natural agents are listed in Table 3.

Depending on the method of film production, AM additives can affect physical, chemical or mechanical properties of the AM film such as water vapor, carbon dioxide or oxygen permeabilities, tensile strength (TS), elongation at break (EB), moisture content (MC), solubility (S), or color expressed as delta-E the total colour difference, or luminosity (*L*). Physico-mechanical and AOX properties of different chitosan films with natural additives are shown in Table 4.

4.2. Addition of Sachet/Pads Containing Volatile AM Agents into Packages

The most successful commercial application of AM packaging has been sachets that are enclosed loose or attached to the interior of a package. Three applications have predominated: oxygen absorbers, moisture absorbers and ethanol vapor generators. Oxygen and moisture absorbers are used primarily in bakery, pasta, produce and meat packaging to prevent oxidation and water condensation. Although oxygen absorbers may not be intended to be AM, a reduction in oxygen inhibits the growth of aerobes, particularly moulds. Moisture absorbers can reduce a_w, also indirectly affecting microbial growth. Both oxygen and moisture absorption technologies have been reviewed in detail by Rooney [109].

Ethanol vapor generators consist of ethanol absorbed or encapsulated in carrier materials and enclosed in polymer packets. Ethanol permeates the selective barrier and is released into the headspace within the package. Since the amount of ethanol generated is relatively small and effective only in products with reduced water activity ($a_w < 0.92$), this application have mainly been used to retard moulds in bakery and dried fish products [110]. Commercial examples include Ethicap®, heat sealed packets containing microencapsulated ethanol in silicon dioxide powder, and Fretek®, a paper wafer in which the centre layer is impregnated with ethanol in acetic acid and sandwiched between layers of polyolefin films [111]. One of the drawbacks is the characteristic off-flavor of ethanol.

The disadvantage of the addition of a sachet is the negative consumer response to the presence of material strange to the product, possibly causing economic losses to the producer. Another disadvantage is the risk of accidental rupture of the sachets or consumption of their contents [6].

Absorbing pads (diapers) are used in trays for packaged retail meats and poultry to soak up meat exudates. Organic acids and surfactants have been incorporated into these pads to prevent microbial growth in the exudates, which are rich in nutrients [112].

4.3. Incorporation of Volatile and Non-Volatile AM Agents Directly into Polymers

AM films produced by incorporation involve the integration of AM agents into the polymer matrix. The molecules of AM additives are physically bound in the structure of the polymer, and are released during the storage of the product. There are several types of incorporation mechanisms including absorption and impregnation.

Table 3. AM effects of chitosan films

Model system	AM agents (concentrations)	Microorganisms	Effects observed on microorganisms	References
Compound gelatin-chitosan films	BG (2% w/v) + Ch (0.75% w/v)	*S. aureus*	*S. aureus* surface growth was inhibited by film	[102]
	TG (2% w/v) + Ch (0.75% w/v)			
	BG (2% w/v) + Ch (1.5% w/v)			
	TG (2% w/v) + Ch (1.5% w/v)			
Chitosan films	Ch(2%) + CEO (0.4% v/v)	*L. monocytogenes*	Inhibitory zone (38 mm^2)	[103]
		L. sakei	≈ (39 mm^2)	
		P. fluorescens	≈ (34 mm^2)	
		E. coli	≈ (36 mm^2)	
	Ch(2%) + CEO (0.8% v/v)	*L. monocytogenes*	Inhibitory zone (39 mm^2)	
		L. plantarum	≈ (43 mm^2)	
		L. sakei	≈ (41 mm^2)	
		P. fluorescens	≈ (36 mm^2)	
		E. coli	≈ (38 mm^2)	
	Ch(2%) + CEO (1.5% v/v)	*L. monocytogenes*	Inhibitory zone (53 mm^2)	
		L. plantarum	≈ (49 mm^2)	
		L. sakei	≈ (56 mm^2)	
		P. fluorescens	≈ (41 mm^2)	
		E. coli	≈ (51 mm^2)	
	Ch(2%) + CEO (2.0% v/v)	*L. monocytogenes*	Inhibitory zone (52 mm^2)	
		L. plantarum	≈ (53 mm^2)	
		L. sakei	≈ (57 mm^2)	
		P. fluorescens	≈ (43 mm^2)	
		E. coli	≈ (51 mm^2)	
Chitosan films	Ch(2%) + TO (0.2% v/v)	*E. coli*	(+) contact area	[104]
		Klebsiella pneumonia	≈	
		P. aeruginosa	≈	
		S. aureus	≈	

Table 3. (Continued)

Model system	AM agents (concentrations)	Microorganisms	Effects observed on microorganisms	References
Chitosan films	Ch(2%) + TO (0.4% v/v)	*E. coli*	(+) contact area	
		Klebsiella pneumonia	≈	
		P. aeruginosa	≈	
		S. aureus	≈	
	Ch(2%) + TO (0.6% v/v)	*E. coli*	(+) contact area	
		Klebsiella pneumonia	≈	
		P. aeruginosa	≈	
		S. aureus	≈	
Chitosan films	Ch(2%) + TO (0.8% v/v)	*E. coli*	(+) contact area; Inhibitory zone (15.5 mm)	[104]
		Klebsiella pneumonia	(+) contact area	
		P. aeruginosa	(+) contact area	
		S. aureus	(+) contact area	
	Ch(2%) + TO (1.0% v/v)	*E. coli*	(+) contact area; Inhibitory zone (16 mm)	
		K. pneumonia	(+) contact area; Inhibitory zone (16 mm)	
		P. aeruginosa	(+) contact area	
		S. aureus	(+) contact area; Inhibitory zone (16 mm)	
	Ch(2%) + TO (1.2% v/v)	*E. coli*	(+) contact area; Inhibitory zone (17 mm)	
		K. pneumonia	(+) contact area; ; Inhibitory zone (19 mm)	
		P. aeruginosa	(+) contact area; Inhibitory zone (16 mm)	
		S. aureus	(+) contact area; Inhibitory zone (16 mm)	

Ch: Chitosan. CEO: cinnamon essential oil. TO: thyme oil (*Thymus vulgaris*). BG = bovine-hide gelatin. TG = tuna-skin gelatin +: represents an inhibitory effect

Table 4. Physico-mechanical and AOX properties of chitosan films

Model system	AM or AOX agents (concentrations)	Physico-mechanical and AOX properties	References
Chitosan films	Ch (1.5% w/v) + α-Tocopherol (0.1%)	(~)S; (~)MC; (~)WVP; (↓)TS; (↓)EB; (↓)*L*; (↑)AOX	[105]
	Ch (1.5% w/v) + α-Tocopherol (0.2%)	(~) S; (↓)MC; (↑)WVP; (↓)TS; (↓)EB; (↓)*L*; (↑)AOX	
Chitosan films	Ch (2% w/v) + ZEO (5%)	(↓)WVTR; (~)AOX; (↓)TS; (↓)EB; (~)color	[106]
	Ch (2% w/v) + ZEO (10%)	(↓)WVTR; (↑)AOX; (↓)TS; (↓)EB; (~)color	
	Ch (2% w/v) + GSE (10%)	(↓)WVTR; (↑)AOX; (↓)TS; (↓)EB; (↓)*L*	
	Ch (2% w/v) + ZEO (5%) + GSE(10 %)	(↓)WVTR; (↑)AOX; (~)TS; (↓)EB; (↓)*L*	
	Ch (2% w/v) + ZEO (10%) + GSE (10 %)	(↑)WVTR; (↑)AOX; (↓)TS; (↑)EB; (↓)*L*	
Compound gelatin-chitosan films	BG (2% w/v) + Ch (0.75% w/v)	(~)EB; (↓) S; (↓) WVP	[102]
	TG (2% w/v) + Ch (0.75% w/v)	(↑)EB; (↓)S; (↓)WVP	
	BG (2% w/v) + Ch (1.5% w/v)	(~)EB; (↓)S; (↓)WVP	
	TG (2% w/v) + Ch (1.5% w/v)	(~)EB; (↓)S; (↓)WVP	
Chitosan films	Ch (2%) + CEO (0.4% v/v)	(~)MC; (↓)WVP; (~)S; (~)ΔE; (↑)TS; (↓)EB	[95]
	Ch (2%) + CEO (0.8% v/v)	(↓)MC; (↓)WVP; (↓)S; (↑)ΔE; (↑)TS; (↓)EB	
	Ch (2%) + CEO (1.5% v/v)	(↓)MC; (↓)WVP; (↓)S; (↑)ΔE; (↑)TS; (↓)EB	
	Ch (2%) + CEO (2.0% v/v)	(↓)MC; (↓)WVP; (↓)S; (↑)ΔE; (↑)TS; (↓)EB	
Chitosan films	Ch (2%) + GTE (2% w/v)	(↓)*L* ; (~)WVP; (~)TS; (~)EB; (↑)AOX	[107]
	Ch (2%) + GTE (5% w/v)	(↓)*L* ; (↓)WVP; (~)TS; (~)EB; (↑)AOX	
	Ch (2%) + GTE (10% w/v)	(↓)*L* ; (↓)WVP; (↑)TS; (↑)EB; (↑)AOX	
	Ch (2%) + GTE (20% w/v)	(↓)*L* ; (↓)WVP; (↑)TS; (↑)EB; (↑)AOX	
Chitosan films	Ch(2%) + TO (0.2% v/v)	(↓)TS; (↓)EB; (~)WVP; (~)OTR; (~)AOX	[104]
	Ch(2%) + TO (0.4% v/v)	(↓)TS; (↓)EB; (↑)WVP; (↑)OTR; (~)AOX	
	Ch(2%) + TO (0.6% v/v)	(↓)TS; (↓)EB; (↑)WVP; (↑)OTR; (↑)AOX	
	Ch(2%) + TO (0.8% v/v)	(↓)TS; (↓)EB; (↑)WVP; (↑)OTR; (↑)AOX	
	Ch(2%) + TO (1.0% v/v)	(↓)TS; (↓)EB; (↑)WVP; (↑)OTR; (↑)AOX	
	Ch(2%) + TO (1.2% v/v)	(↓)TS; (↓)EB; (↑)WVP; (↑)OTR; (↑)AOX	

Table 4. (Continued)

Model system	AM or AOX agents (concentrations)	Physico-mechanical and AOX properties	References
Chitosan films	Chi(1%) + OA (1%v/w)	(↑)TS; (~)EB; (~)WVP	[108]
	Chi(1%) + OA (2%v/w)	(~)TS; (~)EB; (↓)WVP	
	Chi(1%) + OA (4%v/w)	(~)TS; (↓)EB; (↓)WVP	

Ch: Chitosan. ZEO: *Zataria multiflora* Boiss essential oil. CEO: cinnamon essential oil. GTE: green tea extract. TO: Thyme oil (*Thymus vulgaris*). OA: oleic acid. ↓ and ↑ indicate increase and decrease, respectively, while ~ shows no significant difference respect to control chitosan film. WVTR: water vapor transmission rate. WVP: water vapor permeability. OTR: oxygen transmission rate. TS: tensile strength (MPa). EB: elongation at break (%). S: solubility. MC: moisture content (%).ΔE: total color difference. *L*: Luminosity. AOX: antioxidant capacity.

4.3.1. Incorporation by Absorption

During the absorption process, a swelling agent can be used to enhance the absorption of AM agent in the film. For example, Weng et al. [113] used acetone as a swelling agent, which can be evaporated afterwards. A swollen polymer can uptake more AM agents into its matrix. Following evaporation, active AM agents will remain in the polymer.

Indeed, Weng et al. [113] studied the absorption of benzoic and sorbic acids into poly(ethylene-co-methacrylic acid) (PEMA). The PEMA films were prepared in a hydraulic heat press and pre-treated in two different ways: soaking in HCl and in NaOH. The films were next soaked in an acetone solution containing the AM agents. The AM films that were pre-treated with NaOH had better inhibitory effects on *Penicillium* sp. and *Aspergillus niger* than those pre-treated by HCl. The release study showed a higher concentration of the AM agents released from NaOH-treated films whereas the release from the HCl-treated films was very low. Infrared (IR) spectra of AM films confirmed that there was a higher absorption of AM agents in the NaOH-treated films than in HCl-treated films. Higher polarity of NaOH was proposed as an explanation of its capacity to promote absorption of AM organic acids.

4.3.2 Incorporation by Impregnation

AM agents can be mixed with polymer pellets (Figure 1.7) and melted together before the AM films are extruded from polymer blend [114]. However, it was reported in a study carried out by Han and Floros [115] that the retention of AM agents in extruded films is limited by the processing conditions. In this study, most of the volatile AM agents were evaporated during the extrusion process, thus it was suggested to use low extrusion temperatures.

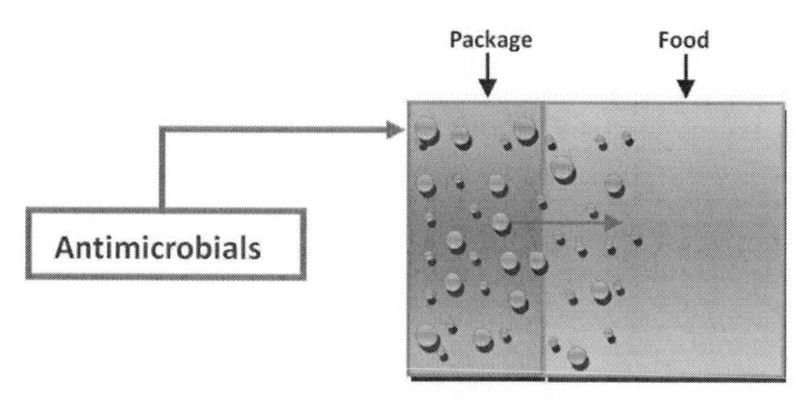

Modified from Han, [70].

Figure 1.7. Incorporation of AM agents in a package.

4.4. Coating/Spray AM onto Polymer Surfaces

Early developments in AM packaging include fungicides incorporated into waxes to coat fruit and vegetables and shrink films coated with quaternary ammonium salts to wrap potatoes [116] Other early developments included wax paper and cellulose casings for wrapping sausages and cheeses coated with sorbic acid [117].

Antimicrobial agents that cannot tolerate the temperatures used in polymer processing are often coated onto the material after forming (Figure 1.8) or added to cast films. Cast edible films, for example, have been used as carriers for AM and applied as coatings onto packaging materials and/or foods.

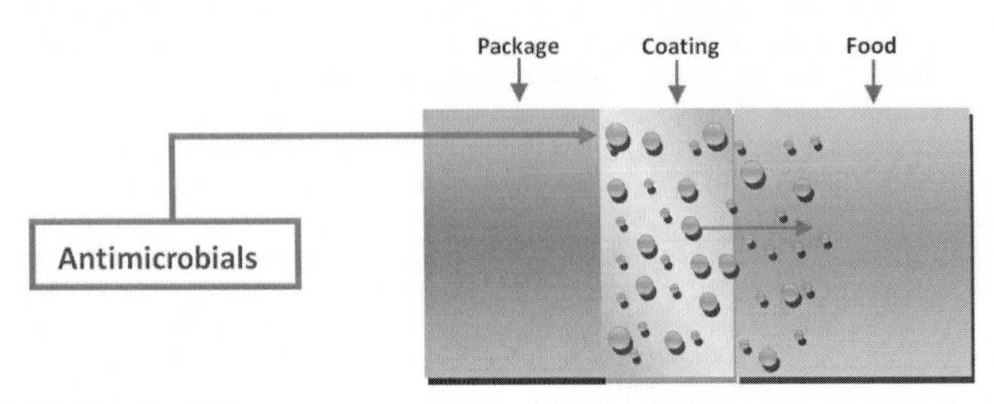

Modified from Han, [70].

Figure 1.8. Incorporation of AM agents in a package.

Ouattara et al. [48] made a chitosan film incorporating acetic acid and propionic acid by pouring mixed solutions into a plexiglass mold. The film thickness was varied by changing the volume of the casting solution in the mold before drying at 80 °C for 4-5 h. The AM activity and the release rate of acetic acid from the produced film were studied, aiming to develop a slow-release packaging for applying the acid onto processed meat. Hydrophobic compounds e.g. cinnamaldehyde and lauric acid were also added into the matrix of the hydrophilic chitosan to increase the tortuosity of the film. Such polymer modification was expected to obstruct the diffusion of molecules through it, which could slow the release rate and extend the activity period.

However, only lauric acid slowed the release of acetic acid, while the AM activity was not significantly changed. Cinnamaldehyde did not decrease the release, while increasing the inhibitory effect due to its own AM activity.

4.5. Immobilization of AM to Polymers

The production of AM films by the method of immobilization involves attaching AM enzymes to the polymer, producing non-migratory bioactive polymers. Unlike other types of AM packaging, the AM enzymes do not migrate into the food but remain active on the packaging surface (Figure 1.9).

This advantage makes this type of packaging desirable for the modern market, where customer requirements are high and safety regulations are strict. Nevertheless, the non-migration systems have limited application to some food types which lack the circulation of the food in a package. The utility of this packaging is then restricted to liquid food only [4].

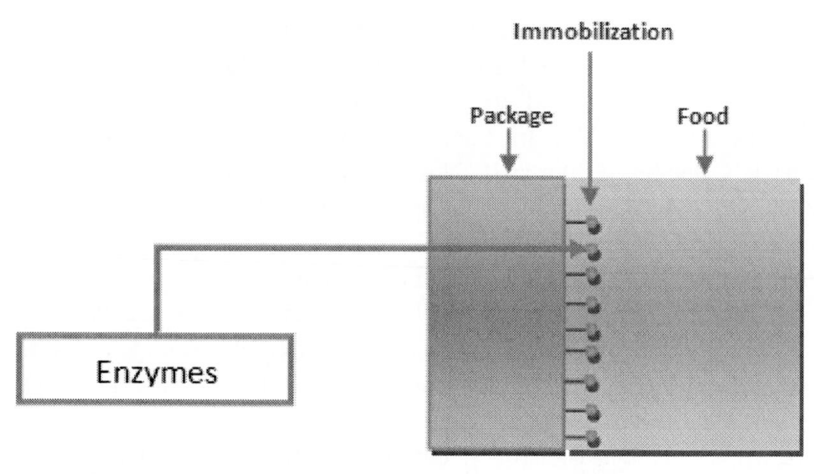

Modified from Han, [70].

Figure 1.9. Chemical immobilization in a package.

Conclusion

Chitosan seems to be a highly promising additive for bio-based films due to its unique cationic and versatile properties. The chitosan-based active packaging materials can be useful for preserving and extending the shelf-life of foods.

The use of this type of packaging materials will probably increase in the near future, due to the consumer's preference for naturally preserved food and also due to the industry pursuit in shelf-life extension of packaged food while preserving product quality and safety.

Acknowledgments

The author Javiera F. Rubilar would like to thank to the financial support of the DIPEI of the Pontificia Universidad Católica de Chile (Postdoctoral research). The author Rui M. S. Cruz would like to thank Fundação para a Ciência e Tecnologia (grant SFRH/BPD/ 70036/2010).

References

[1] Guarda, A., et al., The antimicrobial activity of microencapsulated thymol and carvacrol. *International Journal of Food Microbiology*, 2011. 146: p. 144-150.

[2] Tiwari, B.K., et al., Application of natural antimicrobials for food preservation. *Journal of Agricultural and Food Chemistry*, 2009. 57(14): p. 5987-6000.

[3] Appendini, P. and J.H. Hotchkiss, Review of antimicrobial food packaging. Innovative Food Science and Emerging Tehcnologies, 2002. 3: p. 113-126.

[4] Han, J.H., Antimicrobial packaging systems, in Innovation in Food Packaging, J.H. Han, Editor 2005, Elsevier, Academic Press: London. p. 517.

[5] Suppakul, P., et al., Active packaging technologies with an emphasis on antimicrobial packaging and its applications. *Journal of Food Science*, 2003a. 68: p. 408-420.

[6] Cruz, R.M.S., et al., New Food Processing Technologies: development and impact on the consumer acceptability, in Food Quality: Control, Analysis and Consumer Concerns, F. Columbus, Editor 2010, Nova Science: New York, USA.

[7] Robertson, G.L., Active and intelligent packaging, in Food packaging: principles and practice 2006, CRC Press: Boca Raton, Fl.

[8] Falguera, V., et al., Edible films and coatings: Structures, active functions and trends in their use. *Trends in Food Science & Technology*, 2011. 22(6): p. 292-303.

[9] Padgett, T., L.Y. Han, and P.L. Dawson, Impact of edible coatings on nutritional and physiological chamges in lightly-processed carrots. *Postharvest Biology and Technology*, 1998. 14: p. 51-60.

[10] Ouattara, B., et al., Diffusion of Acetic and Propionic Acids from Chitosan-based Antimicrobial Packaging Films. *Journal of Food Science* 2000. 65(5): p. 768-773.

[11] Huff, K. Active and Intelligent Packaging: Innovations for the Future. *Department of Food Science and Technology*. 2008. p. 1-13.

[12] de Kruijf, N., et al., Active and intelligent packaging: applications and regulatory aspects. *Food Additives and Contaminants*, 2002. 19: p. 144-162.

[13] Gill, C.O., A review. Intrinsic bacteria in meat. *Journal of Applied Bacteriology,* 1979. 47: p. 367-378.

[14] Maxcy, R.B., Surface microenvironment and penetration of bacteria into meat. *Journal of Food Protection,* 1981. 44: p. 550-552.

[15] Yalpani, M., et al., Advance in chitin and chitosan, 1992, Elsevier Applied Science, London.

[16] Ghosh, K.G., et al., Development and application of fungistatic wrappers in food presearvation. Part I. Wrappers obtained by impregnation method. *Journal of Food Science and Technology,* 1973. 10(4): p. 105-110.

[17] Rubilar, J.F., et al., Antioxidant and optimal antimicrobial mixtures of carvacrol, grape seed extract and chitosan on different spoilage microorganisms and their applications in different food matrices. *International Journal of Food Studies*, 2012a. Accepted.

[18] Suppakul, P., et al., Antimicrobial properties of basil and its possible application in food packaging. *Journal of Agricultural and Food Chemistry*, 2003b. 51: p. 3197-3207.

[19] Brody, A.L., E.R. Strupinsky, and L.R. Kline, Active packaging for food applications. Technomic Pub. Co., 2001, Lancaster, Pa.

[20] Ahvenainen, R., Active and intelligent packaging: an introduction. , in Novel Food packaging techniques, R. Ahvenainen, Editor 2003. Woodhead, CRC Press: Boca Raton, FL, USA. p. 590.

[21] WHO, N.D., Food safety and foodborne illness. *Biochimica Clinica*, 2002a. 26(4): p. 39.

[22] Leistner, L., Hurdle effect and energy saving, in Food quality and nutrition, W.K. Downey, Editor 1978, *Applied Science Publ:* London. p. 553-557.

[23] Silva, K.T. A manual on the essential oil industry. in A manual on the essential oil industry. 1996. United Nations Industrial Development Organization (UNIDO).

[24] Smid, E.J. and L.G.M. Gorris, Natural antimicrobials for food preservation. *Food Science and Technology* 1999: p. 285-308.

[25] WHO, World health report 2002: Reducing risks, promoting healthy life. *World Health Organization*, Geneva, pp. 248., 2002b.
[26] Burt, S., Essential oils: their antibacterial properties and potential applications in foods-a review. *International Journal of Food Microbiology*, 2004. 94(3): p. 223-53.
[27] Van de Braak, S. and G. Leijten, Essential oils and oleoresins: a survey in the Netherlands and other major markets in the European Union1999: CBI, Centre for the Promotion of Imports from Developing Countries.
[28] Guenther, A., The essential oils1948, New York: Van Nostrand.
[29] Boyle, W., Spices and essential oils as preservatives. *The American Perfumer and Essential Oil Review,* 1955. 66: p. 25-28.
[30] Shelef, L., Antimicrobial effect of spices *Journal of Food Safety*, 1983. 6(1): p. 29-44.
[31] Nychas, G., Natural antimicrobials from plants, in New methods of food preservation, G.W. Gould, Editor 1995, Blackie Academic and Professional: London. p. 58-89.
[32] Mourey, A. and N. Canillac, Anti-Listeria monocytogenes activity of essential oils components of conifers. *Food Control*, 2002. 13(4): p. 289-292.
[33] Bishop, C.D., Antiviral activity of the essential oil of Melaleuca alternifolia (Maiden and Betche) Cheel (tea tree) against tobacco mosaic virus. *Journal of Essential Oil Research*, 1995. 7: p. 641-644.
[34] Mari, M., P. Bertolini, and G. Pratella, Non-conventional methods for the control of post-harvest pear diseases. *Journal of Applied Microbiology*, 2003. 94(5): p. 761-766.
[35] Juglal, S., R. Govinden, and B. Odhav, Spice oils for the control of co-occurring mycotoxin-producing fungi. *Journal of Food Protection*, 2002. 65(4): p. 683-687.
[36] Pessoa, L., et al., Anthelmintic activity of essential oil of Ocimum gratissimum Linn. and eugenol against Haemonchus contortus. *Veterinary Parasitology*, 2002. 109(1): p. 59-63.
[37] Karpouhtsis, I., et al., Insecticidal and genotoxic activities of oregano essential oils. *Journal of Agricultural and Food Chemistry*, 1998. 46(3): p. 1111-1115.
[38] Mahmoud, S.S. and R.B. Croteau, Strategies for transgenic manipulation of monoterpene biosynthesis in plants. *Trends in plant science*, 2002. 7(8): p. 366-373.
[39] Rubilar, J.F., et al., Physico-mechanical properties of chitosan films with carvacrol and grape seed extract. *Journal of Food Engineering*, 2012b. http://dx.doi.org/10.1016/j.jfoodeng.2012.07.009.
[40] Penney, V., et al., The potential of phytopreservatives and nisin to control microbial spoilage of minimally processed fruit yogurts. *Innovative Food Science & Emerging Technologies*, 2004. 5(3): p. 369-375.
[41] Nguyen, P. and G. Mittal, Inactivation of naturally occurring microorganisms in tomato juice using pulsed electric field (PEF) with and without antimicrobials. *Chemical Engineering and Processing: Process Intensification*, 2007. 46(4): p. 360-365.
[42] Belletti, N., et al., Antimicrobial efficacy of citron essential oil on spoilage and pathogenic microorganisms in fruit-based salads. *Journal of Food Science*, 2008. 73(7): p. M331-M338.
[43] Chanjirakul, K., et al., Effect of natural volatile compounds on antioxidant capacity and antioxidant enzymes in raspberries. *Postharvest Biology and Technology*, 2006. 40: p. 106-115.

[44] Singh, N., et al., Efficacy of chlorine dioxide, ozone and thyme essential oil or a sequential washing in killing Escherichia coli O157:H7 on lettuce and baby carrots. *LWT-Food Science and Technology*, 2002. 35(8): p. 720-729.

[45] Gutierrez, J., et al., Impact of plant essential oils on microbiological, organoleptic and quality markers of minimally processed vegetables. *Innovative Food Science and Emerging Technologies*, 2009a. 10(2): p. 195-202.

[46] Uyttendaele, M., et al., Control of Aeromonas on minimally processed vegetables by decontamination with lactic acid, chlorinated water, or thyme essential oil solution. *International Journal of Food Microbiology*, 2004. 90(3): p. 263-271.

[47] Lemay, M.J., et al., Antimicrobial effect of natural preservatives in a cooked and acidified chicken meat model. *International Journal of Food Microbiology*, 2002. 78(3): p. 217-226.

[48] Singh, A., et al., Efficacy of plant essential oils as antimicrobial agents against Listeria monocytogenes in hotdogs. *LWT-Food Science and Technology*, 2003. 36(8): p. 787-794.

[49] Careagaa, M., et al., Antibacterial activity of Capsicum extract against Salmonella typhimurium and Pseudomonas aeruginosa inoculated in raw beef meat. *International Journal of Food Microbiology*, 2003. 83: p. 331-335.

[50] Mytle, N., et al., Antimicrobial activity of clove (Syzgium aromaticum) oil in inhibiting Listeria monocytogenes on chicken frankfurters. *Food Control*, 2006. 17(2): p. 102-107.

[51] Perumalla, A. and N.S. Hettiarachchy, Green tea and grape seed extracts—Potential applications in food safety and quality. *Food Research International*, 2011. 44(4): p. 827-839.

[52] Cowan, M.M., Plant products as antimicrobial agents. *Clinical Microbiology Reviews*, 1999. 12: p. 564-582.

[53] Ha, J., Y. Kim, and D. Lee, Multilayered antimicrobial polyethylene films applied to the packaging of ground beef. *Packaging Technology and Science*, 2001. 14(2): p. 55-62.

[54] Kuorwel, K.K., et al., Essential Oils and Their Principal Constituents as Antimicrobial Agents for Synthetic Packaging Films. *Journal of Food Science*, 2011. 76(9): p. R164-R177.

[55] Nicholson, M.D., The role of natural antimicrobials in food/packaging biopreservation. *Journal of Plastic Film and Sheeting*, 1998. 14(3): p. 234-241.

[56] Beuchat, L.R., R.E. Brackette, and M.P. Doyle, Lethality of carrot juice to Listeria monocytogenes as affected by pH, sodium chloride, and temperature. *Journal of Food Protection*, 1994. 57: p. 470-474.

[57] Gadang, V.P., et al., Evaluation of antibacterial activity of whey protein isolate coating incorporated with nisin, grape seed extract, malic acid, and EDTA on a turkey frankfurter system. *Journal of Food Science: Food Microbiology and Safety*, 2008. 73(8): p. M389-M394.

[58] Over, K., et al., Effect of organic acids and plant extracts on Escherichia coli O157: H7, Listeria monocytogenes, and Salmonella Typhimurium in broth culture model and chicken meat systems. *Journal of Food Science* 2009. 74(9): p. M515-M521.

[59] Cortinas, L., et al., Influence of the dietary polyunsaturation level on chicken meat quality: Lipid oxidation. *Poultry Science*, 2005. 84 p. 48-55.

[60] Grun, I.U., et al., Reducing oxidation of meat. *Food Technology*, 2006. 60: p. 36-43.
[61] Huang, D., B. Ou, and L. Ronald, The chemistry behind antioxidant capacity assays. *Journal of Agricultural and Food Chemistry*, 2005. 53(6): p. 1841-1856.
[62] Gramza, A., et al., Antioxidant activity of tea extracts in lipids and correlation with polyphenol content. *European Journal of Lipid Science and Technology*, 2006. 108: p. 351-362.
[63] Mitsumoto, M., et al., Addition of tea catechins and vitamin C on sensory evaluation, color and lipid stability during chilled storage in cooked or raw beef and chicken patties. *Meat Science*, 2005. 69: p. 773-779.
[64] Rice-Evans, C., N. Miller, and G. Paganga, Antioxidant properties of phenolic compounds. *Trends in plant science*, 1997. 2(4): p. 152-159.
[65] Lin JK and L. YC., Cancer chemoprevention by tea polyphenols. *Proceedings of National Science Council ROC (B)*, 2000. 24(1): p. 1-13.
[66] Turkoglu, A., et al., Antioxidant and antimicrobial activities of Laetiporus sulphureus (Bull.) Murrill. *Food Chemistry*, 2007. 101(1): p. 267-273.
[67] Han, J.H., Antimicrobial food packaging, in Novel food packaging techniques, R. Ahvenainen, Editor 2003, CRC Press: yBoca Raton, FL, USA. p. 590.
[68] Cruz, R.M.S., et al., Nanotechnology in Food Applications, in Advances in Food Science and Technology - Volume 1, S. Thomas, et al., Editors. 2011, Scrivener Publishing: Massachusetts, USA.
[69] Sánchez, C., et al., Development of a new antimicrobial active film incorporating naturals extracts effectiveness in vapor phase, 2005: 22nd IAPRI Symposium.
[70] Han, J.H., Antimicrobial food packaging. *Food Technology*, 2000. 54(3): p. 56-65.
[71] Goldberg, S., R. Doyle, and M. Rosenberg, Mechanism of enhancement of microbial cell hydrophobicity by cationic polymers. *Journal of Bacteriology*, 1990. 172(10): p. 5650-5654.
[72] Cuq, B., N. Gontard, and S. Cuilbert, Edible films and coatings as active layers, in Active Food Packaging, M.L. Rooney, Editor, 1995, Blackie Academic and Professional: Glasgow, UK. p. 111-142.
[73] Pardini, S., Methods for imparting antimicrobial activity from acrylics 1987. US Patent: 4708870.
[74] Olstein, A., Polymeric biocidal agents, 1992. US Patent: 5142010.
[75] Hagelstein, A., et al., Potential of antimicrobial nylon as a food package: Abstract, in Conference-Proceedings. IFT annual meeting 1995.
[76] Lee, J.H., et al., Cell behaviour on polymer surfaces with different functional groups. *Biomaterials*, 1994. 15(9): p. 705-711.
[77] Paik, J.S., M. Dhanasekharan, and M.J. Kelly, Antimicrobial activity of UV-irradiated nylon film for packaging applications. *Packaging Technology and Science*, 1998. 11(4): p. 179-187.
[78] Tharanathan, R.N. and F.S. Kittur, Chitin—the undisputed biomolecule of great potential. *Critical Reviews in Food Science and Nutrition*, 2003. 43(1): p. 61-87.
[79] Shahidi, F. and J. Synowiecki, Isolation and characterization of nutrients and value-added products from snow crab (Chionoecetes opilio) and shrimp (Pandalus borealis) processing discards. *Journal of Agricultural and Food Chemistry*, 1991. 39(8): p. 1527-1532.

[80] Synowiecki, J. and N.A.A.Q. Al-Khateeb, The recovery of protein hydrolysate during enzymatic isolation of chitin from shrimp crangon cragon processing discards. *Food Chemistry*, 2000. 68(2): p. 147-152.

[81] Knorr, D., Use of chitinous polymers in food: A challenge for food research and development. *Food Technology*, 1984. 38: p. 85-97.

[82] Ravi Kumar, M.N.V., A review of chitin and chitosan applications. *Reactive and functional polymers*, 2000. 46(1): p. 1-27.

[83] Srinivasa, P. and R. Tharanathan, Chitin/chitosan—Safe, ecofriendly packaging materials with multiple potential uses. *Food Reviews International*, 2007. 23(1): p. 53-72.

[84] Chen, C.S., W.Y. Liau, and G.J. Tsai, Antibacterial effects of N-sulfonated and N-sulfobenzoyl chitosan and application to oyster preservation. *Journal of Food Protection*, 1998. 61(9): p. 1124-1128.

[85] Dutta, P.K., et al., Perspectives for chitosan based antimicrobial films in food applications. *Food Chemistry*, 2009. 114(4): p. 1173-1182.

[86] Agulló, E., Rodríguez, M.S., Ramos, V., Albertengo, L. , Present and Future Role of Chitin and Chitosan in Food. *Macromolecular Bioscience*, 2003. 3 p. 521-530.

[87] Rabea, E.I., et al., Chitosan as antimicrobial agent: applications and mode of action. *Biomacromolecules*, 2003. 4(6): p. 1457-1465.

[88] Shahidi, F., J.K.V. Arachchi, and Y.J. Jeon, Food applications of chitin and chitosans. *Trends in Food Science & Technology*, 1999. 10(2): p. 37-51.

[89] Papineau, A.M., et al., Antimicrobial effect of water-soluble chitosans with high hydrostatic pressure. *Food Biotechnology*, 1991. 5(1): p. 45-57.

[90] Sudarshan, N., D. Hoover, and D. Knorr, Antibacterial action of chitosan. *Food Biotechnology*, 1992. 6(3): p. 257-272.

[91] Helander, I., et al., Chitosan disrupts the barrier properties of the outer membrane of Gram-negative bacteria. *International Journal of Food Microbiology*, 2001. 71(2): p. 235-244.

[92] Liu, H., et al., Chitosan kills bacteria through cell membrane damage. International Journal of Food Microbiology, 2004. 95(2): p. 147-155.

[93] Cuero, R.G., G. Osuji, and A. Washington, N-carboxymethyl chitosan inhibition of aflatoxin production: Role of zinc. *Biotechnology Letters*, 1991a. 13(6): p. 441-444.

[94] El Ghaouth, A., et al., Antifungal activity of chitosan on post-harvest pathogens: Induction of morphological and cytological alternations in Rhizopus stolonifer. *Mycological Research*, 1992. 96 (9): p. 769-779.

[95] Hadwiger, L.A., et al., Chitosan both activates genes in plants and inhibits RNA synthesis in fungi, in Chitin in nature and technology R.A.A. Muzzarelli, C. Jeuniaux, and G.W. Gooday, Editors. 1986, Plenum Pub Corp: New York, USA. p. 209-214.

[96] Savard, T., et al., Antimicrobial action of hydrolyzed chitosan against spoilage yeasts and lactic acid bacteria of fermented vegetables. *Journal of Food Protection*, 2002. 65(5): p. 828-833.

[97] Zheng, L.Y. and J.F. Zhu, Study on antimicrobial activity of chitosan with different molecular weights. *Carbohydrate Polymers*, 2003. 54(4): p. 527-530.

[98] Bhaskara, M.V., et al., Effect of chitosan on growth and toxin production by Alternaria alternata f. sp. lycopersici. *Biocontrol Science and Technology*, 1998. 8(1): p. 33-43.

[99] Dornenburg, H. and D. Knorr, Evaluation of elicitor- and high-pressure- induced enzymatic browning utilizing potato (solanum tuberosum) suspension cultures as a model system for plant tissues. *Journal of Agricultural and Food Chemistry*, 1997. 45(10): p. 4173-4177.
[100] Li, B., et al., Antibacterial activity of chitosan solution against Xanthomonas pathogenic bacteria isolated from Euphorbia pulcherrima. *Carbohydrate Polymers*, 2008. 72(2): p. 287-292.
[101] Chung, Y.C. and C.Y. Chen, Antibacterial characteristics and activity of acid-soluble chitosan. *Bioresource Technology*, 2008. 99(8): p. 2806-2814.
[102] Gómez-Estaca, J., et al., Effects of gelatin origin, bovine-hide and tuna-skin, on the properties of compound gelatin-chitosan films. *Food Hydrocolloids*, 2011. 25: p. 1461-1469.
[103] Ojagh, S.M., et al., Development and evaluation of a novel biodegradable film made from chitosan and cinnamon essential oil with low affinity toward water. *Food Chemistry*, 2010b. 122(1): p. 161-166.
[104] Altiok, D., E. Altiok, and F. Tihminlioglu, Physical, antibacterial and antioxidant properties of chitosan films incorporated with thyme oil for potential wound healing applications *Journal of Materials Science: Materials in Medicine,* 2010. 21(7): p. 2227-2236.
[105] Martins, J.T., M.A. Cerqueira, and A.A. Vicente, Influence of α-tocopherol on physicochemical properties of chitosan-based films. *Food Hydrocolloids*, 2012. 27(1): p. 220-227.
[106] Moradi, M., et al., Characterization of antioxidant chitosan film incorporated with Zataria multiflora Boiss essential oil and grape seed extract. *LWT-Food Science and Technology*, 2011. 46: p. 477-484.
[107] Siripatrawan, U. and B.R. Harte, Physical properties and antioxidant activity of an active film from chitosan incorporated with green tea extract. *Food Hydrocolloids*, 2010. 24(8): p. 770-775.
[108] Vargas, M., et al., Characterization of chitosan–oleic acid composite films. *Food Hydrocolloids*, 2009. 23(2): p. 536-547.
[109] Rooney, M.L., Active food packaging1995, Glasgow, UK: Blackie Academic & Professional. p. 255.
[110] Smith, J., J. Hoshino, and Y. Abe, Interactive packaging involving sachet technology. *Active food packaging*, 1995: p. 143-173.
[111] Rice, J., Gas emitting wafers a cost-effective MAP approach. *Food Processing*. September, 1989. 42.
[112] Hansen, R., et al., Antimicrobial absorbent *Food pad*, 1989. US Patent 4865855.
[113] Weng, Y.M., M.J. Chen, and W. Chen, Antimicrobial food packaging materials from poly (ethylene-co-methacrylic acid). *LWT-Food Science and Technology*, 1999. 32(4): p. 191-195.
[114] Suppakul, P., et al., Antimicrobial properties of basil and its possible application in food packaging. *Journal of Agricultural and Food Chemistry*, 2003b. 51(11): p. 3197-3207.
[115] Han, J. and J. Floros, Casting antimicrobial packaging films and measuring their physical properties and antimicrobial activities. *Journal of Plastic Film and Sheeting*, 1997. 13: p. 287-298.

[116] Shetty, K.K. and R.B. Dwelle, Disease and sprout control in individually film wrapped potatoes. *American Journal of Potato Research*, 1990. 67(10): p. 705-718.
[117] Labuza, T. and W. Breene, Applications of active packaging for improvement of shelf-life and nutritional quality of fresh and extended shelf-life foods. *Journal of Food Processing and Preservation*, 1989. 13(1): p. 1-69.

EDITORS' CONTACT INFORMATION

Dr. Franco Pedreschi Plasencia
Associate Professor
Chair of the Department of Chemical and Bioprocesses
Pontificia Universidad Cat6lica de Chile Av.
Department of Chemical and Bioprocesses
Vicuna 4860 Macul, Santiago, Chile
Telephone: (56-2) 3541229
E-mail: fpedreschi@ing.puc.cl

Zuzana Ciesarová
VÚP Food Research Institute, Priemyselná 4
824 75 Bratislava, Slovak Republic
Telephone: + 421-2-250237 (ext. 192)
Fax: + 421-2-50237111
E-mail: ciesarova@vup.sk.

INDEX

#

A

B

C

D

E

F

G

H

M

W

Y

Z